1st 15th

BOOKS BY JOHN BARTLOW MARTIN

the pane of glass

John Bartlow Martin

HARPER & BROTHERS, NEW YORK

THE PANE OF GLASS

Portions of this book were published in The Saturday
Evening Post under the title of Inside the Asylum.

FIRST EDITION

A-I

To Mrs. W. Tom Jones

Contents

Introduction

■ *The Pane of Glass* is a great achievement and a singular service to the mentally ill and all who work in their behalf.

It is one thing to convey knowledge and understanding of a complex problem, and this John Bartlow Martin has done in a masterful way. It is quite another thing to impart to such knowledge a depth of feeling that moves one to constructive action. Mr. Martin has also accomplished this.

This book should promote public enlightenment greatly, for it tells the reader what he needs to know about psychiatry and tells it in layman's language. And it should promote the education of more psychiatrists, for I know of no other nontechnical book which provides the medical student with so full a view of the practice of psychiatry, and I like to think that it will therefore encourage many young men and women to enter what many of us consider the most demanding and rewarding of professions.

In these pages the reader will find a warm, thorough and objective account of what it really is like to live and work in a large public mental hospital. It is as though the author had arranged to lend us the very senses of the doctors, nurses, aides and patients as we traverse with him the world of the schizophrenic, the manic and the depressed.

Taking Columbus State Hospital in Ohio as his prototype, Mr.

Martin in the first instance brings home to us how great is our debt to the doctors and their coworkers and to thousands of others like them in mental hospitals throughout the land. Lacking money and staff, by dint of pure devotion, energy and skill they succeed, almost miraculously, in sending scores of thousands of patients home to their families every year.

In the second instance, Mr. Martin elaborates in sensitive perspective and detail the grim and monolithic structure of the state mental hospital systems of today. He gives us a meticulous accounting of where we stand in our treatment of the mentally ill after nearly two hundred years of effort. He pin-points the assets, modest as they are. He documents the deficits, overwhelming as they are. He explains how we came to this state of affairs, and how bleak is the future if we do not drastically revise our methods of dealing with mental illness.

In the third instance, Mr. Martin's scholarly work comes at a time when the seeds of new approaches to mental illness are sprouting throughout the land. He describes some of them—the general hospital psychiatric units, the clinics and rehabilitation facilities, day and night hospitals, greater reliance on general practitioners of medicine, intensified research, intelligent understanding by political parties and the public, and so on. These auspicious developments add up to a sharing of responsibility for mental illness by all. The future lies in these directions.

One may cherish the hope that students and practitioners of medicine, psychology, social work, religion, nursing, education, the law and, indeed, community leaders everywhere will read this book. If enough of them do, history may record that *The Pane of Glass* was a kind of valedictory challenging us to leave the patterns of the past, taking with us that which was good, as we move to stronger positions for a fresh attack on the greatest remaining health problem—the problem of mental illness. It is an intriguing prospect.

DANIEL BLAIN, M.D.
Medical Director
American Psychiatric Association

Washington, D. C.

"There is a pane of glass between me and mankind."
—A SCHIZOPHRENIC EXPLAINING HOW HE FEELS

the pane of glass

1

State Hospital

■ The way out to Columbus State Hospital in Columbus, Ohio, is on the West Broad Street trolley-bus line, running westward from the Statehouse and downhill across the Scioto River, past the new veterans' memorial and beneath the New York Central and the C & O viaducts, past an ice plant and a lumberyard, used-car lots and pool halls, filling stations and taverns, hamburger stands and pizza parlors, rooming houses and the Inn Towne Motel. A schoolboy stops traffic in the middle of the street, and kids scamper across, and banners are flying before a television store, and a sign on a store-front church says, "JESUS SAVES." The bus's motor whirs loudly, and all the way the uniformed driver calls the streets, stops suddenly at the curb, the door flying open. Broad Street, today a wide busy asphalt thoroughfare, was once the National Road, the main wagon road leading west, and the Central Ohio Lunatic Asylum, as the present State Hospital was called, was one of the first state hospitals for the care of the insane built "west of the mountains." Men brought their troubles with them pioneering.

The bus passes a flat expanse of fields behind a wire fence, and in a cornfield men in blue denim are pulling a wagon, driving a tractor, harrowing. They are patients, tilling the hospital's farm, and the shoppers on the bus turn as one to peer at them. The bus climbs a hill, and above the treetops on the hill appear the red and gray

1

castle-like spires and turrets, smokestack and water tank, slate-gray roof and white gingerbread trim, of the Columbus State Hospital. It looks pretty from afar, like a wedding cake. The bus halts at the drive—the driver does not call out this stop, this one alone—and an old woman and a middle-aged one step down amid dead silence and as the bus hastens away they begin the long walk, no doubt familiar, up to the hospital doors.

The drive curves up the breast of the hill, lined by old trees, marked with a sign, 20 MILES PER HOUR. The grounds embrace 333 acres. The lawn is well kept, burnt brown now in September. It looks like a park, cool, quiet, shady. One would think nothing ever happened here. Two old men, patients, are sitting together on a bench, staring out at the traffic on Broad Street. On a big boulder is a fat old man: He sits there every day, barefoot, painstakingly examining his dirty worn-out socks and wetting one finger and washing his feet. A legless emaciated man rides by in a wheelchair, propelling himself rapidly. A young man alone suddenly arises, takes two steps forward, and stands stiffly at attention; he is making a speech, you can see his lips move, his hands are tense, his body quivers, his features work passionately, but no sound comes forth. Finished at length, he slumps and wearily sits again. A woman visiting her husband is eating lunch with him out of a paper bag. An old man, stooped and dressed in sweater and coat though the day is hot, is carefully stuffing paper into a hole in the bole of a tree. Near him an old man sits with a leaf shielding his bald head. In a circle of benches under a tree where the grass is all worn away, sit thirty old men, talking, shoulders hunched, leaning forward, breaking up sticks that have fallen from the trees. The leaves are coming down, winter is not far away, when the old men cannot sit out here. Far off across the landscape at the rim of the hill a young patient is striding rapidly along. In the distance beyond the trees rise the towers of Columbus.

All these patients out on the lawn, and perhaps a hundred others scattered about the grounds, are privileged patients—those deemed well enough to let out unattended. The rest of the 2,700 others are kept locked up inside. From inside comes a low murmur of garbled sound—talk, song, howls, laughter. The shrubbery against the wall is festooned with pants and socks and toilet paper thrown from a disturbed ward. The brick walls rise up four stories. From a high barred window a thin arm stretches forth, naked to the shoulder, and behind the bars a gaunt black face appears, a man gesturing with his hand, motions that at first seem to be some kind of signal but that soon are seen to be the motions one makes catching flies. From another window a man is singing "The Prisoner's Song" and higher up another patient is perched on a window ledge, squatting on his haunches, pressed against the wire mesh.

Across the drive from the hospital door flies the American flag. The main building is an enormous pile of bricks, four stories high, built in a stepped-back zigzag shape, two long wings extending out and back from the central structure. It is the Kirkbride building plan, originated a hundred years ago by Thomas A. Kirkbride, superintendent of a Pennsylvania hospital and one of the "Original Thirteen" founders of the American Psychiatric Association. Most older mental hospitals in America are built on this plan. They are enormous solid structures which never seem to wear out. The outside wall of this enormous building is more than a mile long. Local legend terms it the longest perimeter wall in the world except for the Pentagon. The front is white gingerbread and white-painted brick. Worn stone steps ascend to the columned porch. The double doors are old and dark with much varnish, and above them is a stained-glass window. Through these doors have passed no fewer than 44,000 persons mentally afflicted. "Columbus State Hospital"—over the years what human suffering and human hope have those words conveyed.

2.

Dr. Benjamin Kovitz, clinical director of Columbus State, said a while back, "The hospital is not necessarily the best place for psychotic patients but at present it's the only place." Kovitz, head of Columbus State's medical staff and the man to whom is entrusted the patients' care and treatment, is a rather slight man with a round bald head and a square face and a shy smile and a habit of leaning forward intently, inquiringly. He has a probing analytical mind; it is a practical mind too, restlessly inquiring, "Will it work?"

Kovitz said, "The first reason mental hospitals came into existence was that we had to have a place for people that just couldn't fit in. They had to go somewhere. The state hospital started a hundred years ago or more when it was realized that local county homes and jails could seldom do an adequate job. So one thing the mental hospital does is to give the community some place to send a person who is disturbing, incomprehensible, fighting, and so on. Then, from the start it was observed that our patients get better simply by being sent into this kind of place. So in addition to the original purpose of custody for the benefit of society, you had the hospital for the benefit of the patient. Then in the last part of the last century the emphasis changed. Freud came along, and dynamic psychiatry, and we began to make an effort really to understand what was before considered meaningless. And we began to try to apply this understanding in therapy. In this century the somatic therapies developed—hydrotherapy, insulin, and Metrazol shock, electroshock—and they worked a minor revolution in the life of the mental hospital. It had suddenly become possible to do something about these diseases fairly easily and simply. The hospital came to be viewed as a place to help people get well— not just a way to keep them out of other people's hair. This was revolutionary. Today we feel we have the obligation to the patient to help him achieve some kind of a healthy life—the best he can whether it's in here or out. The new drugs are just one step in what started with insulin therapy and electroshock—physical things you can do to do something for emotional illness."

He smiled gently. "In addition, we've come to feel that it is desirable to make a hospital serve as a place where people can do research —can find out more about mental illness and treatment. There's such a wonderful amount of source material here to study. Furthermore, in the routine of dealing with patients—examination, psychiatric interview, and so on—the hospital collects a great amount of standardized data. It contributes something toward the enormous fund of information that is accumulating about mental illness. And at the same time we can train new doctors in psychiatry. And so the third hospital function has developed—research and training. Treatment and investigation have to go hand in hand because we don't know what we're treating." Again he smiled. "Some people approach the problem through large statistical studies, studying the epidemiology of mental disease. That's one way to go at it. Telescopically. Others look microscopically—at the details of the individual. There are all kinds of ways. Everybody does his best.

"This place is really pretty good as such places go. We can't give patients the individual attention that we'd like. You can only do that in a very small place. On the other hand, if there's a sore point sticking up, someone will run into it, because we've got enough conscientious people around. Our problems are mainly those of numbers and size. And the present state of knowledge."

Kovitz went on, "The whole idea of a hospital needs thorough inspection. It's worked, it's served some social need, as has the penal system, but it needs a lot of overhauling and a lot of its time-honored conceptions challenged. We need more use of community clinics. We certainly shouldn't hospitalize everyone with a problem. Sometimes a patient just needs to be tided through a crisis. The hospital is all right for a patient in the acute disturbed phase of illness. It's risky if prolonged. These patients will do better if you get them out fast, as soon as they've passed their acute stage. You shouldn't wait for them to get completely well. The longer they wait, the more scared they get—scared to try to go outside. Some go out and come back, go out and come back, forced by pressure from their parents at home, by pressure from us here."

The treatments patients receive in the hospital help them get well. But often just being there helps too. For one thing the hospital makes it extremely difficult for a suicidal patient to kill himself. For another, it is a haven. Kovitz said, "Even the patient that resents being brought here feels relieved here. He's been rescued from the problems he couldn't cope with." In this sense the old word "asylum," correctly used—a sanctuary from trouble—was better than the newer term, "mental hospital." Kovitz said, "For some, coming here is a tremendous relief of tension. For others, it is the beginning of the end. They like the hospital too well. To them it is an invitation to surrender. Schizophrenics often get worse here, much worse. The hospital encourages them to deteriorate, give up, for it removes every inducement to struggle. Every schizophrenic senses this danger. That's why they resist and fear the hospital. And that's why the hospital should not pamper the patients. I don't mean we ought to beat them and keep them in dungeons. The hospital ought to treat them decently, with dignity and with respect for their rights. But it shouldn't be too hotel-like, shouldn't be too comfortable, for if it is you're doing the patients a disservice unless you have really skilled help to get them out."

3.

There were some 1,400,000 people on the books of mental institutions in the United States during the past year. On any given day the country's mental institutions contained about 850,000 people. Mental patients occupy half the hospital beds in America. It has been estimated that one of every twelve children born today will spend some part of his life in a mental hospital. Mental illness is unquestionably America's No. 1 health problem.

Private psychiatric care is expensive. Only 10 per cent of the U.S. population can afford to pay for it. So most of America's seriously mentally ill are in public hospitals—only about fifty thousand are in private sanatoriums or psychiatric wings of general hospitals.

Traditionally the state hospital has been viewed as the American snake pit, a place to be shunned and, if possible, forgotten. But in recent years people have paid increasing attention to state hospitals. In state after state citizens have voted to tax themselves to improve their state hospitals. For the average citizen is learning how costly and scarce private psychiatric care is, and he has begun to realize the truth: If *you* get mentally sick, the state hospital is *your* hospital, the one *you'll* go to.

Even so, the average citizen knows little about what goes on in his state hospital. He doesn't know who the patients are, or what is the matter with them, or what is done for them. Do they ever get well? Who are the doctors, and how much do they know? What of the superintendent's burden? What of the governor and the legislators, on whom rests ultimate responsibility?

And to what other kinds of places do the mentally ill go? What of the university hospital, the psychiatric wing of the general hospital, the private sanatorium? How do they compare with the mainline state hospital?

And what are our national needs in combating mental illness? More doctors? More nurses? More buildings? More money? More knowledge? What, especially, are we doing about research? What do we know and what do we need to know?

What, in short, do we Americans do today for those among us with serious mental troubles?

This book is about the care of the mentally ill in America, especially about their care in state hospitals—about the hospital itself, the doctors and attendants who work there, the patients who live there. It is a book about psychotic people as the doctors and attendants see them inside a state hospital. It is also the patient as he sees himself.

There are in America today 218 state hospitals. Columbus State is one of them, not the best, far from the worst. In this book it is taken as representative of many state hospitals. Let us first take a long, hard, careful look at Columbus State as it was in the fall of 1955. Since then numerous changes have taken place at Columbus State, and we shall note them when we return for a second visit in the final chapter. No hospital stands still. Just so, conditions have changed all over the country, for psychiatry today is in a state of great ferment, and changes wrought by new discoveries and new thinking are occurring every day. Many people, indeed, believe psychiatry today stands on the threshold of a new age. This book, then, contains a description of what life was like in a representative American state mental hospital in the mid-1950s. It takes up the national problem of mental illness and the national search for more knowledge about mental disease, the hope of the future. Someday, what this book shows may be regarded as a view from just below the top of the hill which mankind reached after a long and arduous journey and from which he beheld the truth about himself.

4.

Columbus State Hospital in 1955 was in many ways like all the state hospitals in America. It was big. It was overcrowded. It had too few doctors, nurses and attendants. It was full of human suffering.

Columbus State held 2,700 patients. This was not an unmanageable number—Pilgrim State in New York had 14,000—but it was approaching unmanageability. As Dr. Kovitz said, "I'd sure hate to see it get any bigger. You can't treat patients on an assembly line basis." The 2,700 sick people at Columbus State were occupying space big enough for only 1,800 by American Psychiatric Association standards.

Columbus State Hospital was really several institutions. It was a sort of old folks county home. It was a maximum security hospital for extremely dangerous patients. It was a hospital for the heroic treatment of acute psychotics. And it was a more or less permanent custodial home for a host of steadily deteriorating chronic psychotics.

To care for all these patients there were eighteen doctors. This included the administrators and doctors who handled only physical ailments. This left ten ward doctors who were actually seeing to the day-to-day psychiatric care of 2,700 patients. Not one of these ten ward doctors was a full-fledged certified psychiatrist—that is, none was fully trained and had passed the examination of the American

Board of Psychiatry and Neurology. There were, indeed, only three certified psychiatrists at the hospital and they could give little time to patients. They supervised the work of the ward doctors. Most of the ward doctors were "residents in psychiatry," in training here for Board examinations. They were young doctors just out of medical school or older general practitioners who wanted to become psychiatrists.

Attendants were so scarce that frequently at night one attendant had to try to handle three wards alone. Three wards comprised a block-long labyrinth of rooms and corridors and locked doors, with up to 250 psychotic patients sleeping in them.

And all this was about average for state hospitals in America; many were much worse off. Not a single state hospital in America met the standards of the American Psychiatric Association.

5.

Inside, Columbus State was huge, high-ceilinged, old. The lobby, its woodwork dark with many years of varnishing, its floor tiled in black and white, was furnished with a row of wooden chairs and a brass cigarette receptacle and an old-fashioned showcase of embroidery done by patients, decorated with potted philodendrons and a framed homily, MENTAL ILLNESS IS NO DISGRACE, intended to reassure visiting relatives. The lobby was a quiet, pleasant decorous place, where white-capped nurses and white-coated doctors paused to pass the time of day beside the Coke machine. But the wards beyond were not so decorous.

From the lobby narrow passageways led to the wards. There were twenty-eight of them, stretching back through the zigzag arms of the building, one after the other, separated from each other by heavy solid doors made of steel. Narrow walled-in stairways ascended to the upstairs wards, four stories high. The door to every ward was always locked. Behind each door up to one hundred patients lived, cared for by a couple of attendants. The ward was, mainly, a long, narrow, high-ceilinged hall. But off it lay a honeycomb of sleeping rooms and alcoves and winding passageways, all labyrinthine and complex. The ancient walls were massive—more than two feet thick. The plastered doorways to the sleeping rooms were high and arched at the top; the architecture seemed vaguely Moorish. The sleeping rooms were tiny, cell-like, beds crammed close together. Once they had had doors but the superintendent ordered them removed because they were too prisonlike.

Some wards, inhabited by patients nearly ready to go home, were as quiet and pleasant as the lobby—nicely furnished, with patients sitting in rocking chairs, knitting or watching television. Others, inhabited by disturbed patients, were bare as a prison cell block, the windows barred, the air uproarious with psychotic screaming.

On one ward patients strolled about, fully dressed, or sat on benches along the wall, reading; they might have been members of a club. Always to a visitor the strangest thing about a mental hospital is that the patients are not in bed as in a general hospital but are up and about; they look well, indeed many appear in the pink of health. But then, passing into a disturbed ward, he sees in the dark gloomy narrow passageways psychotic patients wandering about aimlessly, dim figures moving slowly and silently in the shadows, and, turning a corner and passing through a narrow doorway he suddenly comes upon a man standing rigid in a corner, frozen in catatonic trance, squeezed tight against the wall as though hoping to press himself into the very wall and so into oblivion; he does not move as the visitor passes, nor make a sign that he sees him; his bony face is contorted by the demons that torment him. In a little toilet room a dozen men are crowded: They are forbidden to smoke on the ward, since its floors are wood, so they smoke in the toilet, where the floor is tile. The hospital seems quieter than many. It always has been quiet, no one knows why. Old-time attendants say that when the patients get noisy, it's going to rain.

A doctor passes through, and a small man emerges noiselessly from a side room; the doctor pauses and asks, "How do you feel," but the man replies, "You're talking to a dead man, Doctor." "Now, now." But the man shakes his head and watches the doctor go. High on an upper-story ward half a hundred dangerous combative disturbed men sit packed together on benches around the walls, guarded by a husky attendant standing watchfully in the center of the room; they sit all day in silence broken only by an occasional animalistic cry. On a disturbed women's ward, dim-lit, bare of all furniture, a woman lies on the floor covered with a rug, and another is perched birdlike on a window ledge, and another lies curled on a bench in fetal position, and a tall woman with a rag bound turban-fashion round her head strides up and down the ward in intense agitation, gibbering nonsense, fists clenched, her eyes flashing angrily at all who come near, and out on the porch old women naked or wrapped in sheets sprawl on benches or on the floor, which is covered with urine.

6.

The hospital has always been sharply divided into two halves: The wards in the north wing of the building are for women, those in the south wing for men. The new patient goes to one of the acute wards. Here he receives treatment for a few weeks or months. If he responds well, he goes home. If he doesn't, he is moved to one of the chronic wards. (Acute and chronic refer to the stages of the disease, just as they do in a physical illness.) As patients get worse they tend to get moved upstairs and farther and farther back in the building, until finally they are shoved clear out of the main building and back into the dim recesses of the cottages, separate small houses behind the main building. Sometimes a new patient hangs on for months in an acute ward midway back in the building, his doctor knowing he is not well enough to be moved to the front and home but reluctant to give up and send him upstairs to the "back wards," where reside the patients for whom everything has been done and for whom, at least until early in the 1950s when the new drugs came along, there was nothing to await but death. Nearly all mental hospitals concentrate treatment on the acute wards—concentrate on giving each newly admitted patient his chance. A patient's best chance to recover comes as soon as he reaches the hospital. He must be helped then, in most cases, if at all. The trouble is, of course, that other patients are neglected.

Dr. Kovitz said, "You've got to try on everybody, and you've only got so many doctors and so much medicine and so much time. The ward doctors are encouraged to spend some time regularly reviewing their individual patients, taking a few each day and seeing if they can't do something for them. They're supposed to write progress notes from time to time." But often only luck determines which chronic patient receives treatment. "Our day is spent tackling individual problems that are forced on our attention. Somebody clamors for attention, we have an emergency, it has to be dealt with—it's hard to find the leisure to get a long view and see who hasn't been reached lately."

Ordinarily on the chronic wards the patient who gets attention is the one who makes trouble, or whose relatives bother the doctor. Any doctor, asked about a given patient, may say, as one has said, "I don't have her in mind at all. She's an axle that hasn't squeaked much. It's the axle that squeaks the loudest that gets the grease." Most tragic of all, perhaps, are the patients who improve quickly on the acute wards and with a slight extra push could go home—but they have no home, and so, as time passes, they slip back and end up on the chronic wards, forgotten.

A survey of Columbus State Hospital in 1955 showed that about a third of the patients were getting some kind of treatment—the new tranquilizing drugs, shock, sedation, psychotherapy, occupational therapy or recreational therapy. This was a generous estimate and seemed to include every patient who at some time saw a movie or a ball game (activities that are termed "recreational therapy"). It included only 117 patients on shock treatment, 213 on the new tranquilizing drugs, 24 on individual psychotherapy, 31 on group psychotherapy —a total of 385 on active treatment out of 2,700. Dr. Kovitz estimated that perhaps another 1,400 patients might benefit from active treatment were it possible to give it to them. About 900 were purely custodial. This was probably at least an average treatment record for a state hospital.

Kovitz said, "It could be worse. If we had more money for drugs, more doctors to do individual psychotherapy, more nurses and attendants and more recreational activities we might help two-thirds of the patients instead of one-third. If you neglect them they deteriorate; if you show them they've got some place to go in life they'll get better. But there is always a sizable population, maybe a third, that would be very hard to get out of the hospital under any conditions—old people with no place to go, schizophrenics whose process seems irreversible. I'd say we're doing better than we were when I came here ten years ago. Some of the worst features are fading away. There used to be a lot more restraint, more intimidation of patients, a lack of concern for the patient's feelings."

Once a patient is assigned to a ward, he is the responsibility of the ward doctor. He may stay on one ward for years, watching doctors and attendants come and go. Or he may be bounced around continually from ward to ward. The ward doctors try to put each patient in the ward best for him. But the doctor is human, and if a patient gets to be a nuisance, it is only human to get rid of him. Moreover, the doctor is not free. His ward becomes overcrowded; he has to move patients out. Or an attendant, weary of a difficult patient, daily tells the doctor he "doesn't belong" on the ward, and finally, to placate the attendant—for a doctor must get along with his attendants or they can nullify his best efforts—the doctor transfers the patient. But often the doctor on the new ward doesn't want him either and shunts him off to another ward. And so on endlessly. Moreover, in a few troublesome cases, said Superintendent M. R. Wedemeyer, "we deliberately move patients around to share the burden—we have one woman who's always setting fires, making everybody anxious, so we occasionally move her to another ward to give everybody a rest." Nobody approves of bouncing patients around. Everybody agrees that a patient is more likely to be helped by constant treatment by the same doctor and attendants. But only a few state hospitals, such as Topeka State in Kansas, claim to have abolished the practice, and they have bigger staffs and more money than Columbus State.

7.

In 1955, on the first floor of the north wing of Columbus State close to the lobby was a ward which had been taken over by the doctors for their offices. Its corridor was brightly lit and empty and spotlessly clean. The little rooms opening off it, once patients' sleeping rooms, were now offices, one for each doctor. Here he kept his records, wrote case notes and letters, interviewed patients and relatives. In each office was a small desk and two chairs, usually a few books. At such private institutions as the Menninger Clinic the doctors' offices were fitted with couches, used in psychoanalysis. Only one doctor here had a couch—the rest were not analysts and had little time to interview patients at all.

One of these offices, exactly like the others, was the office of Dr. Kovitz, the man who runs the psychiatric staff at this hospital. Kovitz is a quiet man, inward turned, somewhat diffident in manner but with firm views and a clear grasp of problems. He wears glasses; his gaze is piercing. Usually he wears a dark blue suit. One of the other doctors has said, "Kovitz doesn't drive a car, doesn't mix well, likes clinical work, hates administrative duties." In 1955 all the doctors considered him an ideal teacher—good teachers are rare in psychiatry, as in other branches of medicine—and a brilliant diagnostician. Sometimes at a staff conference, after the questions of other doctors had elicited only the fuzziest answers from a patient, Kovitz would take over and with a few incisive inquiries lay bare the patient's mind. Though quiet and gentle he somehow conveyed authority, and often a patient who had stubbornly resisted other doctors would do what Kovitz directed. He knows what he is about, and patients know he knows. Kovitz knows psychiatric theory and relishes intellectual discussion of it but at the same time he never loses his humanity. He can be as erudite and abstract as any professor but on the ward talking to a patient he resembles more a country doctor on his way to deliver a baby. One of the other doctors said, "Kovitz would make a name for himself in psychiatry if he were at a hospital where names are made." And another: "He's the wheel this whole place turns on."

Ben Kovitz was born in Superior, Wisconsin, some forty-five years ago, the son of an immigrant tailor from Lithuania. His parents urged medicine on him—it would give him independence. He graduated from the University of Wisconsin Medical School in 1938. He interned in Kansas City and then "got my first taste of psychiatry" at the state hospital at Osawatomie, Kansas. From there he went to Michael Reese Hospital in Chicago as a resident in pathology, a natural choice of specialties for one of his analytical bent. But his interest in psychiatry remained, and it was not merely by chance that his first job as a pathologist was in a mental hospital, the Jacksonville State Hospital in Illinois.

He has said, "There wasn't really enough pathology there to keep busy so I started sitting in with the staff and making rounds on the wards and before I knew it I was up to my neck in psychiatry." He discovered he was allergic to formaldehyde, a substance used constantly in a pathology laboratory. Smiling he has said, "This provided a handy excuse for giving up pathology and going into psychiatry." He stayed at Jacksonville through the war—the war brought crisis to every state hospital, for its stringencies nearly strangled them—and by its end he had put in four years as, in effect, a staff psychiatrist. He wanted to be certified as a full-fledged psychiatrist by the American Board of Psychiatry and Neurology; Jacksonville was not approved for residency training but Columbus State Hospital was so he came to Columbus. By 1948 he had passed his Boards. He was already clinical director of the hospital. Younger psychiatrists now coming along are likely to undergo a more rigidly prescribed training—undergraduate college, medical school, internship, three years of residency training in psychiatry in an approved hospital, two years of psychiatric practice, and then Board certification. Kovitz's slightly erratic education is typical of that of many psychiatrists practicing today.

As clinical director Kovitz was in sole charge of the residency training program—he taught psychiatry to the young MDs. They were the ward psychiatrists, and Kovitz supervised their work. He spent one day a week teaching at Ohio State University. He lived with his wife and four children in one of the state-owned houses on the hospital grounds. One morning a week he made ward rounds with the doctor who had the acute male wards, another morning with the doctor who had the acute female wards. Doctors on the chronic wards brought their problems to him. He conducted the staff conference every morning from ten to noon. Every Tuesday afternoon he led a discussion on some theoretical aspect of psychiatry. He brought in consultants—a neurologist, a neuroanatomist, others—to lecture on their specialities.

Kovitz is absorbed in his subject. If he belongs to any school of psychiatric thought it is likely to be that identified with Harry Stack Sullivan, who, while recognizing the importance of psychoanalysis, thought it needed to be supplemented by a study of the impact of cultural or social forces on personality. (Kovitz thinks, for example, that if a physically healthy man doesn't work for several years it is quite likely he is mentally ill.) Well versed in Freudian theory, at staff meetings Kovitz was likely to be impatient if a young resident dwelt on it; he probably thought that most of them didn't know enough about it to handle it and furthermore that a theory that a patient's illness originated in a failure to resolve the Oedipal triangle is interesting but has no practical application in a mental hospital. Kovitz's health was not good and he was inclined to overwork. In addition to his duties as teacher and clinical director he was obliged to see several patients on trial visit and numerous relatives of patients still in the hospital. And he also treated three or four patients by psychotherapy, seeing each of them an hour a week.

One day in his bare little monastic office, with its narrow window overlooking the hospital parking lot and the fringe of trees on the rim of the hill, Ben Kovitz was talking about his work. Asked to define psychosis, he said, "I'd rather talk around it. When you're dealing with people with troubles, you find they fall into two groups. In the first group is the person who seems like you or me but something is interfering with his life, he's unsatisfied with life, tensions and moods and ideas bother him, he feels nervous, feels he's not well and wants help—this is the neurotic type. But then there are other people who seem, as you get to know them, obviously different from the rest of us. Their way of thinking, of experiencing reality, is different. Their way of behaving just doesn't fit into the life around them. They can't get integrated. They're out of joint with their environment. These are the psychotic."

The psychoses as they are now understood fall into two groups— organic, with a known physical basis, such as paresis and arteriosclerosis of the brain, and functional, without known physical basis, such as schizophrenia. (It is possible that *all* psychoses have a physical basis as yet undiscovered.) Dr. Kovitz, sitting at his desk, said, "There are certain classical examples of what we call the functional psychoses, the psychoses with no known organic basis. We use the term affective psychosis to refer to reactions in which emotion is the striking feature. This includes people in an overwhelming depression. When the depression becomes so severe that they can't carry on, that their way of thinking about people is distorted, that they experience a delusional type of guilt—this is an affective psychotic reaction. A woman came in this morning all agitated and depressed and was sent to Ward 15. She's pacing, agitated, she thinks the other girls somehow resent her, they're working, doing something useful, and she's not. If she goes into the bathroom ahead of someone else, she feels guilty. Yet nobody said anything to her, there is no basis for her judgment. To the normal person this seems unrealistic. It is. When a person becomes dominated by unrealistic thinking, he is psychotic.

"Another affective type is the manic. He may not show an obvious delusional system but he can't hold himself down, can't slow down, he talks too much, he talks too fast and too long, he's jumping around, new ideas come to him a mile a minute. He might be making a very successful career for himself but he has no brakes, he's all drive. He becomes sarcastic and insulting, and he is very witty. But he can't adapt any of this to the situation he finds himself in.

"But," and Kovitz leaned back in his chair, "the psychotic reaction par excellence, the one that really goes the limit, is that of schizophrenia. The so-called break with reality is the most extreme. Any man in the street who tries to understand a schizophrenic tends to give it up as hopeless. And the doctor does too. You can make sense out of a manic-depressive. But not out of a schizophrenic. They think about experience in a very strange way. They live a sort of waking dream. It is very dreamlike. Their way of feeling comes from a very deep primitive level. It's been theorized that the schizophrenic point of view starts very early in infancy, even before the infant has acquired language. Some of the conscious experience of schizophrenics seems to go back as far as experience goes. They often can't put it into words, or else the words seem odd to John Doe. To talk to schizophrenics you have to think in terms of feelings and symbols, for that's the way they think. The schizophrenic may shout at you that he's embalmed and dead. He seems in every sense to mean it literally, but it's merely a way of speaking, he knows that a part of him isn't living, and that's what he's trying to tell you.

"As to the cause of schizophrenia, it is unknown—and I object to the word 'cause' itself. Some of the causes are understandable. But the crucial explanation is missing. Many factors must conspire to produce the schizophrenic. Psychological factors are important in explaining it but they don't completely explain it. Other people confronted with the same difficult life situations break in different ways—some people drink, for example, or become narcotics addicts, in order to escape reality. But why do schizophrenics escape this way? I don't know. Nobody knows. Some people think it's a matter of constitution. Presumably 'constitution' means factors that are present at birth or are acquired so early that they become practically irrevocable, an ingrained permanent part of the personality. But this just pushes the whole question one step farther back. And the constitutional factors are constantly being influenced by experience. These people just can't handle the great crises of life—adolescence, marriage, jobs, competition, failure, childbearing, the climacteric. A new child may represent a terrible threat to some people. I had one man who relapsed into catatonic schizophrenia every time his wife had a baby. We all undergo certain stresses. Some people can take stress well. Some can't. The type that gives up most completely is the psychotic. The regular methods are not enough, so they fall back on others, and the ultimate in trying to stand the stress of putting up with people is the schizophrenic pattern. Schizophrenics have tremendous sensitivity to people. Schizophrenia can be viewed as one way of trying to stand the intolerable.

"Some schizophrenics have lost all control. They fly into a rage and attack people. The schizophrenic seems either to hit back or to give up. They hit people for no apparent reason—their imaginary voices make a disgusting remark and they hit the nearest person. Anybody who happens to come near a schizophrenic while he's hallucinating is likely to get hit, for the bystander materializes the phantom in the patient's mind—the voices that are taunting or threatening or abusing him. Sometimes a schizophrenic kills. When he says the voices told him to kill someone, he is really trying to kill the thing in himself that he hates. We have to keep many of them here permanently. We may hate to do it but they'd mess up themselves and their families outside. Some of them get well enough to be tolerated, to hold a job, to salvage something out of life. But it is not a real cure."

Is there a cure for schizophrenia? Kovitz said, "A lot of sick people don't get well. People with tuberculosis, or cancer, or heart disease— they don't get completely well. In general, most schizophrenics have a pretty gloomy outlook. Some manic-depressives can have a few attacks and get well. Their illness is different. It's a self-limiting process, and even without treatment the depression probably would clear up in two or three years, but they pick up after two to four months on EST [electro-shock treatment]. But paranoid schizophrenia is a self-perpetuating process. A paranoid schizophrenic has built up a fixed system of delusions, and he gets something out of it, it helps him, and he doesn't dare give it up. He's a fighter, he hates to lose his self-esteem. Other types have as bad or worse an outlook as the paranoids. There is the defeatist, the surrendering, kind of schizophrenic. We call this hebephrenia, and it has a very poor outlook indeed, though occasionally one surprises us. People with fight and emotion, full of tension, striking out, who haven't given up, seem to have the best chance. It's partly a matter of how long they've been sick. But more important it's a matter of how much energy they can put into patching up their self-respect and admitting what they are. Some whom you have a feeling will improve do but then they slip back—one day they'll be doing fine, the next day they're tearing the plaster off the ceiling. Ordinary psychotherapy such as can be given in a place like this may be worse than useless. It may be dangerous. I know of one girl who was suffering tremendous tension at facing what was wrong in her life. The pressure was intolerable. So a psychotherapist trying to help her face it made her feel she was at the brink of hell. She went from bad to worse."

Some doctors think that there is really only one functional psychosis— that schizophrenia, manic-depressive psychosis, involutional melancholia and paranoia (a rare condition) are really all the same. In any case, the cause of all the functional psychoses is unknown. So is the cure. The cause of only a few major disorders, all organic, such as paresis, is known. Abraham Myerson has written, "The major mental diseases, the psychoses, are not in the least curable by psychotherapeutics, including psychoanalysis. Many of these diseases are favorably *influenced* by insulin coma, electric shock, and prefrontal lobotomy, but they are not cured in any final sense at all." One psychiatrist in a moment of wry despair defined psychiatry as "That branch of medical science which treats of a disease in which the pathogenesis is obscure, the symptoms dubious, the diagnosis difficult, and the cure unknown."

Dr. Kovitz said, "Apparently abnormal bodily processes help produce mental illness. Knowing how the new drugs work may help us understand this. It's something to start working on. There's evidence that the adrenal glands function differently in schizophrenic patients than they do in normal people, though nobody knows whether this is cause or effect." And there are many other promising research leads now under investigation, as we shall see.

Kovitz thought concern over "curing" psychosis useless. "Even the new drugs can't make a new person. There's a complexity of forces affecting the course of a patient here—physical, physiological, the conditions of hospital life, the attitudes of others. And the potential within the person himself is always of utmost importance. Not just in psychiatry but all throughout medicine you are trying to relieve symptoms and trust to nature and God to cure. In the case of a sprained ligament, the doctor doesn't heal it—he puts the patient to bed, and the ligament heals itself. Or in the case of heart failure, digitalis slows the heart and minimizes the effects—it doesn't cure anything. What we're trying to give is the same thing—symptomatic help, not cure. We help the patient and he gets along better. That's not so hopeless or tragic as some think. That's what all life is like. We give aspirin for a headache and I could give you a long theoretical discussion of what the aspirin does but it's just a lot of words. The point is, it makes you feel better. All our therapy here at the hospital is intended to make the patient more manageable, if you want to put it that way. And that's another way of saying that we're helping the patient to help himself. What do we mean help? Help him to feel better, act better, be more acceptable to the world. What we try to do is stop the malignant circle of the psychotic process and reverse it and start a benign circle, or at least slow down its velocity. The psychotic patient is a person who has gone into a tailspin. We try to give him a chance to pull out of it. That's all—and it isn't bad."

With so little known, why does anybody get well? Spontaneous remission, say most doctors—about a third of psychotic patients recover spontaneously. Sometimes the hospital, being a haven, helps—gives the patient a rest from the world he cannot face. And sometimes good things happen mysteriously. Once at Columbus State the doctors decided to perform brain surgery on a young girl. Despite insulin shock and electroshock, she had become more and more withdrawn and inaccessible. "She was deteriorating before our eyes," Kovitz recalled. "We decided to try surgery as a last resort." As a preliminary test they did a pneumoencephalogram on her—made an X-ray of the brain after draining away the spinal fluid and replacing it with air. Oddly, she seemed greatly improved after the pneumoencephalogram. So the doctors held off on their operation. Little by little she continued to improve. "The time came," Kovitz said, "when she was able to leave here—and remember, she was a chronic schizophrenic. She got a clerical job and so far as I know she's still got it. That was five years ago. So sometimes good things happen without your knowing why."

Perhaps the most hideous thing about mental illness is that the mentally ill suffer. Asked if this was so, Kovitz said, "Unquestionably," and doctors everywhere would agree. The depressed patient is truly depressed, just as you are when you are depressed, only infinitely more painfully. The catatonic who sits mute and stuporous, pulled to pieces by warring complexes, is in the grip of a terror almost beyond comprehension. "It is true," Kovitz said, "that some patients find a measure of peace through their illness—psychosis is one way of dealing with reality. But anyone who thinks that the patient likes this way of life is very much mistaken. A delusional world is not necessarily painless. Some delusional experiences are worse than the worst nightmares.

"Many people seem to think that a patient is either completely broken with reality or is not. This is wrong too. All of us have a side that is not in contact with reality. Just so, patients have a side that *is* in contact with reality. It is wrong to talk about patients in front of them. They know you're doing it. I once had a patient who said her head ached and I ordered aspirin, and the attendant laughed and said, 'No brains, no feeling.' This is an idea that Dorothea Dix was fighting a hundred years ago. In those days hospitals didn't bother to heat the wards because they thought the lunatics didn't know whether they were cold or not. It just isn't so. You've seen catatonics sitting in a stupor, they act as if they didn't know or care where they are. But even they know. Often after they come out of it they can tell you what was happening around them. They sit mute, like vegetables, but if you put them under Amytal they talk and you find out there's a lot going on inside them and some of it is pretty horrible. It would be comforting to think that psychotic patients don't suffer, that they're crazy and don't know what's going on anyway, that because they're living in their own world they're not hurt. But it just isn't so. A place like this is packed with human tragedy, people blocked off and locked off from life. Yet it is not so terrible as outsiders think, in one way. There have to be places like this for some people. But in another way it's ever so much worse than outsiders think, for the people here suffer terribly." He smiled a little. "The same tensions and inconsistencies and problems plague all of us. Sometimes I'll see in a patient's history problems so similar to my own it makes me jump. But I don't know why he's schizophrenic and I'm not quite."

In the twentieth century there has been a tendency to abandon the old word "insanity" and substitute "mental illness." This is inspired, no doubt, by a desire to erase the age-old stigma of "insanity" and by a recognition of kinship among normal people, neurotics and psychotics. But unfortunately the impression has arisen that "mental illness" is no worse than a bad cold. In America, perhaps the most psychiatrically oriented country in the world, it has become almost fashionable to visit a psychiatrist, to make light talk of "upsets" and "emotional disturbance." People tend to forget that serious mental illness is still, as it always was, a crippling shattering sickness. Kovitz has said, "Having a mental illness is a disastrous experience. It's hard to recuperate. It's hard to believe in yourself again. And many never do really get well again." Lately there has been heard the cry, "Buck up—there's nothing much wrong with you, you're just a little disturbed, and even if there is something seriously wrong, you can take a miracle pill and be as good as new." It just isn't so, any of it. The mentally ill are not merely a "little disturbed"—they are terribly and quite horribly sick. And there is no "miracle pill." Just as the word "asylum" was, in a strict sense, more apt than "mental hospital," so is there good reason for returning to the old word "insane," for if words have a meaning these people are not sane.

2

Inside the Asylum

■ When a new patient arrives at the hospital, whether in his own car or a police car, he is brought up the front steps and through the front door into the lobby. Sometimes a new patient comes in screaming, dragged by police, kicking at the nurses and doctors, crying out, as a wiry little old woman did, "Take me back, take your hands off me. Charles, bring me my medicine, Charles, take me back." An experienced attendant has said, "I'd rather see them come through that door fighting than any other way." Doctors agree: Patients who arrive most highly disturbed seem to have the best chance of recovery. But most arrive quietly and wait docilely beside the policeman while the switchboard girl calls over the echoing loudspeaker system the name of the admitting doctor.

This morning he was Dr. Robert Dane, a quiet soft-spoken twenty-nine-year-old man with bushy black hair and liquid features and dark brown sympathetic eyes. Coming to the lobby he checked the court commitment papers, then sat down beside the new patient and talked to him. How did he happen to come here? Who brought him here? Where is he? What is the date? When was he born? How does he feel? How have things been going at home? Can he substract 3 from 100, and 3 from that, and 3 from that, and so on? Can he name the months of the year backwards? From the answers to a few such questions, and by looking closely at the patient, Dr. Dane could form an impression of what was wrong with him. A catatonic schizophrenic, for example, may not answer at all but may merely sit mute; a man with cerebral arteriosclerosis may not be able to reverse digits. Dane's manner was friendly and casual, the offhand disarming way psychiatrists have of asking life-and-death questions; and to the most bizarre or hostile replies he was likely to merely nod and say, "Sure, sure." After a few minutes Dane called a nurse and told her where to take the patient—to the regular admitting ward, or, if Dane thought the patient dangerous or suicidal, to Ward 8, the acute disturbed ward. The nurse, a girl in white, took the patient by the elbow and led him away.

Dane stayed to talk to the patient's relatives. He told them when they might visit—any afternoon from one to three—and when they might consult the ward doctor—Wednesday and Friday from one to three—and what the patient must not have: matches, a cigarette lighter, nail file, pocket knife, more cash than a dollar or two, a watch. More importantly, Dane tried to reassure the relatives. "They have terrible ideas about this place. They think that over here we cut people up, tie them down, throw boiling water on them. They feel guilty about having brought the patient here at all. If you can allay their fears it helps an awful lot. Because a lot of our patients will be ready to go home on trial visit after a few months, and you want to pave the way. If you handle them well at the beginning it helps."

The men's admitting ward was Ward 2. The way to it from the lobby lay down a long narrow curving passageway which ended at a heavy solid steel door. The nurse unlocked it and the patient got his first look at a ward in a mental hospital. The place looked crowded and busy. Patients were mopping the floor, a nurse in white was walking rapidly down the ward, a tall thin patient was wandering slowly about, another was sitting huddled on a chair, knees drawn up to chin. About twenty-five patients were sitting in chairs ranged along the wall. One old man was sitting in a chair with his head down on his arms on a little table; his shoulders were shaking as though he were weeping inconsolably. The doorways of a few sleeping rooms were blocked by screens marked "Isolation." In these rooms were patients who had arrived with tuberculosis, and although the doctors tried to move them out quickly to the separate tuberculosis cottage, they might stay here a week or longer with the other new admissions. In other rooms were patients sick in bed with physical ailments, for Ward 2 was not only the male admitting ward, it was also the hospital's male medical ward. Psychotic patients are like anybody else in one respect: They get sick or hurt, and when they do they must be treated, and so the hospital is not only a psychiatric hospital but also a general medical hospital, performing appendectomies, setting fractured legs and dealing with pneumonia. Therefore at any one time the admitting ward might have a conglomerate assortment of patients of all sorts—a mischievous kid just in from jail, an eighty-five-year-old deteriorated schizophrenic with a broken hip, an acute raging maniac, a middle-aged man in a catatonic stupor for years who has now contracted pneumonia.

The new admission was stripped on arrival, bathed and examined physically. His clothing was sent out to be marked. He was given a short white hospital gown and a pair of floppy white hospital overalls. Young Dr. Dane interviewed him again and ordered any further studies he thought necessary—extensive psychological testing, including a Rorschach test; an electroencephalogram if the patient had a history of having "spells" or "fits"; spinal fluid and blood tests if there was a possibility of paresis. Ordinarily these tests took about a week. Then Dane presented the case to all the doctors on the staff, and they diagnosed his illness, prescribed treatment, assigned him to a ward, and in large measure charted his course in the hospital.

Let us sit in on a staff meeting.

2.

Staff was held every morning from ten to noon in a large open sunny room on the ward used for doctors' offices. The floor was terrazzo, the bare walls were painted pale green, sunlight slanted in through six high narrow windows in a bay. It was a pleasant though austere place. The doctors and social workers, ten or a dozen of them, sat around a long oak table, papers spread out before them. At the head of the table was a vacant chair for the patient. On his left sat Dr. Dane; on his right Dr. Kovitz; and the other doctors ranged down both sides of the table. At staff, Kovitz carried the load. The others might disagree as to diagnosis or treatment; Kovitz decided. The residents considered staff the most valuable part of their training. They were somewhat tense during staff, anxious to give correct opinions, listening closely to everything the patient said. Often they riffled through the APA diagnostic manual, hunting a category to fit the patient before their eyes. Staff put tremendous pressure on the patient too. Two patients had died at staff. It was worse at other hospitals, where staff was conducted formally in front of a hundred nurses, doctors and visitors. At some hospitals staff was used primarily for teaching, the staff seeing only a few admissions carefully selected. At Columbus staff saw virtually all new patients, five or six in an ordinary morning. Most took fifteen or twenty minutes.

This morning Dr. Dane was presenting the case history of a new patient, a middle-aged man who lived with his parents on their farm. His brother said he had been "worried and sad" for several weeks. His mother said, "Just wasn't himself. He wanted to be on the go all the time. Wouldn't go to bed. He wouldn't sleep over two hours at any time. He has threatened people and his own life." On admission he had gone immediately to bed and had told Dr. Dane he couldn't get up (but by subterfuge Dane had got him to do so). He had told Dane that he had had several fights recently, that since his most recent one he had not "felt right inside" and had been "suspicious and frightened." Dane, reading now rapidly and softly from his own admission notes, concluded, "He was flattened during the admission interview [that is, his capacity for emotional response was low]. I'm presenting him as a schizophrenic reaction, catatonic type with paranoid features." Dane put down his papers and went out into the hall and returned in a moment with the patient.

He was a tall thin man with sparse curly red hair, wearing white overalls and needing a shave. He looked at the doctors, bewildered and hesitant. They sat silent, looking at him. Dane invited him to sit down but he did nothing, only stood. Dane took him by the elbow and pushed him gently toward the chair. He sank slowly into it and sat with his elbows on the arms of the chair, his hands hanging limp, his mouth agape, looking down at the table, not looking up at anyone. Dane began, "Can you tell us how you happened to come here?"

After a long time he said, "I don't know."

"Was it your own idea?"

A pause, then, "No."

"They brought you?"

He did not answer. Dane asked, "Who brought you?"

He said, "I don't know."

Dane asked, "Are things different now than they used to be?"

The patient said, "Huh?"

Dane repeated the question, and after a long pause the patient mumbled something altogether unintelligible. His answers were agonizingly slow, his voice flat and toneless, his expression did not change—he looked scared to death. The interview seemed excruciatingly painful to him. He looked and acted like a very sick man.

Dane asked if he felt himself under strain, or tension.

"Yes."

"You described some unusual experience to me—do you remember?"

No answer.

"You said that sometimes you hear voices that talk to you. Do you still?"

With evident effort he said, "Not seldom."

Dane said, "Do you mean you frequently hear voices?"

"No."

"Is something chasing you, or after you?"

"I reckon."

"Can you tell us about that feeling?"

The patient paused a long time. Then, running his hand around his lips, he said, "I don't think so."

Dane looked at the other doctors around the table, and one, Dr. Saul C. Bookspan, a man in his forties with a clipped little mustache, asked, "Have you changed lately or have other people changed?"

The patient did not answer but he did look up at Dr. Bookspan.

"Would you tell us a little about what has happened to you?"

"I don't know what to say."

"Do you find it difficult to think at times?"

"Yes."

"About what?"

"About home."

"Is something wrong at home?"

"I think my mother's sick."

"Why?"

"She is worried about me."

"Why should she worry about you?"

He waited a long time, as though about to say something, but then he muttered, "I dunno," and gazed down at the table again, and one felt that the spark of human recognition which had been kindled had died.

Dr. Kovitz, hunched down a little in his chair, took up the questioning. "How do you feel about being here?"

"It's all right," the patient said in the same dull monotone.

"Do you feel there is a need for you to be in the hospital?"

He nodded.

"You realize you are not well?"

He nodded.

"Are you afraid of us?"

He did not answer, did not look up.

Dr. Kovitz looked around at the other doctors. None spoke. Dr. Kovitz asked the patient, "Is there anything you want to ask us?" He made no response. Kovitz ended the interview as he did all of them: "Thank you for talking to us. You can wait out in the hall." Dane had to get up and help him out. He limped a little, leaving, and Bookspan asked, "Is there anything wrong with the left leg?" Dane said he didn't know but it was difficult to get him to walk.

Dr. Kovitz said, smiling a little, "Well, what do you think, Dr. Bookspan?"

Bookspan said, "Catatonic schizophrenic. He's very perplexed. I *think* he's got a lot of tension. He's certainly withdrawn to the point of being schizophrenic. Whether shock treatment will help I don't know. It'd be worth a try."

"Dr. Lande?"

Dr. Elizebeth Lande, a tall middle-aged woman, said, "Catatonic schizophrenic." Dr. Mary Lou Hippert, an attractive young resident, agreed, but added that she thought she detected paranoid as well as catatonic features in the schizophrenia. To this Dr. Maria Madi, a distinguished-looking middle-aged Hungarian woman, added that "there was a little silliness in the last response," suggesting the hebephrenic type of schizophrenia. Kovitz spoke for himself: "I think he's almost surely catatonic and if there's no physical contraindication we ought to try EST. In view of his limp, though, we'd better get a pelvic X-ray before we do it, to make sure he didn't fracture his pelvis a long time ago." (Patients sometimes break hips or backs during the convulsions of EST.) "He ought to improve. The first onset in the early forties gives a favorable prognosis." The social worker was still making notes on all this when Dr. Dane began presenting the next patient.

3.

He had just been received from the State Hospital for the Criminally Insane at Lima, Ohio. Columbus had sent a violent patient of its own to Lima, one too difficult to handle, and since Lima was full to overflowing, had been obliged to accept this man in exchange. Dane, reading from the papers before him, said the patient had been sick off and on since about 1915. The son of well-to-do parents, he had gone to college and once had owned a farm but then he had fallen ill, had thought people and animals and Indians were following him, and finally in 1930 had been committed to a state hospital. In the ensuing twenty years he had escaped from it a dozen times, and the last time it had taken three deputy sheriffs to return him from his sister's home, where he was threatening her with a hatchet. After that he had been put in Lima. Dane said, "He told me he came here from Bushong's Better Boarding House," and the other doctors laughed—Dr. Bushong was superintendent of Lima. Dane brought the patient in.

He was in his sixties, a tall man with a fringe of white hair on his bald head. Smiling, he sat. Dr. Dane asked, "How are you feeling, sir?"

He replied, "Do you believe in air conditioning?"

"What happens when the air conditioning is on?"

"Might cover your face up," said the patient, with some conviction. "I was never signed in by the court."

Dr. Bookspan asked, "Do you feel you have been sick?"

"I've never been sick."

"Then why are you kept in the hospital?"

"Well, the air conditioning came down and they got in touch with the witches and the witches came in." He went on about the witches.

Bookspan asked if he knew where he was. He replied, "He got in trouble across the street. Berry came down. They came in and wanted me to come to the hospital for protection—I got hit several times. My shoulder." (His shoulder actually had been injured many years ago.) He lounged in his chair, at ease.

Dr. Kovitz took over. "Do you want to ask us any questions?"

He said, "I'd like to get the key and get out of here."

"You want to leave, do you?"

"Right this instant."

"How long have you been here?"

"Wednesday. The eleventh or twelfth." (Wrong.)

Dr. Kovitz said, "I think you'll have to stay with us for a while."

"Think I'll have to? I'll have to get an attorney then." But there was no threat in his voice at all.

Kovitz nodded, murmuring, "Get an attorney and get a writ. Do you have an attorney you could write to?"

"Mr. Johnson," he said promptly. "But whether he's still there or not I don't know. Can I get my clothes? Can I get a pencil and write him?"

Kovitz assured him he could, and the patient left.

Kovitz polled the doctors. Most thought him an "old paranoid schizophrenic," though two, pointing out that he did not seem sufficiently deteriorated for a man who had been schizophrenic forty years, suggested he might be suffering from a chronic brain syndrome, senile brain disease or paresis.

Kovitz said, "We should remind ourselves that age doesn't make the diagnosis. Nothing about him suggests CBS with senility. He's a typical deteriorated paranoid schizophrenic. You can just see the faded remnants of paranoid trends in his talk about getting a key but if you give him an order he'll do it. He has poor judgment and is impractical, you can't say he's undeteriorated. What we're seeing is a hebephrenic change in a man who was paranoid. How you classify him by the textbook I don't know. Now he's more hebephrenic than anything else. He has the chronic schizophrenic affect, the washed-out persecutory feeling. His thinking is, 'I ought to be out'—but he doesn't act that way. Your true paranoid schizophrenic is more consistent. But they burn out. You find a lot of them here, sitting on the bench talking to someone who isn't there."

Dr. Bookspan asked, "Is the classification, then, what we see now or the basic one?"

Kovitz smiled. "The terms don't fit. Our classification of schizophrenia is absolutely unscientific. But it doesn't matter. He is purely a custodial problem—there is nothing to do but take care of him."

Young doctors, as they are the first to admit, tend to lay great store by diagnosis. Actually, as an older doctor has said, "diagnosis is often an academic question—the treatment is the same anyway," for the methods of treating mental disease are few. Nonetheless, diagnosis has its uses; it is a shorthand way, as Dr. Kovitz has said, of speaking about the past experience of psychiatry—"What do this kind of people do, what are their problems, what are the dangers?"

Dr. Wedemeyer, the superintendent, who had come in and now sat against the wall, added, "We ought to keep an eye on him—he wants to walk off." Kovitz agreed.

4.

The next patient was another old man, nearly eighty, and he too had been in a mental hospital before but the doctors reached an entirely different conclusion about him. He was a large florid-faced man, extremely garrulous, and he greeted the doctors pleasantly. Dr. Dane said, "How are you feeling, Dad?"

"Oh, fine."

"That's good. By the way, do you remember my name?"

"Your name? No, can't say as I do." (Dane had told it to him twice on Ward 2, most recently a few hours ago.) "What is your name, anyway?"

Dane told him and spelled it. The patient spelled his own name, then, rising, shook hands with Dane. Dane invited him to be seated and asked why he was here.

The patient said, "I'm here for a checkup."

"I see. How are things going at home?"

"Well, my wife she's awful nervous."

"Do you have any children?"

Five, he said.

How old were they?

"Well, the oldest was born at the time of the big flood—that'd be 1913—well, it'd be 1913 to 1955, that'd be—" and he thought hard. "I used to be able to do that in my head but I can't any more." (Dane had asked him previously to take 3 from 100 in series but he couldn't.)

Dane asked him about a "black-out" he had described.

"Well, yes. I was going out and buy fifty pounds of beans, I was writing checks and everything else, and I had this black-out, guess I tried to lift too much, I get a little stiff in my legs sometimes," and he chattered on about his legs then about the hospital, saying, "Couldn't nobody treat me better in my life than they treated me here," saying the medicine was free, the food all right, he didn't mind being here at all, but he didn't like his ward—"too many wallflowers settin' around there. But they don't bother me, I don't have anything to do with 'em. Other day a nurse asked me if I'd take one of 'em to the sixth ward and I said, 'No, I'll sweep out the rooms if they take the sick people out but that's all.' "

Kovitz asked if he had any questions.

He said, "I'm not asking any questions. I don't think it's for me to ask questions." They excused him and he left, still talking, asking Dane's first name, shaking hands with Dr. Kovitz, Dane assuring him he'd get him off the admitting ward soon "and when you get on a ward there'll be other fellows that you can go out in the yard with."

When he had gone, Kovitz polled the staff. They agreed: Chronic brain syndrome with arteriosclerosis. Kovitz asked, "What shall we do with him? Think we can improve him? He was here before and went home. We don't have Metrazol right now."

Another doctor said, "The pharmacist says he can make some up on prescription."

Kovitz said, "Is that so? Then let's try nicotinic acid and Metrazol." He turned to Dane, asked, "Is he better than on admission?"

"Yes."

"Let's also give vitamin B complex. If he becomes overactive he should be considered for low doses of Serpasil."

5.

The next patient was a Negro with an odd steady stare, his mouth slack, his voice slow and hesitant, with long pauses between sentences. He said he felt "all right." He'd been "nervous" about four years. How did his nerves bother him? "Oh, you heard me—sweep the sidewalk." He had spells, sometimes falling down. What happened after the spells? "Feed the dog."

Kovitz asked if he could say "Methodist Episcopal."

He replied, "I go to church every Sunday."

Kovitz said, not unkindly but with authority, "Will you say the words Methodist Episcopal for me?"

He did, but slurred them badly.

Kovitz asked him to write his name and address, and he did, with difficulty and in a deteriorated script.

Dr. Wedemeyer said, in a loud and distinct voice, "A long time ago did you have treatment for bad blood?" ("Bad blood" is a colloquialism for syphilis.)

"Yes."

"How long ago?"

"About one year."

"But I mean a long time ago."

"No, I went to college. I husked corn."

He left. Kovitz said, "It's probably open and shut—he fits the picture of a paretic in every respect. He shows slight slurring of speech, mild euphoria, slightly unequal pupils, and he is partly disoriented." A younger doctor seemed surprised, and Dr. Kovitz said, "We wouldn't think of paresis because we don't see many any more. When I came here in 1946 from 7 to 10 per cent of our admissions were paresis. Now less than 2 per cent are. It's traded places with alcoholic psychosis." Paresis had disappeared because a specific cure, penicillin, had been found for the disease that causes it, syphilis. It is not impossible that one day some specific cure will be found for schizophrenia and other mental diseases. Kovitz said, "We'll make the diagnosis CBS with syphilitic brain disease. But confirm the diagnosis with a spinal."

6.

On alternate days the staff saw male and female patients. One day before them came a Negro woman in her thirties. She had been here several years earlier when she had heard voices and suspected people of persecuting her. Diagnosed schizophrenia, mixed type, catatonic and paranoid, she had been discharged as improved after several months of electroshock treatment. The hallucinations and delusions had disappeared.

Now they had reappeared. She had been brought to the hospital a few days ago after a fight with a "neighbor girl." Upon admission she had told Dr. Wilson P. Shortridge that the neighbor girl put a Dictaphone in her house to spy on her, the voices told her so. She had said the girl accused her, wrongly, of carrying on a love affair with the girl's husband. She had said her own husband did not want her in the house and she did not want to be there. Her husband, she had said, threatened to return her to the hospital unless she did as he wished. She was not really married to him, though they had lived together a long time and had several children. To Dr. Shortridge she had seemed oriented—known where she was, who she was, what time it was—but very nervous. Nearly weeping she had told Shortridge, "I don't want any more electric shock treatments. I am afraid of them." In response to Shortridge's routine question about the meaning of the proverb that a bird in the hand is worth two in the bush, she had said, "Hold on to what you've got and don't reach out. But I don't have anything." Shortridge had thought her judgment only fair. Asked what she would do if permitted to leave the hospital, she had said, "I've just got a dollar. I'll take fifty cents for a show and fifty cents to go find a job."

Shortridge had been interested in her. He brought her in now, a handsome well-built woman carrying a toothbrush. She stated correctly where she was, when she had come here and why. She told them about the neighbor girl. "The idea of her pickin', just plain pickin', she's picked on me too long, she picked up something, I went in the house,

I was nervous. Before they came her sister had me by the hair, because I don't fight two women, she had a stick so I give up." She was full-figured and might once have been almost beautiful.

Shortridge asked, "Do you think it's possible you're not well?" She said, her fingers tensely intertwining, "I'm nervous," and then, in a taut strained voice, "I wasn't loved. That's a lot of it. I wasn't loved enough."

Shortridge, his face boyish, said, "Have you felt unhappy?"

"Yes. I couldn't help it. They didn't have enough love. God knows somebody loves me."

Shortridge paused. Kovitz took up the questioning, leaning forward close to her, his voice quiet: "Does your husband love you?"

"He doesn't care. I have two children. Next time a man wants me he can marry me, he can get a license."

"Why didn't he get a license?"

"Because I had a baby."

"How old were you?"

"Twenty-four. I didn't know any better. I came from the South. I was scared. That's why I did it. I had my first big lovin'," and she broke and sobbed deeply. Her sobbing was the only sound in the room.

Kovitz said, "How many children do you have?"

"Two children. My husband, the first thing he bought me was a suit."

"How does your husband treat you?"

"He fights with me. And he drinks."

"So you couldn't stand it any longer and you got too nervous."

"I didn't care. I was going to leave my children and the whole business."

Her voice was rising; Kovitz's was soft and even: "Does this Dicta-phone continue to talk to you here?"

"Yes. Sometimes."

"What does it say?"

She sat silent a long time, she seemed to gather herself, you could see her body tautening; she leaned forward and burst out: " 'Women's rights! Women's rights!' it says." She sank back in her chair wearily.

Kovitz looked swiftly around the table then said, "Is it referring to your rights especially?"

"It just refers to people," and her voice sounded tired.

"Do you feel you haven't had your rights?"

She did not answer.

"How do you feel about staying at the hospital?"

No answer.

Kovitz said gently, "You're not really well enough to go home, you know. Are you afraid of being here? Afraid of the treatment?"

She looked up, her dark eyes apprehensive: "Yes."

"Would you try some other kind of treatment?"

"It won't help."

Kovitz said, "I can't promise you it will help but it helps some people and I can promise you it won't hurt you or frighten you. Will you try it?"

She looked at him a long moment then nodded slowly.

He said, "Thank you for talking to us. You can wait out in the hall now."

She got up slowly, almost painfully, as an old woman moves, though she was just past her twenties, and walked out into the hall.

The doctors were silent a moment. Kovitz smiled a little and looked around the table, saying, "She feels that she was at fault because she embarked on the situation with her 'husband' in the first place. The general philosophic ideas in schizophrenia always can be turned back to the personal problem. It's interesting that the Dictaphone speaks of women's rights. She feels that she had been denied *her* rights. And in a sense she has. I'd like to hold her off EST and try Frenquel when we get some." (Frenquel was then a new tranquilizing drug.) He looked at Dr. Gordon Smith, smiling a little. "This is a patient worth spending some time with if you're able to do so. I don't know if you can."

Dr. Smith, the resident in charge of the acute women's ward where this patient would go, shook his head—single-handed, he was trying to take care of three hundred patients.

Kovitz said to young Dr. Shortridge, "Maybe you can do it."

Shortridge said, "I would be very glad to." He would see the patient an hour a week for individual psychotherapy.

Kovitz polled the doctors. Bookspan said, "She shows the features of a paranoid schiz but she's not flat enough."

One of the doctors remarked that she had become disturbed without any apparent reason. Kovitz said, "No one is ever disturbed without reason. Even if it's nothing disappointing that we can see, it's disappointing to the patient. She can't handle her situation. Dr. Smith?"

"I think I'd vote for paranoid. Though I'm well aware of the catatonic features."

Kovitz nodded. He said, "Let's call it acute undifferentiated with paranoid and catatonic features. It will be interesting to test Frenquel on someone so schizophrenic. If she were an emergency I'd start her on something else while we're waiting for the Frenquel—though she's already depressed and Thorazine seems to make depressions worse." He thought a moment, then, to Shortridge: "Well, Doctor, you keep an eye on her and if she's disturbed we'll start her on something."

7.

"What we need above all else," said Superintendent Wedemeyer, "is more people to do more things—doctors, nurses, attendants, occupational therapists, everything." He was sitting in his modest office overlooking the flowerbeds in front of the hospital. Wedemeyer said he could use at least half again as many nurses and attendants as he had. He needed a few fully-trained, Board-certified psychiatrists to supervise more closely the work of the residents. The three he had "can only spread themselves just so thin." Moreover, more Board-certified doctors would attract more residents and encourage the Board of Psychiatry and Neurology and the Council on Medical Education and Hospitals of the American Medical Association to approve the hospital as a three-year residency training center. The hospital's most pressing physical need was for a separate medical and surgical building so it could stop mingling the physically sick with new admissions. As to the basic building, old though it was, Wedemeyer felt it was adequate.

Dr. Wedemeyer, a big, affable crew-cut man of forty-seven, described himself as "a practical man." Born in Gallipolis, Ohio, the son of a farmer who urged him to become a doctor, he graduated from Ohio State University Medical School in 1933, went into the army, and served at army hospitals in Indiana. In 1936 he went into private general practice in Oak Hill, Ohio, a town of two thousand. When the war began he went back to the army. He became interested in psychiatry. He went to England in 1944 as flight surgeon of a combat squadron—"a general practice with a good many psychiatric problems." He got out in 1945 and went back to general practice in Oak Hill.

"But I was looking for opportunities in the psychiatric field," he said. "I felt it was going to be my primary interest. I had contracted

undulant fever and general practice was much too strenuous for me."
In April, 1946, he came to Columbus State Hospital as a resident in
psychiatry. He stayed a year, spent two years across the street at Columbus State School as a resident, then went to work as a psychiatrist at
Ohio State Penitentiary, examining new prisoners and making psychiatric evaluations for the parole board. He resigned to become director
of the Toledo Mental Hygiene Center, a community clinic. The superintendent of Columbus State Hospital died and Wedemeyer replaced
him June 16, 1952. Wedemeyer was not a Board-certified psychiatrist,
though he was eligible to take his Board examinations.

He was, however, certified by the American Psychiatric Association
as a mental hospital administrator. A great deal of Wedemeyer's time
was taken up with nonpsychiatric work—hiring employees, settling
their grievances, dealing with breakdowns at the powerhouse, making
speeches in town, above all making up his budget—but nevertheless
he agreed with the APA that a mental hospital superintendent should
be a psychiatrist. Many relatives of patients insist on seeing the superintendent, the highest authority, and Wedemeyer thought it important
that the highest authority be a psychiatrist. And everything that happens in a mental hospital, including administrative actions, affects the
mental condition of the patient, whether it is intended to or not.
Wedemeyer and his wife lived in a large apartment in the main
building. Formerly he had paid only a nominal sum for his rent and
food. In 1955 he and all other superintendents and doctors and attendants were taken off maintenance and given higher salaries. Wedemeyer's pay rose to $18,500 a year.

Wedemeyer got onto the first-floor wards frequently; he visited other
wards occasionally; he sat in on staff several times a week. He rarely
saw his own superior, the Director of the Department of Mental
Hygiene and Corrections in the downtown office. "I spend my time
running this place day to day," he said, "operating the place with what
is handed to me, hoping I'll get what I need."

When Wedemeyer took over the job, as he said, "the entire operation showed evidence of having had a sick man for superintendent.
The rolls were all confused. We had people in the hospital that we
couldn't legally keep. We had voluntary patients who had been here for
years and years and years—some seemed to be simply living off the state.
There was a little clique of alcoholics who lived here, stayed long enough
to sober up, left and got drunk, came back for a while. We had to clean

house. Then, there was friction between the nurses and the attendants. The attendants had been here a long time and thought they ought to run things. The registered nurses were new. I put the nurses in charge. There was considerable dissatisfaction among the doctors—there hadn't been any promotions for a long time. There were dissatisfied attendants who thought they were doing the work of a charge attendant [one in charge of a ward] but were only getting the base pay. We began to get more nurses and more doctors. When I came here there were eleven doctors. Now we've got eighteen and we've had up to twenty. There were ten or twelve registered nurses; now there are twenty-eight or twenty-nine. We reorganized the psychology department and Social Service. We've rehabilitated all but seven of the twenty-eight wards in the main building—painted them, rewired them to eliminate fire hazards, replaced wooden floors with terrazzo. There's been no basic change in therapy—but all in all, I think we're giving the patients better care now than they used to get."

Wedemeyer was trying to run a good hospital. He said, "We try to impress on attendants that the patients are human beings with some rights and dignities." Not only attendants forget this: A while back a research foundation had requested permission to implant cancer tissue for research purposes in patients; Wedemeyer had indignantly refused: "Not at *my* hospital, you won't."

8.

Columbus State was a vast establishment. No fewer than fifteen buildings were scattered about its 333 acres. It was a huge rural or parklike tract, plunked down not far from the center of modern Columbus. When it had been built it was on the edge of town but in 1955 Columbus State was surrounded by a neighborhood of small homes and flats and a small shopping district on Broad Street. This was an old part of town, a workingman's section, with houses crowded close to one another.

The main building of Columbus State sat on the brow of a hill commanding a fine view of the city. Below and in front of it stretched its fields and farms. Behind it were its other buildings—greenhouse, powerhouse, tuberculosis cottage, commissary, homes for the doctors and a cluster of one-story and two-story buildings called "the cottages" where aged and chronic patients were kept. Far back toward the railroad tracks was the hospital's little cemetery, where the unclaimed bodies of patients lay buried. (But recently such bodies have been turned over to Ohio State University for research.)

Blacktop driveways wound round the buildings through the trees. The place looked peaceful but not uninhabited. It had a life of its own. Patients were working in the greenhouse and in the garden, digging, hoeing, pushing wheelbarrows. At mealtime lines of patients from the cottages moved slowly along the sidewalk toward the main building. Children of the doctors played on the grass in front of their homes. They talked to privileged patients who were strolling about the grounds; sometimes they formed friendships with the patients and were saddened when they died. One doctor's son delivered newspapers to the hospital. Sometimes patients baby-sat for the doctors' wives of an afternoon; sometimes doctors' wives took patients out for drives in the city. Patients washed the doctors' cars and cleaned their houses and did their housework.

In the small brick commissary behind the main building privileged patients sat with their relatives in booths along the wall, sipping milkshakes served by patients. A former attendant dropped in to drink a Coke with an attendant still working here. A former patient joined them. Something draws people, attendants and patients alike, back to the hospital long after they have left. Do they miss its security?

The heart of the whole vast establishment was the enormous sprawling main building. It was always busy, never still. Throughout its echoing corridors the loudspeaker blatted continually, paging doctors. At lunchtime the bare cafeteria was filled with white-capped nurses and white-coated doctors, and their talk was of patients who had become such problems that they were known all over the hospital, of doctors who had left, of newcomers to the staff, of parties they had been to or were going to, of a drinking party in the out-patient clinic some years before when two doctors got into a fight. In the lobby relatives lined up at the receptionist's desk to register to visit, looking apprehensive and shamefaced. A patient passed through, running an errand for a doctor. A doctor and two nurses chatted by the Coke machine. Dr. Kovitz stopped by the assistant superintendent's office to discuss a patient: "Do you know her? She's in her teens. She came to us after she'd nearly killed her brother or her sister, I forget which. She wants to go home for a weekend and her father wants her to but I don't know, it's a decision I don't like to make by myself. The father doesn't seem to have much of an idea of the risks involved, she might be all right for a short time but I'd worry if she was there very long."

At lunchtime long lines of patients, escorted by nurses and attendants, filed through the building to the enormous dining hall, eating at long tables. (The infirm and acutely disturbed ate on their own wards.) Below was the kitchen, a vast place, and the storerooms. Below that in a sub-basement was a labyrinth of dark corridors and rooms, like catacombs—locked bins filled with many years' accumulation of trash, desks, unclaimed clothing left by patients, moldy suitcases, couches, coffins. In the workshops at the rear patients were at work painting and hammering and sawing, repairing the hospital's furniture.

9.

The problems of such a hospital, however well run, are enormous, and often very odd. In 1954 the hospital had to replace 1,677 pieces of window glass broken by patients. Patients are totally unpredictable. A patient who worked at the commissary, seemingly nearly well, one day went downtown to see the governor. (She only wanted to tell him what a nice place the hospital was.) Escapes were frequent, not from the wards, but from the grounds, whence privileged patients could simply stroll to Broad Street and take a trolley bus downtown. In one Eastern hospital, when a patient escaped, the whole staff went out to search the swamp, but here the superintendent either notified the police if he considered the patient dangerous or more often did nothing, figuring that the patient would go home and if his relatives didn't want him they would bring him back.

The problems of treating the physical ailments of psychotics are great. Dr. Raymond T. Beitzel, who handled them, said, "They're so involved in their own world of fantasy that they can't give you any kind of a medical history to aid your diagnosis. Half the time they don't bother to tell you they're sick. One morning the ward nurse will notice that so and so doesn't look right, looks tired, didn't eat his breakfast, and she'll send him down to us and he'll have pneumonia—but he may not run a temperature at all. Then, they just can't co-operate with the doctor. After an operation they'll tear the dressing off, or take a pair of scissors and cut the stitches. They won't settle down and rest and do what they're told, so you have to sedate them—but in some cases you can't, in pneumonia, for example, so you have to decide whether it's better to restrain them physically or let them go as they are."

No matter how carefully perils are estimated, some are overlooked.

Once a patient fell ill, ran a high temperature, was given all imaginable tests, baffled the doctors and finally died; an autopsy showed that her stomach had been perforated in thousands of places, for she had eaten the seeds from a canary cage on the ward. Suicide is always a danger but the most elaborate precautions cannot anticipate every method a psychotic can devise. The hospital usually had about one a year. One patient tore up a book and stuffed the pages in her mouth, suffocating. Another crawled through a basement window and hanged himself. Another cut his throat with a toothbrush container.

Fire in a mental hospital is a nightmare, yet well-meaning relatives cannot be dissuaded from giving patients matches, even on disturbed wards. Homicidal attacks are not uncommon. One night an attendant was labeling bottles in the ward office alone when a patient came in and, as he did every night, said he was going to write a check to the attendant for a million dollars; instead he grabbed a pair of scissors and stabbed the attendant in the chest. Every so often doctors or attendants find weapons hidden on the wards—switch knives, a doorknob in a sock, a sharpened spoon, a fork bent into the shape of a pair of brass knuckles, a butcher knife. One day a patient told her ward doctor she had something she wanted to give him. She gave him a gun and one hundred rounds of ammunition. She had ordered it from a mail-order house and it had been delivered by express, despite regulations that no patient may open a package on the ward except in an attendant's presence. (The doctor said, "I don't think she intended to use it—I think she just wanted to create an impression. She did that all right.")

One night about 1 A.M. an attendant who had to take care of three chronic men's wards alone, entering Ward 14, found a flower stand wrecked on the floor. In a six-bed dormitory he found a patient, a sixty-five-year-old deteriorated paretic, in bed with his head crushed. The weapon, a leg from the flower stand, lay nearby. The patient was dead by the time Wedemeyer arrived. The night supervisor had visited the ward about twenty minutes before the killing and found him wandering around the hall, mumbling to himself, as he often did; the supervisor suggested he go back to bed, and he did, and was killed a few minutes later. The attendant who found him noticed that the man in the next bed, a husky catatonic schizophrenic Negro of forty-three, was restless. Superintendent Wedemeyer took the Negro to a seclusion room on Ward 16. He seemed confused and said only that the voices "up there" were bothering him and that he had been moved from his bed because "it was wet there." (It was, with blood and tissue.) Another patient in the dormitory said he had been awakened by a noise, had looked up and had seen the Negro standing beside the dead man's bed. Next morning the Negro said he had done it: He had broken up the flower stand and taken the leg of it in both hands and hit the patient because the voices "from down there" told him to. The Negro was sent to Lima State Hospital.

Not surprisingly, the affair upset all the doctors. Before the day passed they requested Wedemeyer to transfer dangerous patients off their own chronic wards. Could the killing have been prevented? Should the Negro have been on a disturbed ward, and locked in a seclusion room? He had been considered dangerous for years, often in restraint or seclusion. He was tubercular but could not be handled in the tuberculosis cottage, where there were female patients and no seclusion room. An attendant once wrote of him: "Patient fights to kill." By 1949 his behavior had improved, and he was moved to Ward 16, a quiet chronic ward. Occasionally he still became noisy at night and had to be put in seclusion. On March 4, 1955, he was transferred to Ward 14 because Ward 16 was being remodeled. The ward doctor noted that he should be moved back to 16 as soon as possible so he could be secluded at night. But he never was returned; he was kept on 14 and given Amytal at night, and it was on 14 that he killed his fellow patient.

Now, ideally, he should have been kept in seclusion every night. Ideally, if he had to be moved off Ward 16, he should have been sent to another ward with seclusion rooms, not to 14. But he wasn't. Why not? Doctors and attendants are too busy to give such problems careful consideration. But even had they had unlimited time it is doubtful if they would have considered the Negro dangerous enough to take any unusual steps. Superintendent Wedemeyer said, "It's all very well to say that you shouldn't have potentially dangerous patients on an open ward like that—but a large percentage of our population are potentially dangerous. You can't lock up everybody all the time. Originally all the sleeping rooms had doors on them—they were just cells. Over the years the doors have been taken off. Basically we're trying to get away from doors and locks. Any catatonic schizophrenic is potentially dangerous. Any catatonic can sit on a bench for days, then suddenly for no reason clench his fist and hit the patient next to him. They tend to turn all their troubles inward—that's why they sit speechless and won't eat—and bottle them up inside and all at once it all boils over and for a short period a terrible explosion takes place." The only solution Wedemeyer could suggest was to hire enough attendants—impossible on his budget—to have at least one attendant on every ward on all three shifts. The killing took place on a ward that an attendant had to leave unguarded because he was responsible for three wards. Had he been on hand he might have seen or heard the Negro breaking up the flower stand. But of course he might not have. The plain truth is that the problems of such a place are enormous and many of them can't be solved.

10.

The shortage of attendants is only one result of the chronic financial starvation of this hospital and of all state hospitals. In 1955 Columbus State spent $2.60 a day a patient. It fed a patient for 16¢ per meal. There were only four stenographers for the entire hospital and they were constantly leaving, for they were paid only $162 a month. "You call up an employment agency and they laugh at you," Wedemeyer said. The hospital records of many patients were inadequate. There were virtually no patients' records on the wards, where the doctors needed them; Wedemeyer couldn't put them there because he couldn't buy a filing cabinet for each ward. "We might be able to get them over a period of five years," he said, "but if we do we'll have to go without something else." When two generators in the power plant wore out, they were replaced at a cost of $225,000, all the money that had been appropriated to build a new cottage. "So we got the two new generators, but we suffered one new building," Wedemeyer said. Disturbed patients must be fed on the wards, which had no electric refrigerators —only old-fashioned iceboxes, and not only milk and butter but some medicines had to be kept in them. Wedemeyer was installing a drinking fountain on every ward "as fast as I can get a hundred dollars here, a hundred dollars there." The hospital had no bread slicer, and so bread came to the wards in long loaves and had to be sliced there with sharp knives—on disturbed wards. Moreover, the unwrapped bread sometimes fell off the trucks and rolled into the gutter, then was picked up and sent on. "I put a bread slicer and wrapper in my budget twice and it was cut out," Wedemeyer said. Then he exploded: "And I'm going to get one this year if I don't buy another damn thing for the culinary department. A bread slicer and wrapper. And a bean snipper— a bean snipper costs only four or five hundred dollars, but we haven't got one, and every time we have a good crop of beans we have fifty

men standing around snipping beans for two months out of the year—
patients."

Patients' families make problems too. One visitor brought a bottle
of wine to the ward, and when Wedemeyer barred her from the
hospital, she went to see the governor. One husband who had abandoned his wife when she fell ill became interested in her again when
she improved; he visited her and took her out on the grounds and
there got into an argument with her, twisted her arm, and called her
names; she relapsed and became disturbed again. Relatives badger
doctors for favors they can't grant—to take the patient home or out
for a ride before he is well enough. Sometimes relatives neglect
patients; sometimes they bedevil them. Disturbed themselves, they
confuse the patient. One doctor has said, "In most cases my big problem
is that the families don't care enough. The patient has been here fifteen
or twenty years, nobody cares about him any more." A while back a
doctor finally got a patient well enough to go home and so notified
his brother; the brother replied: "I regret to inform you that there are
no adequate provisions to accommodate him. . . . Perhaps you could
find employment for him around the hospital." The doctor remarked,
"So you see, once in a while we do help patients—and then this."

Relatives, of course, suffer too, and deeply. A widow who received
her eldest son home with high hopes was soon obliged to write the
superintendent:

DEAR DOCTOR,
    In regard to [my son], I was just wondering what I am to do. . . . You
can't tell where you are at with him some days seem real good then again
he gets real fussy have to let him have his own way can't talk to him. He
still has his three guns loaded and here of late been shooting the revolver
off two different times in the alley after I go to work so the neighbors tell
me. . . . Smokes cigarettes in bed and has hole burnt in rug in front of
his bed clear through the rug beneath, matches on the floor or on furniture where ever he is at. I'm just afraid he going to burn us out, it's a
worry when I leave till I get home again. At the table he handles all the
pieces of meat on the plate till he decides what one he wants, then if he
don't want it throw it back for you to eat. . . . He worried his Dad to
death, now he is gone and I am left to get along the best I can.

The hospital took him back.

When relatives brought a new patient to the hospital they were
given a little green booklet, crudely mimeographed by patients, telling

them what they should know. It closed: "By having the patient admitted here, you and the hospital have embarked on a co-operative plan to help him. You cannot cure the patient alone; neither can we do it without your co-operation. We need each other's help in this and hope that we can be successful in accomplishing what you and the patient want most, his return home to a successful and happy life." It is a brave, almost heroic, hope, and sometimes it comes true.

3

The Past

■ The Central Ohio Lunatic Asylum, as Columbus State Hospital originally was called, opened its doors to its first patient 120 years ago, on November 30, 1838. It was a pioneer state hospital. The states were only beginning to assume responsibility for the care of the insane. Columbus, like other such institutions, offered its patients little but sheer custody. Even this represented great progress, for previously the insane had been allowed to roam the countryside or had been locked up in jails.

2.

Psychiatry as a term is only about a hundred years old. But mental illness is as old as man. And as widespread—not only have men been mentally ill since the beginnings of history but they have been mentally ill wherever they lived and whether in civilized societies or in primitive tribes.

The history of psychiatry and of the treatment of the mentally ill goes back to the Greeks and the ancient Hindus, but such isolated monuments as their altars and healing temples, where "cures" were effected by gods and priests, emphasize the "union of religion and psychology . . . destined to play a critical and almost fatal role in the history of psychiatry," as Gregory Zilboorg has noted in his authoritative book *A History of Medical Psychology.* Similarly, though Hippocrates, the "father of medicine," devised a classification of mental

44

diseases that included terms still in use—epilepsy, mania, melancholia, paranoia—he established no continuing or meaningful science, for the Church of the Middle Ages returned to ancient mystique and treated the problem in terms of demonology—the mad were still "possessed." The "cure" for madness—as for heresy—in this system was by fire or water. The rebirth of scientific inquiry in the Renaissance led to the "physic" of the seventeenth century, when the treatments were emetics, purgatives and bloodletting. Still treatment was for only the fortunate few, and the poor insane wandered as pariahs, sometimes permitted to seek alms, or were imprisoned in chains and fetters. Such early "hospitals" as Bethlehem in England (which gave the language "bedlam") and the Bicêtre in Paris used neck chains fastened to walls as restraint and daily whippings as "treatment." And a favorite Sunday sport of Shakespeare's day was to visit Bethlehem to watch the mad disport themselves, a practice that survived long enough to account for the fence around Columbus State. Near the end of the eighteenth century Joseph Daquin stated the ends of modern psychiatry when he declared that a hospital for the mentally ill should have as its objectives not confinement but treatment and research. Philippe Pinel, director of the Bicêtre during the French Revolution, struck the chains from some of his patients because "it is my conviction that these mentally ill are intractable only because they are deprived of fresh air and of their liberty." And when in 1795 the Quakers, urged on by William Tuke, a merchant who had been roused by a woman's death in an asylum, opened the York Retreat, a humanitarian hospital where kindness replaced restraint and abuse, a new day had begun.

The barbarisms of the Old World were at first paralleled in the New. The American colonists put the insane in stocks, in jail, in the poorhouse; they sold them like slaves; at Salem they burned them for witches. The first American hospital to receive mentally ill patients was the Pennsylvania Hospital in Philadelphia, opened in 1752. It kept them chained to the walls under guard of "cell keepers." But it did attempt to treat them—shaved and blistered their scalps, bled and purged them. In 1768 Virginia passed a law providing for the care by the state of the mentally ill, and in 1773 it opened a hospital at Williamsburg, Virginia. Thus was established the principle that the states—not the cities, not private individuals—are primarily responsible for the hospital care of the mentally ill, the principle that guides American policy today.

3.

The first Ohio law providing for the care of the mentally ill was passed in 1815. In 1821 the state began to contribute to the support of patients in a county hospital in Cincinnati which is now Longview State Hospital. The Central Ohio Lunatic Asylum, the forerunner of Columbus State Hospital, was Ohio's first true state institution. It was established upon the urging of physicians led by Dr. William Maclay Awl, an early leader of American psychiatry. Born in 1799 in Pennsylvania, he studied medicine there and, in 1826 when twenty-seven, set out on foot for Ohio. He saw his first psychotic patient while practicing in a small Ohio town. In 1833 he moved to Columbus, at that time a town of four thousand with ten physicians. He gained prominence during a typhoid epidemic. On his call and that of other doctors, a convention of Ohio physicians met January 5, 1835, in Columbus, and out of it came the impetus for all the benevolent institutions in Ohio, including those for the insane, blind, and deaf and dumb. Dr. Awl urged the need for an insane asylum upon the community and the legislature. On March 7, 1835, the legislature authorized the purchase of land for "A Lunatic Asylum for the State of Ohio" and appointed three men to direct the project, including Dr. Awl, who became the first superintendent of the hospital. On April 20, 1837, convicts from the Ohio Penitentiary laid the first stone. The first patient was admitted November 30, 1838.

The new hospital stood on a sixty-four-acre tract of land on East Broad Street, then beyond the city limits, now near the heart of town. It cost about $150,000. It was built by convict labor. It could be seen from all parts of town. Dr. Awl wrote—and the description echoes at many points that of Columbus State Hospital today—"It is a stupendous pile of brick and stone work, which presents an imposing appearance." Its main building was ornamented with an Ionic portico. Its center section contained the staffs' offices and sleeping quarters. Its two wings contained the patients. Women occupied one wing, men the other. In each wing was a ward hall one hundred feet long, off which opened individual sleeping rooms. Behind the main building were two smaller buildings where "the violent and filthy classes" were kept in solitary confinement. (The custom of pushing patients into the back wards began early.) The asylum had space for 140 patients. Many people thought it extravagantly large. Within a few years it had to be expanded. A later superintendent wrote, "Since then whenever any hospital has been opened for this unfortunate class, the same hopes have been entertained at its inception; the same delusion has reappeared, only in like manner to be dispelled."

4.

Patients flocked to the hospital. By the end of 1839, its first full year, 157 patients had been admitted; 43 were discharged, 114 remained. Dr. Awl wrote:

They have been gathered up in different Counties of this extensive commonwealth, and consist of every variety and grade of lunacy, from the driveling IDIOT up to the raging MADMAN, who "scrabbles on the doors of the gate and lets his spittle fall down upon his beard" [the last a quotation from the Bible]. As was expected, a large proportion are paupers and their cases are mostly of long standing. Time, neglect and bad treatment in the jails, poorhouses, and private dungeons of the country, have in a great measure established the nature of their complaints and confirmed the frightful delusions that rage in the brain. We have washed them, provided them with food and clothing, and as far as possible have exerted ourselves to make them feel comfortable in their new situation. Their "chaos of illusions" has been attentively examined and studied, and we have endeavored to classify them, and through a mild system of tender respect and philosophic kindness, bring them to submit to the regularities of an efficient moral discipline. . . . In general our Patients soon become reconciled to their new house. . . . Under the smiles of a beneficent Providence, and the care of an intelligent board of directors, [the hospital] must succeed and command attention and respect, both at home and abroad, to the glory and praise of this high minded, great and benevolent state.

A patient of that time wrote:

In the hall in which I am located, there are 22 [patients] who . . . are tended with all possible care and humanity. . . . There is no unnecessary restraint imposed; no tyranny exercised; no undue severity used; no unbecoming punishment inflicted. They are treated with a mild, yet becoming firmness—but should any one evince an unruly spirit, or be guilty of any glaring or mischievous infringement of the rules of propriety, or so far forget the respect which is due to proper rank, and act so as may be injurious to himself or to those around him . . . he is either confined in his own room, or perhaps conducted to the shower box, where water is admitted upon him from a cistern above, in such copious streams as may cool his blood down to a degree of temperature sufficient for enabling him to reflect on the impropriety of his conduct, and to train him for again becoming a harmless member of society.

(Years later hydrotherapy was introduced into psychiatry and though for a time it was hailed as curative it actually was used as was this ancient cistern: to quiet and restrain excited patients.)

Doctors here did not starve their patients or nearly bleed them to death, this patient wrote; rather, they gave them medicine which would "under God, rekindle the almost extinguished embers of the soul, convert the shadow into some tangible mental consistence and gradually strengthen and confirm the intellectual powers." Medicine was served out three times daily in small cups labeled with the patients' names, as it is to this day. Patients had access to books and newspapers. Attendants took them on walks about the spacious grounds. The superintendent assembled the patients in a large room every evening after supper and conducted family worship. The patient wrote: "To a person like myself, who had, before I was brought here, experienced the horrors and almost solitary confinement of a county jail, the place seems a paradise in which one might live with pleasure and leave with regret."

5.

Dr. Awl considered classification of the patients important. He felt it aided treatment, promoted self-respect, and enabled the superintendent to sort out the patients and put like with like. His classification of their "apparent form" of insanity included maniacal, melancholic, epileptic, demented, monomaniacal and moral insanity. (Not for fifty years would Kraepelin devise the system of classification which is, with modification, in use today.) Among the "supposed causes" of the patients' illnesses Dr. Awl listed masturbation, fever, constitution, abuse from husband, measles, fear of want, kick of a horse, puerperal fever, religious fanaticism, intemperance, domestic trouble, disappointment, blasted prospects, disappointed love, fright, injury of the skull, intense application, unfortunate marriage, lost in the woods, hard study, excessive grief.

As for treatment he reported that the patients engaged in "amusements or exercises calculated to invigorate their bodies and interrupt the train of morbid ideas in their minds." They worked if they were able. They received purgatives and other medicines. "Kindness and forbearance on the part of the officers soon induces an effort in the Patient to repress the turbulence of his feelings and respect and confidence are the consequences." Restraint was seldom necessary, and the strait jacket was never used. If a patient became violent he was put in seclusion, and so on the wards "peace and decency . . . now prevail." Dr. Awl felt that "the earlier a case of insanity is treated, the greater the prospect of success."

In a report a few years later, the superintendent described the treatment for "acute mania." The patient's bowels were first emptied by purgatives, then he was given from four to six ounces of wine three or more times a day, or its equivalent in brandy. "If excessively furious and raving, he is confined to his room, or wholly secluded." After about three weeks when he seemed "saturated" with wine, he was given such tonics as tincture of iron. In cases of extreme irritability and restlessness, opium was given, "always with excellent effect." In "puerperal mania," the superintendent wrote, "our main reliance is upon purgatives." He said, "The completeness and stability of a cure depend much upon the treatment which a Patient receives after returning home." And: "We know too little of the matter to dogmatize, but we know enough to indicate how much we have to learn." Much of all this could have been written today.

6.

On October 16, 1844, thirteen state hospital superintendents, including Dr. Awl, met at Philadelphia and formed the Association of Medical Superintendents of American Institutions for the Insane, a name eventually changed to the American Psychiatric Association. It was the first national society of medical men in the United States.

During the middle years of the nineteenth century, however, the greatest force for improving the care of the mentally ill was not the APA but a lone woman, Dorothea Lynde Dix. A retired Boston schoolteacher, she visited the East Cambridge jail and was shocked to find the insane locked up in filth with criminals. For two years she visited other jails and almshouses in Massachusetts and then memorialized the legislature: "I come to present the strong claims of suffering humanity. I come to place before the Legislature of Massachusetts the condition of the miserable, the desolate, the outcast. . . . I proceed, Gentlemen, briefly to call your attention to the state of Insane Persons confined within this Commonwealth, in *cages, closets, cellars, stalls, pens: Chained, naked, beaten with rods,* and lashed into obedience!" The legislature enlarged Worcester State Hospital so it could receive the insane poor. Miss Dix moved onward—between 1840 and 1850 she crusaded in every state east of the Rockies for the establishment of state hospitals. In 1848 she petitioned Congress to subsidize state care of the insane poor, urging that they ought to be considered "wards of the nation," an idea never adopted. By the time she died, writes Albert Deutsch in his history of *The Mentally Ill in America,* she was directly responsible for the founding or enlarging of thirty-two mental hospitals and had played an important role in the founding of the Government Hospital for the Insane in Washington, D.C., now called St. Elizabeths.

The first reform in the care of the mentally ill in America, that of Dorothea Dix, put the insane into state hospitals. Swiftly state hospitals grew bigger and bigger—it was cheap to pile enormous numbers of the insane into gigantic institutions. The second reform is now in progress —to get them out.

7.

The spirit which informed that first revolution was humanitarianism. And indeed it was humanitarianism which dominated American psychiatric practice during the last half of the nineteenth century. Institutionalization became an end in itself. And the purpose of the institution was kind treatment, not therapy.

The earliest psychiatrists in America, such as Benjamin Rush, a signer of the Declaration of Independence, had used physical treatments. Now the tendency was toward "moral treatment." The superintendent regarded the patients with respect. He knew them all. Hospitals were small and permeated with human warmth. Dr. Awl believed that no hospital should be so large that the superintendent could not greet every patient personally every day. His purpose was to appeal to his patients' emotions and to influence them with kindness and understanding to return to sanity. He denounced the restraint of violent patients. He believed mental patients were not very different from "normal" people, a distinctly modern idea. He tried to improve the quality of his attendants, called them "keepers" no longer and required them to treat the patients as human beings. His hospital, and others, was suffused with an atmosphere of hopefulness. Indeed, a "cult of curability" arose, as Deutsch says, and superintendents vied with one another in reporting high percentages of "cures," until Dr. Awl reached apogee by reporting in 1843: "Per cent of recoveries on all recent cases discharged the present year, 100." (Some called him "Dr. Cure-Awl.")

The journal of the Association of Medical Superintendents of American Institutions for the Insane was full of notes about moral treatment. One superintendent wrote: "The character of the moral management is activity without excitement, progress and the combination of self-government, with appeals to the intellect and sentiments. There is always something to expect, to prepare for; some anticipation, or some retrospect. . . . [Patients] are their own gardeners, laborers, players, musicians, percentors, librarians, and, under certain restrictions, their own police." The superintendent of the famed Bloomingdale Asylum in New York wrote: "In the Lunatic Hospital as in society and in the state, the individual must be prominent." At the Illinois State Hospital for the Insane at Jacksonville, ladies from the town formed a benevolent association to visit the institution every Saturday. Many institutions had similar visiting groups, a custom that all but died out as state hospitals became larger, more forbidding, more impersonal, and more isolated from their communities.

The superintendent of an institution in Frankford, Pennsylvania called "The Asylum for the Relief of Persons Deprived of the Use of Their Reason" wrote, "The moral treatment of insanity . . . comprises all the varied means which are employed for occupying the mind and body, for promoting cheerfulness and contentment, and recalling natural and healthy trains of thought," and among these means he mentioned walking, riding, visits to the neighborhood, the use of the library and museum, lectures, "exhibitions with the Magic Lantern," neat apartments, regular visits by friends and relatives, and such exercise as "pumping," that is, turning a crank and wheel.

In 1955, a hundred years after the zenith of moral treatment, Dr. Winfred Overholser, superintendent of St. Elizabeths, wrote:

> Moral treatment was the only remedy our great forebears knew. Today we have electro-shock; we have insulin; we have new drugs, scientifically designed activities and the whole range of psychotherapy, including those two American contributions, narcoanalysis and group psychotherapy.
>
> We have learned much about the anatomy, physiology, and pathology of the nervous system, as well as of the other organs of the body. Our

surgery, both general and neurologic, has developed to an astounding extent. Much is known about biochemistry, the functions of the vitamins, minerals and other elements of nutrition. In the field of treatment, the development of insulin, of the antibiotics and of chemotherapy is enormous. We have conquered general paresis, first by the use of malaria and later by penicillin. The present treatment of involutional melancholia has strikingly improved the prognosis of that illness.

As far as the understanding of mental mechanisms is concerned, we have come far indeed. Freud cast brilliant new light in the field of psychopathology, and contributions from Jung, Adler, and later, Horney and Sullivan, are significant. Adolf Meyer and William Alanson White did much to emphasize the importance of body-mind unity. Psychotherapy, including psychodrama, is advancing rapidly.

"Drastic" treatments, too, have been tried, more or less successfully, and some of the newly developed drugs seem to offer much promise, at least as adjuncts or as palliatives. Psychiatric nursing, clinical psychology and psychiatric social work, though new, have developed far. The sciences of anthropology and sociology are contributing much to the understanding of individual and group behavior.

Despite all this, in 1955 we have 700,000 patients in our mental hospitals. Much of the stigma and superstition regarding mental illness has persisted. Schizophrenia, which accounts for nearly half of all mental hospital patients, remains an unsolved problem. Possibly, then, our colleagues both of the past and of the future, might call us to account for having accomplished but little during our century, despite our brave new tools.

Might not both past and future hospital men say that, in our scientific pride, we have lost the human touch and that our knowledge has been acquired at the expense of an interest in the patient as a person worthy of respect? Our forebears of 1855, in spite of their shortcomings, their ignorance and their lack of so many of the things we take for granted, respected the "ladies" and "gentlemen" entrusted to their care. What is more, their attitude of hopefulness had undoubted therapeutic value. . . .

The humanitarianism of the future will be based on scientific foundations, but it can be no better in quality and human warmth than it was when a handful of medical men, supported and encouraged by Dorothea Lynde Dix, took "lunatics" from the streets and the jails, and cared for them lovingly in the 1850's.

8.

A few years after it was built, the superintendent of the Central Ohio Lunatic Asylum at Columbus called it badly overcrowded. In 1850, it had to turn away two hundred patients who sought admission. A new institution was needed. The superintendent said about one person out of a thousand in Ohio was insane (today about three of every thousand are in public mental hospitals). Thus there were two thousand lunatics in the state. Assuming that eight hundred of them could remain at home, hospital space was needed for twelve hundred and he could take no more than three hundred. Where were the rest? About 120 were in wretched quarters in the county hospital in Cincinnati. The others were in county jails about the state, their lot "too horrible to be believed—confined in cellars and out-houses, or in dogpens; suffering the extremity of cold in winter, exposed to a burning sun in summer; pelted with sticks and stones, as an amusement, by unthinking schoolboys; a scanty meal tossed in through a narrow aperture, as to a wild beast; their dens . . . cleaned out of the accumulated filth at distant intervals."

The superintendent wrote, "Everywhere the public mind is awakening to a sense of the *humanity, justice,* and *economy* of making *ample* provision for the insane," and he mentioned new state hospitals in Pennsylvania, Illinois, Kentucky, Missouri, North Carolina, Alabama, Michigan, Mississippi. The Eastern seaboard had good hospitals; Massachusetts, Miss Dix's home state, led all the rest. But Ohio was lagging. At the asylum, the superintendent wrote, the greatest hazard was fire. The asylum "has been on fire again and again." In the winter the water froze on the wards, and the superintendent was afraid to turn on the heat to thaw it because of the danger of fire.

At 9:15 P.M. on November 18, 1868, a cold bitter night with snow and rain falling, fire destroyed the asylum. It started on one ward, probably when a patient lit a torch at the gas jet in the hall and threw it flaming into the clothing room; it suffocated six patients on that ward and spread rapidly. Nevertheless, all the 314 patients in the hospital except those six were rescued. The superintendent, describing the scene of "consternation and terror," expressed amazement that no more were killed and gave thanks to "our kind and merciful Heavenly Father." Of the patients who survived, 198 were sent home or to county institutions and the rest were put in the Deaf and Dumb Asylum temporarily; the state set about making plans to rebuild.

The legislature authorized the construction of a new and slightly larger hospital for four hundred patients on the same grounds at a cost of $400,000. Work was commenced. But a year later the legislature ordered reconstruction stopped and adopted a new plan: It would sell the grounds of the old institution, buy a different tract, and build a much larger hospital capable of holding at least nine hundred patients. It bought a three-hundred-acre farm on the opposite side of town, out on the National Road, which is now West Broad Street, the William S. Sullivant farm, "one of the most beautiful farms in all central Ohio." The cornerstone was laid July 4, 1870, at elaborate ceremonies attended by the governor, other state officials and a large gathering of citizens.

The plans were grandiose. But work proceeded slowly, sometimes halting altogether while legislators argued, architects changed their plans, trustees were removed and winter weather damaged unfinished brickwork. In all, the hospital was seven years abuilding, finished July 4, 1877. The cost was $1,462,634.55. (Its present value is estimated at seventeen million.) The hospital received its first patient August 23, 1877. A few years later its name was changed to Columbus State Hospital. The history of our hospital had begun.

9.

It was—and is—a most impressive edifice. While it was under construction a Californian, inspecting the asylums of America and Europe, pronounced Columbus State "the most complete in all the land . . . one of the best in the world." It was said to be the largest institution of its kind on earth. Each of its two wings was divided into four stepped-back parallel sections, the second set fifty feet back of the first and so on. There were four wards in each wing. Each ward had a long narrow corridor, 15 feet wide and from 160 to 185 feet long, off of which rooms opened on each side. Each ward had two iron stairways, a fire protection. To this day the wards have changed little from Dr. Thomas S. Kirkbride's plans—except that now a ward contains not 15 but 100 or more patients. Dr. Kirkbride thought no hospital should contain more than 250 patients. But Columbus State's capacity was 852 and when soon a fourth story was added to some sections it rose to 902. In 1955 it held 2,700 patients. In all it contained 400 single rooms, 14 rooms for 2 patients each, 86 rooms for 4 patients each, and 16 for 5 each. The floor was laid on arches of brick and corrugated iron supported by iron girders; the roof was iron and slate; the partition walls were brick; only the door frames, window frames and flooring were wooden.

Three months after the hospital opened, it contained 815 patients, nearly all it could hold—387 men, 428 women. "They come from various quarters," the superintendent reported, "some from their homes, many from other hospitals, many from the county infirmaries, some of them from jails and the penitentiary. They represent all grades of society and of suffering; some of them were very violent and excitable, and all of them were more or less agitated with conflicting hopes and fears on their arrival at their new residence among strangers."

By this time, 1877, Ohio had four large state hospitals—at Dayton, Cleveland, Athens and Columbus—with a capacity of 2,700. The state also supported 600 patients in the old county institution at Cincinnati and 100 at the Toledo Asylum. Thus the state was providing for the care of 3,400 insane persons. (Today, 35,000.) In other states "west of the mountains" twenty-five state hospitals had been built and four more were being built. But, Columbus State's superintendent warned, "Glorious as is this prospect we must not tarry too long in self-complacent satisfaction. . . . As soon as the building has been finished, it has been filled, leaving many outside with the same urgent claim for admission unheeded. . . . In a few weeks this building will be filled to its capacity, leaving no margin for those cases which may occur during the coming year, except by vacancies created by recoveries or deaths, and we shall soon be brought face to face with the old dilemma of retaining the old and rejecting the new cases, or accepting the new or recent cases at the expense of the same number of chronic cases sent back to the infirmaries." It was a dilemma still faced in 1955 in only slightly different form.

10.

Of the first 823 patients admitted, 140 of the men were farmers, 106 laborers, 2 molders, 17 carpenters, 6 schoolboys, 11 blacksmiths, 8 merchants, and the rest were a scattering of stonecutters, printers, salesmen, lawyers, coopers, clerks, doctors, teachers, sailors, teamsters, peddlers and others. As to the "form of disease," they were classified this way: mania, 455; mania with epilepsy, 23; monomania, 4; melancholia, 174; dementia, 143; dementia, senile, 10; dementia, with epilepsy, 7; dementia, with paralysis, 7.

As to the "alleged cause of insanity," the medical superintendent reported:

A. PHYSICAL CAUSES
    CLASS 1: Fever, smallpox, measles, erysipelas   14
    CLASS 2: Diseases of uncertain or variable seat, *viz.*, ill health
           and kick of horse   26
    CLASS 3: Diseases of nervous system: epilepsy, injury to head,

paralysis, sunstroke, cerebrospinal disorder, diseases of brain, neuralgia, spinal irritation, nervous debility, chorea   45

CLASS 4: Diseases of the digestive organs: diseases of the liver, dyspepsia   9

CLASS 5: Respiratory organs: asthma   2

CLASS 6: Disease of urinary organs, *viz.*, kidneys   1

CLASS 7: Diseases of generative organs and childbirth, *viz.* puerperal condition, menstrual derangements, change of life, uterine disturbance, lactation, pubescence, uterine tumor, syphilis (2)   75

CLASS 8: Miscellaneous physical causes, *viz.* excessive exertion, masturbation (54), intemperance and dissipation (21), old age (5), overexertion and want, loss of sleep, suppressed eruption, struck by lightning, opium eating, excessive use of tobacco, excessive venery   101

B. MORAL CAUSES:

Business and financial troubles	28
Disappointed affection	24
Disappointment	4
Mental excitement	2
Grief at loss of relative	7
Nostalgia	1
Jealousy	6
Fright	1
Religious excitement	22
Domestic troubles	40
Abuse by relatives	5
Anxiety	1
Slander	1
Remorse	1
Seduction	3
Prison life	30
TOTAL MORAL CAUSES	176
C. UNKNOWN	374
GRAND TOTAL	823

Female patients were kept busy making sheets, pillow cases, towels, shirts, dresses, shrouds, nightgowns. The men worked in the garden, tin shop, blacksmith shop, upholstering shop, storeroom. One evening a week there was music and dancing for the patients; patients who were violent on the wards conducted themselves decorously at the dance.

A "sleight of hand expert" entertained them. Religious services were held every Sunday. The superintendent organized a band. He hoped to build a walled-in exercise court for excited patients. He recommended strongly that separate institutions be built for the epileptic and for insane criminals—"It is neither just nor wise that innocent persons, whose only fault is the terrible misfortune of being bereft of reason, should be forced into companionship with convicted felons." Subsequently such separate institutions were built—a hospital for the criminally insane at Lima, hospitals for the epileptic at Gallipolis and at Orient near Columbus. A state school for the feeble-minded had already been opened in Columbus across the road from the State Hospital. Gallipolis, Orient and Columbus State School now are all state schools for the mentally defective.

In 1878 Columbus State admitted 411 patients and discharged 376, a ratio not unlike that of 1955. This left 850 patients in the hospital. But 48 of those discharged were admittedly unimproved—they were discharged only to make room for new patients. The superintendent, Dr. L. Firestone, was much less optimistic than his predecessors—the "cult of curability" was dead. At least half his patients would probably not live long, for the hospital contained 31 paretics, whose prognosis was "certainly fatal," 27 consumptives, 15 syphilitics, 45 epileptics "and more than 200 others with constitutions seriously broken down."

In his views on the causes of insanity, Dr. Firestone, like most psychiatrists of the day, emphasized organic factors heavily. He wrote, "Physical diseases play an important part in the production of insanity. The reciprocal relations between the body and mind are so intimate that disorder of the former is quite sure to affect the latter." (The next step, to turn the proposition around, as psychosomatic medicine did, took over half a century more.)

Dr. Firestone discerned two causes of insanity: remote and exciting. By "remote" he meant chiefly heredity. Among "exciting" he listed physical ill-health, intemperance and numerous "moral causes," including business worries, disappointed affections, grief, jealousy, religious excitement, prison life and domestic troubles. Dr. Firestone considered heredity of the utmost importance. "Like begets like," he wrote. "Children bear the traces of parentage not alone of body but of mind. A child is in a certain sense circumscribed. Its boundaries are drawn beyond which it cannot pass without unusual exertions. . . . It is strange so little heed is given to this all-important, all-absorbing question.

. . . [Marriage] should be a matter of serious consideration, not merely blind experiment; an affair of judgment as well as of the heart."

He divided the treatments used at Columbus State at that time, 1878, into two categories: medical and moral. Purgatives, painkillers, sedatives, nutrients, tonics—these were his medical agents.

> But little dependence, as a rule, can be placed on medical treatment for the cure of the insane, except so far as employed in conjunction with the moral treatment. . . . Medicine alone will not cure the insane. Friends make frequent inquiries as to the medical treatment pursued, and most generally express dissatisfaction when informed that but little medicine has been given. They appear to be of the opinion some panacea, unknown to members of the profession generally, is used by the specialist to bring back reason that has left the temple of the soul. Mistaken opinion. Specialists having charge of the insane boast of no superior knowledge. They employ no secret agents—are in possession of none.

Many patients had passed through the great crises of life, Dr. Firestone wrote—considering life's disappointments and unexpected trials, it was no wonder that "evil results" ensued, for "the nervous system, strung to the greatest limits of tension, must give way." It is a rather modern concept. He used recreation, walking, carriage riding, manual labor and ward work "to divert the mind and lead it, if possible, away from self." We use the same things today, calling them occupational therapy and recreational therapy.

He tried to get good attendants:

> It has been the aim to secure attendants with a sufficient amount of intelligence to exercise proper mental control, establish and maintain a high moral discipline, and bring into operation pure beneficial influences, that seldom fail to tranquilize patients, put them in love with themselves and those around them, lighten the burden of their afflictions, and cause them to feel that, notwithstanding they have been separated from dear ones at home, yet they are still among friends anxious and willing to bestow every good.

Dr. Firestone was discouraged because he had to turn patients away. In 1879 he wrote that five hundred patients were lodged in county infirmaries because there was no room for them in state hospitals. He tried to enlighten the public at large.

There are many persons [he wrote] in all communities, who harbor the groundless belief that hospitals for the insane are merely the repetitions of dungeons of a thousand years ago, with dark, and filthy cells, in which are mingled the discordant sounds of clanking chains and the wild chorus of shrieks of woe and sobs of despair. . . . It is gratifying to be able to say, that the management of the insane at the present time stands in happy contrast to that of the past. . . . All must realize that science is daily making new advances, triumphing in discovery, and unfolding new truths.

In 1884, looking back fifty years to conditions which existed before the hospital was established, the trustees wrote, "In this wonderful age of progress there has been no greater advancement than in the treatment of the insane. . . . gentleness and benevolence have largely taken the place of those machines of torture known as cribs (or cages for human beings), camisoles, and straight-jackets, not one of which is now in use in this Asylum."

Perhaps progress reached apogee in 1885, when the superintendent unlocked the doors of two wards, one for men, one for women, giving inmates the freedom of the grounds. He reported that no "accident or misdemeanor" resulted. But he added, perhaps with an eye to the superstitious public's fear of lunatics, "It must not be forgotten in our endeavors to widen the scope of liberty and freedom, that 'Ceaseless Vigilance is the Price of Safety, in Lunatic Asylums.'" Today, nearly seventy-five years later, the fad among American hospital superintendents is the movement toward "open," or unlocked, wards and hospitals, as we shall see.

11.

By 1899 the superintendent was complaining that the plant was old, its boilers and plumbing worn out. And it badly needed a fence around the grounds, not to keep the patients in but to keep the public out. The city had grown amoebalike to surround the hospital; strangers wandered through the grounds, picking up clothing thrown from the windows, and at harvesttime people stole the crops, and on Sundays the curious drove out to stare at the lunatics. The following year, 1900, the fence was built, an iron picket fence five feet high, and it stands there yet, though its gates have been removed, for it is no longer needed: State hospitals have become more isolated from the community than they were then, and people no longer willingly go near them. In the nineteenth century the hospital was an object of curiosity and even of sentiment to its community; today it is an object of dread. Then people without relatives in it visited it, in humanitarian spirit; they seldom do today. In 1879 a citizen made a bequest of sixteen thousand dollars to Columbus State for the "comfort and happiness of the patients." With the money the hospital bought five pianos, several music boxes, stage scenery, musical instruments, and a collection of steel engravings, and it built a plant conservatory. Such a bequest is almost unheard of today.

The hospital was getting more and more crowded. New additions had been made but they too were overflowing—the hospital housed 1,409 patients in 1903. A movement had begun in hospital architecture to build not the massive single-unit buildings like Columbus State but, rather, smaller cottages scattered about the grounds. Between 1903 and 1909 three cottages were built at Columbus State and named for former superintendents—Awl, Greer and Harrison. Three more were added later. A tent colony for tuberculous patients was set up (and later replaced by a permanent building). Greer Cottage, opened in 1905 to acute patients, contained the newest marvel in psychiatry: hydrotherapy. For many years, hydrotherapy was a mainstay of "therapy" all over the country. Today it is little used, and few people think it had any lasting or real effect on mental illness: It merely quieted excited patients, was a legitimized form of restraint. Some doctors think the new psychiatric drugs will someday be regarded in the same way.

Except for hydrotherapy, progress at Columbus State in the early years of the twentieth century was recorded largely in terms of sidewalks built, the powerhouse repaired and porches added to the wards. The hospital was beginning to use the diagnostic categories established in the 1890's by Kraepelin, and the old division into "moral" and "physical" causes of insanity was disappearing. But the only new therapy here as everywhere was hydrotherapy. And for many years it remained so. Except for fever treatment for paresis, not until the 1930's and after was there a sudden surge forward in therapy—insulin shock, electroshock, lobotomy and the new drugs. During the first thirty-odd years of the twentieth century at Columbus State, psychiatry's long slumber continued. It was giving patients humane care. But it was doing little more.

A New York doctor complained in the 1890's that while other sciences had progressed, "psychiatry is in the same position of 50 or 60 years ago. . . . It has shut itself up within the asylum walls, discouraged work and thought, and met well deservedly with the fate of China and ancient Egypt. As a science psychiatry is dead and a mummy may be its symbol."

The superintendent of Columbus State defended psychiatry. It had rescued mental disease from mysticism. Lately it had provided two valuable new "clinic forms"—paranoia and paresis. It was achieving "recovery" rates of 33 to 40 per cent. It had made progress in brain anatomy, brain function, nerve cell changes.

But the Columbus State superintendent, like most American hospital superintendents, was in truth shut up inside the walls. He mentioned the work of Kraepelin and Lombroso. But he made no mention of Sigmund Freud. This was in 1898. Five years earlier Freud and Breuer had discovered the unconscious and Freud had discovered psychoanalysis.

12.

Those years—the last in the nineteenth century, the first in the twentieth—were great years. A revolution was wrought in psychiatry (and a second revolution may be under way now). The first landmark of the revolution was the discovery of the cause of paresis. The great names are Kraepelin, Freud and Bleuler. Till then nineteenth-century psychiatrists had been interested only in the management of patients. They were isolated within their asylums. They did not practice in the world.

There were in all asylums large numbers of patients who were partially or wholly paralyzed, in delirium, often in convulsions, and who seemed to progress to dementia and death. This disease is paresis; it was recognized as a separate disease entity in 1826. By mid-century some doctors were guessing at a link between paresis and syphilis but not until 1897 did Richard von Krafft-Ebing prove conclusively by clinical experiment that syphilis causes paresis. Subsequently in 1906 the Wassermann test was discovered and in 1912 the definitive colloidal gold test on spinal fluid. Treatment followed. In 1910 Paul Ehrlich discovered salvarsan. In 1917 the treatment of paretics with malarial fever began, and soon every asylum had its "fever box." After the discovery of penicillin and its effectiveness as a treatment for syphilis, paresis began to disappear, and today it is a rare occasion when a paretic turns up at a state hospital.

The discovery that paresis was caused by the syphilitic spirochete's invasion of the brain was the first discovery of a specific physical cause of a mental disorder. It is a landmark in medical history. It had a momentous effect on psychiatry, for it lent weight to the belief, already prevalent, that mental diseases are really physical diseases of the central nervous system. It gave the ascendancy to the organic theory of mental illness. But even as it did so new discoveries were being made which would swing the pendulum the other way, toward a psychic theory of mental illness. They were made chiefly by Sigmund Freud.

Freud was born in 1856 in a small town in Austria-Hungary, lived most of his life in Vienna, and, driven abroad by Hitler's anti-Semitic program, died in London in 1939. He was a neuropathologist. In 1885 he visited Paris, then the psychiatric capital of the world. Mesmerism had drawn attention to the neuroses. Hypnotism, succeeding it, showed that the psychological has an influence on the physical. J. M. Charcot was attempting to show that hypnotic states could be induced only in people who suffered from hysteria. Freud returned to private practice in Vienna and, working with Josef Breuer, a general practitioner, discovered that a hysterical patient talked freely while in hypnosis and could remember forgotten events intimately related to her symptoms. When she did so, she exhibited intense emotion connected with the fantasies and memories she had suppressed. Upon awakening from hypnosis she usually had lost her symptoms. This marked the discovery of man's unconscious. Soon Freud found he could do without the hypnotic state. He simply let the waking patient talk at random. He called this free association. He analyzed and interpreted for her what she said. Psychoanalysis was born.

Much more followed. Indeed, what followed was nothing less than a whole theory of human personality. Its cornerstone is the unconscious. Freud showed conclusively that man is not wholly a rational animal, that there lies buried in every man an unconscious which obeys no laws of reason and bears no necessary relation to external reality, but behaves only according to its own needs and in doing so determines much of human behavior. Freud was not working with psychotics. He was working with neurotics and with "normal" people. In his classical study of the psychopathology of everyday life he showed that everyday slips of the tongue, omissions, misspellings, and so on are caused by the action of the unconscious. When a man forgets repeatedly to mail a letter, it is because he really does not want to mail it. When a presiding officer, opening a meeting of parliament, erroneously declares the meeting closed, he has some reason for wanting the meeting over with before it started. All this, as Franz Alexander has pointed out,* seems commonplace today but in 1912 it wrought a revolution comparable to the Copernican revolution. The rational philosophers of the seventeenth and eighteenth centuries had made the thinking mind the center of the universe. Freud showed it was not so. He set limits upon the rational and the conscious. He showed that both rational thinking and moral feelings are means by which we adjust to our environment but that they do not entirely determine our thinking and behavior, for a powerful segment of mental life is neither rational nor moral, is adjusted not at all to the external world. Our unadjusted tendencies are in continual conflict with the rational. They disturb us; we suppress them. They become unconscious. The psychoses and neuroses may be understood as a breaking through of the unadjusted unconscious attitudes of the personality.

Alexander writes:

The chief difference between a neurosis and a psychosis is the extent to which the repressed unadjusted mental content breaks through into consciousness after overcoming the resistance of the repressive forces. This outbreak of repressed content is most complete in psychoses. In the end-phases of schizophrenia, for example, the impression is made that the ego has given up all resistance and is dominated entirely by hallucinations. In a psychosis even the earliest adjustment of the ego, the capacity to subordinate imagination to the evidence of sense perceptions, breaks down, and the consequence is a loss of orientation to the world. The later achievements, such as aesthetic and moral restrictions and inhibitions, also disappear in psychoses. A psychosis can thus be considered as an attempted though never wholly successful flight from reality and, more particularly, from adult existence to childhood, to a happier time, when reality did not yet disturb the rule of fantasy. This flight may be temporary or permanent. . . . Psychoneurosis and psychosis can be considered as different stages of the same mental process, the outbreak of the unconscious, repressed, primitive part of the personality. In a psychosis the process goes much further, for the difference between conscious and unconscious disappears to a large degree

* Franz Alexander, *The Fundamentals of Psychoanalysis.* New York: W. W. Norton, 1948.

and the unconscious dominates the whole personality, whereas in a neurosis the principal achievement of the later ego-development, the acceptance of reality, remains more or less intact, and the unconscious tendencies penetrate the ego only in isolated symptoms, which are like foreign bodies embedded in normal tissue.

From Freud's discovery of the unconscious flowed many things, including ideas accepted everywhere today. From it flowed the emphasis upon the earliest experiences of life, especially those connected with the family, as the crucial experiences in shaping a man. From it flowed the psychiatric concepts of repression, regression, rationalization, projection, dream interpretation and the theory of infantile sexuality. From it flowed the idea that the normal, the neurotic and the psychotic constitute a continuum—that the neurotic and psychotic are not beings apart. Freud's work revolutionized psychiatry in his lifetime. It influenced innumerable fields of human endeavor, including several scientific disciplines. At first it was ill received by the medical profession. Many people resist it yet. Zilboorg observes acutely that men resist it because they cannot accept the idea that their own minds are neither omnipotent nor free. Some are repelled by what they consider Freud's overemphasis on sex. Some consider psychoanalysis antireligious. Some say that all Freud's work is "merely theoretical." This last objection is true—nobody has ever seen the conflict between the unconscious and the rational mind. But we have seen its results, in prisons and mental hospitals. Just so, nobody has ever seen an atom split or fuse with another—but we have seen its results at Hiroshima and Bikini. Perhaps because so much of his terminology passed over into layman's conversation, Freud has probably been more misunderstood than any scientist. But his work underlies all psychiatry today, which is to say all our understanding of ourselves. Like Einstein's discovery that $E=MC^2$, Freud's discovery of the unconscious wrought one of those rare and truly cataclysmic revolutions in the history of human thought.

13.

German psychiatry during that same period had posed the argument of soma versus psyche which still goes on—whether mental disorder results from organic or from psychic process. As we have seen, the discovery that syphilis causes paresis—and Sergey Sergeyvich Korsakoff's description in 1899 of chronic alcoholic psychosis which is still called Korsakoff's psychosis—lent weight to the organic theory. So did the work of the neuroanatomists, who in seeking to learn more about the brain neglected other aspects of human personality and organization. Freud's discoveries swung the pendulum toward a psychic theory of mental illness. They dominated psychiatric thought during the first half of the twentieth century. Freud visited America in 1909, and nowhere in the world did his views flourish as in America. America has become the most psychoanalytically oriented country in the world, the capital of psychoanalysis.

Nonetheless, at the same time, such American psychiatrists as Adolf Meyer and William Alanson White struggled to fuse the two views and see man as a psychobiological whole. (So had a few German psychiatrists, such as Ernst Kretschmer.) So did the school of psychosomatic medicine which arose in America in the 1930s.

But today the discovery of the new psychiatric drugs has swung the pendulum violently away from the psychic and toward the organic view. The organicists—especially the biochemists—seem today to be in the vanguard of a second psychiatric revolution, as we shall see.

It was in Germany at the end of the nineteenth century that attempts to classify mental disease reached their peak. As we have seen at Columbus State Hospital, earlier nineteenth-century classification had been of little use, ascribing the symptoms of the insane to "moral" and "physical" causes. In 1896 Emil Kraepelin, a German psychiatrist, laid down the classical classification of mental disease which has left an imprint on today. Kraepelin divided the serious mental illnesses into two large groups: dementia praecox and the manic-depressive psychoses. Dementia praecox was characterized by the symptoms found in catatonia and hebephrenia—auditory hallucinations and persecutory trends. It led inevitably to mental deterioration and true dementia and was irreversible. Manic-depressive psychoses ran a cyclic course as a series of attacks of elation and depression, between which the patient is usually "normal." They were recoverable psychoses.

Kraepelin assumed that mental illness was a disease, that like any other disease it ran a certain course and that it was something definite. He also assumed that mental disease was, like any other disease, due to a defective organ, to heredity, to metabolic changes or to imbalance of the endocrine gland secretions. Thus, after centuries of striving, psychiatry was at last fused with medicine. But Kraepelin's system was a rather hopeless one. It did not look at the patient and ask, "Why is he sick?" It looked at the patient and pigeonholed him as either manic-depressive, in which case he would of course get well, or as suffering from dementia praecox, in which case he was of course doomed. It invited him, properly classified, into a hospital to await his fate. It excluded thoroughly, Zilboorg writes, "any consideration of the human personality."

It was to the study of man as man that Freud returned psychiatry. And it was by using Freud's discoveries that Eugen Bleuler revised Kraepelin's concept of dementia praecox, renaming the disease schizophrenia. After years of studying psychotic patients, Bleuler published in 1911 his monumental *Dementia Praecox, the Group of Schizophrenias.* It led psychiatry out of the blind alley into which Kraepelin had led it. Bleuler thought of schizophrenia as a group of psychotic reactions to reality rather than as a single formal disease. Kraepelin had believed in the incurability and unknown organic origin of schizophrenia; Bleuler, though postulating an organic basis, viewed it also as a reaction to life which may be cured because it sometimes cures itself—many schizophrenics recover spontaneously. He described a psychological loosening of associations as a fundamental characteristic of the disease. Another was autism—the inward-turned break with reality, fantasy thinking rooted in the unconscious, not in external reality. Zilboorg has called Bleuler's book on schizophrenia "the most important contribution to psychiatry made by the twentieth century."

14.

Freud's revolution influenced American psychiatry profoundly. But it had little direct effect upon psychiatric therapy in American state hospitals. It did contribute hugely to hospital psychiatrists' understanding of their patients' condition. But it offered no new therapy that could be used on psychotic patients in state hospitals. Freud's own therapeutic method, psychoanalysis, cannot be used on psychotic patients but only on some neurotic ones, as Freud himself said. Indeed, Freud said only a fortunate few can benefit from psychoanalysis—those who are intelligent, educated, not too old (usually under fifty), co-operative, consciously desirous of recovery (patients forced into analysis by relatives seldom benefit), and rich enough to afford it—analysis usually takes a minimum of 250 hours and may take 1,000 hours, at a fee today of perhaps twenty-five dollars an hour. In some private hospitals, analysis is practiced on psychotic patients with good results claimed. But there are few analysts in state hospitals. In private hospitals and a few state hospitals, a more superficial psychotherapy is used on psychotics. But in most state hospitals doctors have no time for individual psychotherapy. Attempts have been made in America to shorten the analytic process, so that each doctor can reach more patients, by means of hypnoanalysis, narcoanalysis and group analysis. But none of these have been much used in the ordinary state hospital.

Thus it was that the state hospitals had to wait for something else to come along. It came in 1933: insulin shock therapy for schizophrenia, followed by electroshock therapy in 1934. These were physical treatments easy to perform and their use became enormous. Next came lobotomy and its variations—surgical operation upon the brains of psychotics. Finally in recent years the new psychiatric drugs have been discovered. As each therapy came along it was hailed as opening a "new era" in psychiatry, hailed by some, even, as a "cure" for mental disease, only to be discarded as a cure and retained as a palliative. Whether this will happen to the new drugs cannot be said as yet.

We shall study more closely all these therapies as they have been used on individual patients in Columbus State Hospital. And we also shall observe closely patients in each of the main diagnostic categories of psychosis as they are now understood by psychiatrists and defined by the American Psychiatric Association.

Mental disorders today are divided into two broad categories—those of known organic origin and those without known organic cause. Among the organic disorders are chronic brain syndrome associated with convulsive disorder (epilepsy), chronic brain syndrome associated with central nervous system syphilis (paresis), and chronic brain syndrome associated with senile brain disease. The "functional" disorders without known physical cause are involutional psychotic reaction, manic-depressive reactions, paranoia, and the group of schizophrenic reactions, including three chief subtypes, hebephrenic, catatonic and paranoid schizophrenia.

15.

Day after day within the ancient thick brick walls of Columbus State Hospital on a hilltop overlooking the city of Columbus, sick men and women and their doctors resist the ravages of psychosis. But however great the doctors' skill, however great the patients' own courage and their families' devotion, it is in the long run to "downtown" that they all must look for support—to the office of the Director of the Department of Mental Hygiene and Correction in the skyscraper state office building beside the muddy Scioto River, to the governor's carpeted office and the legislature's chambers in the squat, oblong, Statehouse in the center of town. And, ultimately, they must look beyond, to the people of the state of Ohio.

Columbus State Hospital is one of thirteen prolonged-care mental hospitals in Ohio. The state has in addition special hospitals for the defective, tuberculous insane and criminally insane; it also has eight hospitals, called receiving hospitals and psychiatric institutes, for patients needing only short-term care. All are operated by the Department of Mental Hygiene and Correction. It is the biggest state operating department. It spent in 1958 $54,119,210 merely to operate its institutions (it also let contracts for an additional $28,000,000 on new buildings, while another twenty million dollars' worth were under construction). This is by far the largest operating budget of any operating department of Ohio government. In its mental hospitals scattered about the state are some 35,000 patients. They are cared for by more than 10,000 doctors and other employees. In addition the Department administers Ohio's mental hygiene, prison and juvenile retraining programs. In all there are more than 47,000 wards of the state in its thirty-three institutions. The master of this empire is its director, Dr. Robert A. Haines, a bright young curly-haired psychiatrist who rose rapidly in the Ohio mental hospital system and became Commissioner September 24, 1957. His job is often called "the second most important in Ohio," the governor's being first. He succeeded Dr. John D. Porterfield. It was Porterfield who, in 1955, brought about major reform in Ohio's vast state hospital system.

Porterfield is a slender mustached friendly easygoing man in his forties, given to smoking a pipe. Porterfield is a doctor but not a psychiatrist; a public health man, formerly with the U. S. Public Health Service, he was appointed Director of Ohio Department of Mental Hygiene and Correction in July of 1954.

Until 1953 the Ohio mental hospitals were run by a vast sprawling bureaucracy known as the Department of Public Welfare. This fantastic body operated prisons, mental hospitals and all public assistance programs including old age pensions, aid to the blind and aid to dependent children. For several years the Ohio Mental Health Association, a citizens' group, had complained that the mental hospitals were lost in the vast Welfare Department and ought to be detached from it and put in the hands of psychiatrists, not, they said, politicians. The elderly head of Welfare vigorously opposed such a move. But he was unpopular with many legislators, and in 1953 they established the present Department to handle mental hospitals and prisons. Governor Frank Lausche vetoed the bill but the legislature passed it over his veto. To run the new department various people urged Governor Lausche to appoint a psychiatrist. But Lausche, a rumpled shrewd skillful politician whose stock in trade is an independent plain-spoken no-frills approach, is constitutionally opposed to psychiatrists and social workers and people of like ilk, and characteristically he appointed Porterfield, a man he knew and whom almost nobody else favored for the job.

The problem Porterfield faced was a formidable one. The state's population was rising as new industry drew workers from the South. Columbus itself, only a few years ago a sleepy college farm town and state capitol that bragged it had no booms and busts but quietly went its way, had since the war become a booming industrial city bursting at the seams. And the population of Ohio's mental hospitals had not only kept pace with the general population—it had outstripped it, for while the general population had increased 22 per cent in the last ten years the population of its mental institutions had increased 29 per cent. To keep up, Ohio had spent in those ten years no less than sixty million dollars to build or acquire new mental hospitals but yet they were getting ever more overcrowded. In 1944 Ohio had nine prolonged-care hospitals; in 1954 it had thirteen. Moreover to get new patients out of hospitals quickly by intensive treatment, instead of dumping them into prolonged-care hospitals, it had pioneered a system of new receiving hospitals. Even so, despite a decade of unparalleled expansion and pioneering, Ohio was worse off when Porterfield took office than it had been ten years earlier. It had 35,877 patients crammed into space adequate for 23,640 patients—12,237 above capacity compared with 10,732 above capacity ten years earlier. It had patients sleeping on the floor and in the halls and in dayrooms and recreation rooms, in beds crammed so close together that, as Porterfield said, "ordinary health measures are impossible." And patients were pouring into the hospitals at the rate of ten thousand a year. Moreover, many existing buildings were hopelessly run-down, and some, such as the notorious Annex at Longview in Cincinnati, were dangerous firetraps. Unlike some leaders of recent hospital reform in other states, Porterfield moved rather quietly and slowly at first. He made his first big move at the end of 1954 when, shortly before the legislature convened, he announced his budget. In a widely distributed brochure he said the state must spend $81,340,000 to construct new hospital buildings and an additional $25,743,000 to rehabilitate existing ones—a total capital outlay of $107,083,000. In addition, Porterfield asked for $100,487,157 to run his department during the next two years—an increase of about $30,000,000, most of it to be used in hiring more doctors and raising their salaries. Everybody had known Porterfield would launch an expansion program but few people had thought he would launch such an ambitious one. "We caused quite a stir," Porterfield recalls. He had tried to get Governor Lausche's view of the request before making it but without success; Lausche told him to go ahead and announce it on his own.

Governor Lausche, a conservative governor of a tight-fisted state, was committed not to raise taxes. So were legislative leaders. In presenting the program to the legislature Lausche cut back Porterfield's operating request from $100,000,000 to $80,000,000. As to Porterfield's request for a $107,000,000 building program Lausche recommended that the decision be left to the people: They should be asked to vote on a bond issue.

Several legislators introduced mental hygiene bills of their own. All sorts of things were proposed. Everyone realized that Ohio had reached an important turning point in its mental hospital program. Dr. Will Menninger from the Menninger Clinic in Topeka, Kansas, addressed a joint session of the Ohio legislature on February 16, 1955. He said that Kansas was probably the only state in the Union in which the mental hospital population had declined in the preceding five years: It was down 7 per cent in Kansas but up 15 per cent in the nation as a whole. He said, "I believe that Kansas has the only system of state hospitals in the country where there isn't a long waiting list and where people don't have to sit in jail for a week or a month before they can even enter a hospital where a doctor might see them a month later. It is possible and probable, I think, that in Kansas we will never have to build additional hospital beds if we can keep our present program going."

He attributed all this primarily to the fact that Kansas in 1949 had begun spending a great deal of money, not on buildings but on doctors. At that time Kansas had found it sorely needed 3,800 more mental hospital beds. They would cost $38,000,000. A study committee including the Menningers had recommended against buildings and in favor of getting more doctors and nurses. Dr. Menninger said, "Patients get well only if they are treated by doctors, and when there aren't any doctors, they can't get well. To use my brother's words: 'Many patients will get well in a barn if you have the right doctors and the right treatment. We don't want them to live in barns, but staff and treatment must come first.'" (One building at the famed Menninger Clinic actually is a remodeled barn.)

Dr. Menninger said the Kansas legislature first raised the Topeka State Hospital budget by nearly 60 per cent (compared to the 30 per cent increase which Porterfield had requested). Topeka State hired more doctors, psychologists, social workers, nurses, occupational therapists, attendants. But it couldn't hire enough because there aren't enough in the country. So Kansas began to train its own. It set up a five-year plan that pays doctors well for their three years of psychiatric residency training but requires them in return to spend two years in state hospitals before fleeing to private practice. As a result, Dr. Menninger said, Kansas now had one doctor for every 74 patients compared with one for every 343 in 1948. It had tripled its attendants and psychiatric aides. And its patients had begun to go home. Within two years Topeka State's population dropped from nearly 1,800 to about 1,530. Before 1948 about two-thirds of all patients who came to the hospital stayed; now two-thirds went home. (Care must be used in interpreting these figures; for example, Topeka State does not have to accept any patient sent it by the courts, as does Columbus State, and, again, many patients have been sent out of Topeka State into private state-supervised nursing homes.)

All this was costly—in 1948 Kansas was spending $1.06 per patient per day on its mental hospitals, in 1954 $4.19. (Ohio spent $1.77 in 1948 and $2.62 in 1954). But Dr. Menninger thought it had cost less than a building program. He said, "I think one of the blots on our social horizon all across this country is that year after year we go on building more brick and mortar when we don't have enough doctors to staff the hospitals we already have. New York State voted $350,000,000 on last election day for more hospital beds and they can't staff what they have right now."

He urged the Ohio legislature to "give first priority to helping
people get well." He said, "That means buying 'brains.' I am certain
that the only feasible way to do that is to establish training programs
for every type of professional personnel needed, directed by persons of
sufficient professional stature to attract students." He recommended
tying the state hospital training program "as closely as possible" to
university medical schools. He urged the legislature to increase operating budgets "sharply." "You can't expect doctors to work in state
hospitals for $6,000 a year—or $8,000 or $10,000—when they can
earn $25,000 or even $50,000 outside. . . . Unfortunately, at the
moment, psychiatry is a seller's market." He said, "Next in priority
after 'brains' is the replacement of the antiquated firetraps, already
50 to 105 per cent overcrowded." Finally, he urged a program of
public education, saying he believed that in Ohio as in Kansas the
public if it knew the facts would "insist upon the best kind of mental
hospital program possible."

So an issue was joined in the legislature: bricks vs. brains. The
legislators, aroused, decided to make up their own minds. In chartered
buses they drove about the state, visiting hospitals. They were appalled
by some of the things they saw—mattresses on the floor at Toledo
State, sawdust beds at Longview. The ancient Annex at Longview
shocked them, but so did the new "B" Building at Columbus State,
for it housed 130 deteriorated schizophrenic women, nearly all incontinent, and it smelled horribly. A lobbyist for the Mental Health
Association recalls, "My job suddenly was reversed. I used to talk to
the legislators about horrible conditions but this session I had a hard
time to get a word in edgewise, the legislators did all the talking."

Porterfield went before a legislative committee to ask it to restore
the cuts the governor had made in his original budget, thus, in effect,
going over the governor's head. (He had the governor's permission
to do so.) He said he favored both bricks and brains. The governor was
keeping quiet, leaving the decision to the legislature. The legislature's
research service, after investigating other state systems, seemed to lean
toward the Menninger view of brains before bricks. In general this
was the view the legislature finally adopted.

To get brains, it raised the governor's recommendation for an
operating budget to $90,894,954—ten million dollars less than Porter-
field had requested but ten million more than the governor had
recommended and twenty million more than the Department had spent
the previous biennium. The budget would bring Ohio's expenditure

up to $3.19 per patient per day, a little above the average for all states. (The private Menninger Clinic spends about $40.) To pay for the increase the legislature voted no new taxes; instead the governor by executive order raised the price of liquor fifty cents a gallon (liquor is sold only through state stores). Thus the promise not to raise taxes was kept in letter if not in spirit.

The new budget authorized hospitals to hire more doctors, attendants, therapists and others. But the legislature recognized that such people cannot be hired merely because they are authorized. So it raised salaries and, most important, it earmarked five and a half million dollars for research and training programs. (To equal Kansas' program it would have to spend twice that.) This program was to be established at three receiving hospitals—those in Columbus, Cleveland and Cincinnati, which are operated in conjunction with three university medical schools. Under the new training program doctors might choose to stay only for their three-year residency training at a starting salary of $3,400 a year or they might agree to stay five years, three as residents and two as ward doctors at a state hospital, and in this case they would start at $6,000 a year. Thus, it was hoped, the state would get at least two years' service out of the additional psychiatrists it would train. There was no guarantee they would stay longer but as an inducement the legislature authorized Porterfield to raise salaries. Under his new salary schedule psychiatrists received from $12,000 to $17,000 a year without maintenance (they formerly received $8,640 to $10,320 with maintenance). Most hospital superintendents received $18,000 without maintenance (formerly $13,800 with maintenance). Three men in the department got $20,000 or more (the governor's salary is $25,000). These salaries were not the highest in the country but they were close to the top.

In addition to all this the legislature authorized certain specific improvements at Longview, Cleveland, Dayton and elsewhere, and it gave Porterfield the power, formerly vested in Civil Service, to fix salaries, establish qualifications and remove superintendents.

Finally the legislature submitted to the voters a bond issue for a building program. Initially, as has been said, Governor Lausche had proposed a $100,000,000 bond issue for mental hospitals alone, but the school lobby got on the bandwagon, and the legislature finally proposed a $150,000,000 bond issue, half for Porterfield's department and half for school improvements. The bonds were to be paid off by an additional cigarette tax of one cent per pack if the voters approved.

The bond issue went on the ballot November 8, 1955. Since the war no state in America had defeated a bond issue for mental hospitals. But Ohio has a reputation for penny-pinching government and Ohioans have frequently voted down bond issues. Moreover, at this same election the ballot contained three other unrelated referenda, including one put on the ballot by the CIO and fought bitterly by business interests. It is easier to vote "No" on several referenda than to vote "No" on some and "Yes" on others. And of course it is always easier to vote "No" than "Yes" to any complicated proposal, particularly one which will raise your taxes. Finally, on the ballot the mental hospital bond issue was labeled "Bond Issue for Public Buildings," which raises in the tax-burdened citizen's mind visions not of the afflicted untended in gray hospital wards but of plush and marble temples for politicians. It was therefore somewhat surprising that the electorate defeated the other referenda but approved the bond issue. Regardless of the merits of the other proposals, the vote was a tribute to the ability of Ohioans to vote with discrimination, as well as a tribute to the proseletyzing of Lausche, Porterfield, Porterfield's publicity man and the Ohio Mental Health Association.

Everybody interested in mental hospitals was immensely pleased. Roger Cloud, Speaker of the House, a neat intelligent youngish man, said, "It was a joint effort by many of us in the legislature. I was interested because I happen to have some close acquaintances with some problems in the field, and I could realize that it could happen to anybody. We all tend to think it's inherited and miserable and something to feel sorry about and let it go at that. But they improve if they are treated. If not, they regress rapidly. That's the evil of all the states' failure—they've allowed patients that could've been treated to regress beyond treatment. But there's never been so much public interest as today. We've got a good start in Ohio."

We shall see later on how, in the three years since the voters passed the bond issue, the new program has turned out and how it affected our hospital, Columbus State. And we shall see too the effect of other recent revolutions in other states, some far from quiet.

16.

Columbus State is the fourth biggest state hospital in Ohio. (Longview is the biggest, containing about seven hundred more patients than Columbus.) Columbus must accept any patients committed to it by court. Most of its patients are court-committed; only a handful come voluntarily. Those who are able must pay for their hospitalization. What they pay depends upon their means; the maximum is three dollars a day. Many pay nothing. Columbus State spent $2,920,603 for the year ending June 30, 1957; its patients repaid the state $554,736 that year. The doctors at the hospital do not know which are paying patients and which are not; the money is paid to the downtown central office.

Of the approximately 2,700 patients in recent years, 1,270 are men and 1,430 women. About half come from the city of Columbus and half from surrounding counties. Columbus State contains about the same percentage of Catholics, Jews and Protestants—and Negroes— as the population at large. The hospital tries to reject alcoholics who merely want to sober up, though it accepts psychotics whose illness results from permanent brain damage caused by alcohol. The hospital does not keep epileptics unless they are also psychotic but it does keep, reluctantly, a few mental defectives who are not psychotic, for the state school for defectives across the street is jammed to the doors.

Columbus State is always crowded. Yet in 1955 it was not so hideously overcrowded as Toledo State Hospital, where patients slept on the floor, or Cleveland State, which was so crowded that new patients had to await their turn in the county jail. Nor was it so crowded as a hospital in another state where, when a new patient came in the front door someone else had to go out the back, or Elgin State Hospital in Illinois, where in some wards even the dining room was filled with beds—beds pushed so tight together that a patient had to crawl over many other patients' beds to get to his own. Nonetheless, Columbus is always overcrowded. Occasionally it gets so tight that new patients have to be put in the beds of patients who are home on weekend leave. Because of overcrowding old chronic psychotics clutter up acute treatment wards, though the doctors try to keep patients of one kind on a ward.

Columbus State tries not to keep children under sixteen, but if they are psychotic there is no other place for them. Once it had twenty children, and at any time is likely to have a half-dozen. At any given time perhaps half the patients are organics. And among these are many aged persons. Indeed, the hospital in 1955 contained about 650 old folks. Many of these did not really need a mental hospital but there was just no other place to put them.

One patient had been here continuously since 1881. She was nineteen when she arrived, diagnosed "imbecile," her commitment papers saying, "Hears the stove and kitchen utensils talking." She became a "ward favorite"; attendants and patients made a fuss over her. Some years ago she used to sing and dance and mop the floors, and occasionally she became disturbed and heard "the voices" and answered them, saying "hell's fire and damnation," but later she spent most of her time sitting on the floor. She thought she was one year old. She wanted to go home. So far as the records show, she never had had a visitor in the seventy-five years she had been here.

4

The Lovely Schizophrenic

■ One day at noontime in an echoing corridor of Columbus State Hospital, all the doctors were talking about a patient they had just seen at staff. "She is a girl," one said, "who can really show you what it's like to be schizophrenic." And another: "She is a classic case."

Since the mysterious disease called schizophrenia lies at the heart of the whole problem of mental illness, accounting for half the patients in Columbus State and indeed in all American state hospitals, let us study this girl closely.

We shall call her Sally Bennett. She is a tall willowy blonde girl of twenty-three, not missing real beauty by much. She was born in Columbus, delivered by instruments. Her father was middle-aged when she was born, her mother much younger. Sally was their first child. A second daughter born a year later is healthy. Sally's father was a successful businessman. Of her mother a social worker once wrote: "She has dedicated her life to raising her two children. She is somewhat meticulous and overconscientious, but has always been very close to Sally." There was no known history of mental illness in the family. Thus Sally's background does not include the tainted heredity, poverty or social disorganization found in the background of so many state hospital patients.

She grew up in a middle-class Irish home in a middle-class neighborhood. She was bright, a "very good student" through high school. Later, at the hospital her IQ tested only 81, dull normal, but the

77

psychologist thought that her disease was hindering her mental functioning and that she was probably of at least average intelligence. As a child she had a quick temper "and did not hesitate to get into a real fight with even the larger boys," a social worker once wrote. She was athletic. She was "very determined." In high school she felt "left out," excluded from the girls' "cliques." She was active in church affairs. She never had any boy friends. She was a tall girl, too tall for most boys. She felt increasingly shy around young men. She had always been "very meticulous and methodical." She became excessively cleanly, bathing two or three times a day.

2.

She came to the hospital the first time three years after graduating from high school. After high school she had left home and gone to work in Wisconsin. She apparently had been happy. She had stayed in Wisconsin for her vacations. Soon after that she had begun to hear voices. They criticized her. So disturbing were they that she quit her job. "She was quite gay when she told her girl friends about quitting the job," a social worker wrote. "The following day she cried all day. She felt that it was all the fault of the company and the supervisors who kept her from feeling at ease so that she could not work, eat, or sleep. She thought that the manager was in love with her and this upset her. About this time she mentioned her frustrated ambition to have a husband and children. She hinted that something had happened in Wisconsin, but would not say what this was even to her girl friends."

Her father talked to her by telephone. She seemed very upset. People in Wisconsin "were calling her vulgar names." Yet she didn't want to leave. Her father persuaded her to fly home. He met her; he thought she looked much thinner and her eyes looked "different"— "glassy or shiny." She could not sit still. Her father took her to a private sanitarium and after a few days upon the advice of doctors there brought her to Columbus State. She was admitted that first time as a voluntary patient.

The admitting doctor wrote that she was "a 20-year-old single, white girl with a face like the kind one sees on Red Cross posters." She said she wasn't sick, and was here only at her family's insistence. "She is aloof, polite and obviously evasive. There is reason to believe that she is still having auditory hallucinations which are concerned with homosexuality. The patient is definitely schizophrenic with paranoid features." Admitted onto Ward 5 she immediately became excited and had to be taken to Ward 7, a dark and noisy disturbed ward. When the doctor saw her again a few days later she was friendly and co-operative. She was perfectly oriented in all three spheres—knew who she was, where she was, what time it was.

Her attitude toward the psychologist swung wildly—she was flat and apathetic, then aggressive and resentful, then cool and distant, then amiable and almost silly. She said she may have contracted syphilis on Ward 7. "I have never been in such a dirty germy place," she said. "There's so much syphilis on that ward it's pathetic, bacteria, stench, so much disease around here." She resented being here. Her parents had brought her here because of "mental strain" but she wasn't mentally ill. Once she glanced around as if hearing voices; the doctor asked if she ever received messages, and she said, "Yes, I'm talking to people right now." But a few minutes later she denied hearing voices any more, perhaps she never had heard them; and when the doctor asked if other people influenced her, she said guardedly, "I guess it's just a hunch, you can't really say for sure." (Schizophrenics often try to conceal their symptoms.) A Rorschach test showed a narcissistic personality, unstable emotion and meager fantasy, and the psychologist said the findings "suggest an early schizophrenic reaction with catatonic and possibly paranoid components."

The best time to treat her was now, the doctors thought, and they gave her a heavy course of shock treatments, both insulin and electroshock. She improved rapidly. But the ward doctor, having seen other patients relapse when treatment is stopped, continued the treatments in the hope they would "hold." Sally rebelled, refused treatment. The doctor, who had become interested in her, suspended treatments for a week then talked her into resuming them. They went smoothly. She had a total of ninety-three insulin and thirty-five electroshock treatments. Five months after she arrived at the hospital, she was sent home on trial visit. She came back for a checkup two weeks later looking neat, attractive, well dressed and well poised, saying she had been relaxing at home, was thinking of going back to work. Her father would send her to college if she wished. A month later she seemed much the same, though she hadn't tried to go back to work yet and felt self-conscious and inferior.

The hospital records are incomplete in her case, as in many others.

She evidently relapsed and returned voluntarily to the hospital, spending about six months more there, receiving electroshock. In 1952, a social worker, apparently reviewing records routinely, discovered she was there without formal commitment, and she was discharged at once as "improved." (One wonders how much credence to place in the statistics of this hospital and others on discharges, "recoveries" and "improved" cases.)

3.

The hospital heard no more of Sally for more than three years. Then suddenly she arrived, in 1955, committed by court at her parents' request. The court case history had been filled out by her sister. The present onset of disease, her sister said, was "very sudden": While getting ready to go to work one day about a year earlier Sally had abruptly announced that she was quitting her job because the company "had set up a dummy switchboard and was constantly saying stupid things to her to make her quit and she was going to beat them at their own game." She did quit. She began to behave queerly. She told her sister she heard voices. People were "trying to run her life." She was "very irritable" because the voices wouldn't let her alone. Sometimes she was friendly to guests in her home; at other times she would not speak to them. She avoided her own family. She stayed in her own room most of the time. She became destructive, depressed and suicidal. Once, "mad at the voices," she threw a clock through a window. In bed at night she wept. She had visited her former ward doctor, now working in the hospital's out-patient clinic, and had been given Thorazine, but it had done little good and she had gone irregularly, and finally her parents had had her committed.

When she arrived in 1955, Dr. Shortridge, the young fresh-faced crew-cut resident in charge of female admissions, first saw her in the old fashioned lobby by the Coke machine. She said she was "having the same difficulty" as before. She remembered little about her earlier hospitalization: EST had confused her. Shortridge wrote, "She does not understand the necessity of being hospitalized at this time but is willing to accept treatment. She is well oriented in all spheres."

She went willingly with a nurse to Ward 13. Shortridge saw her there three days later. He reported that she sat quietly and talked to him easily, her manner "rather haughty and aloof." She could do simple arithmetic quickly and accurately, knew the names of the three largest cities in Ohio and of the governor and the President. Asked for the meaning of the saying that a bird in the hand is worth two in the bush, she replied, "Something you have a hold of is more valuable than something in the distance." Asked for the meaning of the saying that a rolling stone gathers no moss, she said, "Something active stays fresh or is more luminous, or something to that effect. It doesn't rust or tarnish. Somebody ambitious is less likely to grow old in his ideas."

Shortridge asked about her symptoms.

Patient describes erotic sensations in genital region which were sudden in onset one year ago, one month after breaking off an affair with a young man. . . . She denied having had intercourse with him but describes her sensation like "being in bed with a man." She says she liked him, but progressed little beyond the hand-holding stage. She says he wrote her after [they separated] but she did not answer his letters. She blames him, saying she knows he is causing her erotic sensation; voices, sometimes his voice, have told her and at other times "kidded her about it." States, "They're trying to make a harlot out of me. Why am I here? I'm a healthy, happy normal girl. I want to go back to my job and buy a car. I don't want to be penned up for life. Would you like it? People spit in your face. Who wouldn't fight back? If you can't cure me, promise to put me out of my misery."

Next morning Shortridge presented her to staff. She faced the white-coated doctors angrily. She didn't think it was doing her any good to be in the hospital, it was in fact making her worse, for it was a very depressing dirty place, and furthermore her ideas about sex were more "idealistic" than those of other people here. She demanded to know whether she had been put here for life, she wanted "the facts in the situation." There was "more to life than sleeping," and "I would rather be put out of my misery"—if she went on like this for years, not knowing what was going on, she might "end up as a sex maniac." Living in this place and having EST would "wreck me both physically and mentally." Of Dr. Kovitz she demanded what the future held for her. Quietly he told her she was sick, and she said, "Why can't you give me a straightforward answer? Why? Who's behind this? Someone's got to be. Someone is impressing these ideas on my mind, and it's very degrading. I'm an ambitious happy normal active girl, I'm not a sick person, they just think I am. But why?"

The staff diagnosed her as schizophrenic reaction, paranoid type with catatonic features. Later Dr. Kovitz recalled, "She got rid of a lot of anger at staff. I think it did her good. She felt persecuted, she kept saying here she is trying to do the right thing and be a normal girl and this malevolent interference comes up. 'The whole world's gone crazy, not me, I'm the same as I always was'—that was her attitude. 'They're misinterpreting everything and making revolting suggestions, and now instead of trying to understand me they lock me up in a hospital where I'm likely to end my days.' That was how she felt. For years she's been afraid to show her feelings. As she gets sick her feelings are too hard to control. But this anger is like a flash in the pan. When it's gone, deterioration or withdrawal begins."

4.

Sally interested Kovitz, and a day or so later he went up to Ward 13 to see her. Climbing the narrow walled-in steel stairs to the second floor he said (to the present author), "Many schizophrenics are hard to understand, they have a peculiar symbolic shorthand way of putting things, and you almost have to get your own mind into a sort of schizophrenic pattern to be able to understand them. But you won't have that trouble with this girl, not if she's the way she was at staff the other day. I don't know whether she'll show the same amount of affect today she did then. She may have flattened." ("Affect," strictly, does not mean emotion but we can use it that way. "Flattened affect" means that the patient seems to have lost to some extent the capacity to react emotionally.) Kovitz went on, "It may have been the pressure situation of staff itself that made everything boil up the other day."

He drew a ring of keys from his hip pocket, expertly unlocked the door, stepped onto the ward, relocked the door and moved swiftly down the long hall. It was a quiet rather pleasant place, with tables and sofas ranged along the walls. Women were sitting in rockers and on benches. An old woman in a gray dress touched Kovitz's sleeve, she wanted to talk to him about her bowels, but he said he was sorry, he couldn't listen now, and he made his way through the patients to the ward's living room, fitted with a piano and television set. Sally was sitting on a wooden bench, her long legs curled up, feet under her, reading a magazine. She smiled at Kovitz and got up and walked ahead of him to the nurse's office, a bare bright antiseptic place.

Tall, she moved gracefully, almost gliding; she seemed to hold herself in as she walked, scarcely moving her shoulders at all. Her body was well controlled. She was wearing an attractive blue dress, a blue cashmere sweater, yellow rope sandals that made her big feet look bigger. Her hair was neat and pulled back over her ears into a knot at the neck. She wore lipstick. Her skin was transparent and her features fine and delicate. There was something patrician about her demeanor. She looked like a girl who had gone to a very good girls' school, though she had not.

In the nurse's office, she turned, willowy, supple, and sat in a straight bare-armed wooden chair, sitting very erect. Kovitz pulled a chair up, sat down and asked, "How have you been feeling?"

"All right. I'm eating, I'm much more relaxed and I'm sleeping well."

Smiling, Kovitz said, "You were a little upset in staff the other day."

"I was, Doctor," she said gravely.

"Did it make you feel good to express yourself?"

"It did. To get it out of my chest."

"Do you feel the same way you did then?"

"As long as I get well, that's all that matters," she said.

"What is your difficulty, as you see it?"

"It's all a lie, a loss of memory."

"Do you feel as though something is interfering with your life?"

"Yes, definitely, I do," she said positively. "Being in the hospital, taking away my freedom, that is interfering with my life. I believe the medicine is helping me."

Kovitz asked whether Thorazine had helped her at home. "I stopped taking them right before I came to the hospital. They helped me sleep but I don't know, there wasn't any real advantage in the tablets. Will they erase my memory at all?"

"No, they shouldn't."

Ordinarily her voice was soft and well modulated, though rapid, but now it became louder and coarser: "Am I confined to the hospital with my parents' consent? Why was I fingerprinted? Fingerprinted, like a common criminal! The last time my aunt brought me here. If I do take my medicine will I get to go home someday?" She was leaning forward tensely, her fists balled on the arms of her chair.

Kovitz said, "If the medicine helps you, yes. Your going depends on when we consider you are well enough to go. But what is the medicine for?"

"Whatever is causing the illness, Doctor, and that still has me befuddled."

"Why do we think you're sick?"

"I don't know. Because of the crisis in the case. I was under pressure at the time, I have been for over a year, I've been intimidated or made to believe certain things at certain times. I've heard people remark at me on television," and she laughed somewhat sheepishly.

"What has been said?"

"I don't know."

"Was it said on television?"

"Maybe it means you're being supervised or being watched," she said, frowning a little as she looked at him.

"Does it make you self-conscious?"

"Yes, of course it does—I would say any normal human being likes to live his life in private. When it first hits you it hits as a jolt. You're quite unaware of it and then it happens."

"Is it happening to you now?"

"Yes, it is, Doctor. They're just like people talking about you. Jesting, offering criticism on how you happen to be in the hospital, about you or how you act or on your habits."

"Do the voices remind you of anyone you've ever known before?" Dr. Kovitz asked. It was the first time that either of them had used the word voices but she didn't notice.

She said, speaking more slowly and somewhat guardedly, "They could. But I don't know. I wouldn't want to involve anyone. I don't know what impression I'm supposed to have. That's what befuddles me. What is the purpose behind it?" and she clenched her fists tighter and leaned forward and said again, "What is the purpose behind it?"

Kovitz said quietly, "How long has this been going on?"

"Doctor, it's been a year since last July. Last July I first noticed the effect. I was interrupted, everything I tried to do, I was interrupted, and since then this series has taken place," and she was leaning forward tensely.

"Are the voices unpleasant and personal?"

She nodded. "At times."

"Do they tell you what to do?"

She paused a moment, kneading her long fingers. "Yes, I'd say so."

"Do you have to do what they say?"

"No, I don't."

"Have they ever controlled your thinking?"

"At times. Something could happen if I wasn't particularly aware of it. I might do something to my family if I wasn't aware of it at all times."

"Something unpleasant or improper?"

"I have at times, when at home, thrown things on several occasions. I flared up all of a sudden, I felt violence all over me, I threw a dish, I was lying down on the davenport, I don't know what went over me but I picked up a clock and threw it at the window."

"Do the voices ever discuss unpleasant topics? Do they want to suggest morally injurious ideas?"

"Sometimes."

"Where do they come from?"

"I don't know, Doctor. I have thought different things about it. Being the one that's concerned, I thought maybe it was possible to control someone else's mind through electrical energy and they would get the other person's emotions."

"Why do you suppose they are doing it to you?"

"I don't know, Doctor. That's what I have been trying to figure out. How it happened. What it has come to be. Why? Why, Doctor?" and she leaned forward again tensely. "For what purpose?"

"You know," Kovitz said, crossing his legs, "you're not the first person this has happened to."

"Yes, I can see that."

"I once knew a woman who thought the mad scientists could do it."

She nodded. "I got the idea it might be for scientific experiment, maybe. Using people for guinea pigs."

"Do you really believe a person would do this terrible thing to you for scientific purposes?"

"Well, I haven't had much knowledge of science, Doctor. I believe anything is possible in this world. I've heard about brainwashing." She seemed calm about all this.

"But why did they pick on you, of all people?"

"I don't know—unless it's because of the experience I had this year." She seemed tense again. She rushed on: "I dated a certain young man, he wrote me a letter and told me he was leaving, he wrote me a letter and told me how I could reach him. He was just someone to sit with and talk with."

"How did this make you feel?"

"Over the year this other incident occurred, different things that have been said. At the time I didn't think anything about it."

"Were the things that were said on sexual topics?"

"Yes," in a low voice.

"Do you think you worried about it?"

"At the time I didn't give it a thought. But yes, I believe I acted differently. I wouldn't go out with him. And then this incident happened. I believe the reason it did was that I was under the influence of alcohol and not out of the effect of electric shock. I was still more or less under the influence of shock."

"Did this incident have anything to do with what has been suggested?"

"Well, that is what I think. I never had any trouble up to that time."

"Do you think you are being punished?"

"I wasn't aware of it if I was. Up till then I wasn't aware of it but looking back at it I think I would have acted differently." She was cool again, her chin up.

"Does this make you miserable and unhappy?"

"It has made me very unhappy and miserable in the past year, Doctor. But still I believe that today is today and to go on here is for the best. I am willing to put it behind me. I did make a mistake, though I was under the influence of alcohol and electric shock."

"What was the mistake? What mistake did you make? Listening to him talk about sleeping with you?"

"No."

"Do you have the feeling you have done anything wrong?"

"It's hard to say," she said slowly.

5.

Kovitz began asking her about her first hospitalization three years earlier.

"Why did you come to the hospital the first time?"

"I was on vacation in Wisconsin working for a certain concern and I believe a similar instance happened when I was in Wisconsin, similar to this instance."

"An incident with a young man?"

"Yes, Doctor," and she spoke in a low rapid voice: "It was a sailing party, three of us girls, three or four girls, I don't remember how many, I can't remember, but I can remember the sailing and we went on an island. He was from Chicago."

"You met a young man from Chicago?"

"It was arranged that way, and a similar instance occurred on the island at the sailing party. But nothing happened," she said, clenching her fists. "Something was said, something was suggested, but nothing happened, Doctor. I believe it was meant to enforce that on my mind."

"Did it bother you?"

"Yes, it bothered me. But then I went back to work, just forgot about it, and I just went back to work and it didn't bother me."

"Is it possible that the remarks made now could refer to this earlier incident?"

"No, I think they are put there for a purpose. And the first time that this was put to me was caused by a similar instance. It is meant to give me a feeling that I was in the wrong. Because of what has happened, both instances took place at work, on the job, more or less a sheet was placed for me to resign, to quit, and that is why this is happening. It has happened twice in my life. But nothing happened actually. I was younger in Wisconsin at the time, and it put me in a state of fear and put me in a state where I was afraid I would be caught but I didn't actually do anything. The man from Chicago on the sailing party tried to cover me with a blanket and I could see what was going to happen and I did flee, let's say flee, from him."

"He tried to cover you with a blanket?"

"Yes. Naturally everyone that is a young girl knows when to flee and when not to flee. We went out for a sailing party and he made advances that were improper and it was proper for me to flee."

Kovitz said, "What did he try to do?"

"He was very trying and out of place. I was only going out for a sailing party and he was trying to get serious. He was the influence at the time—he was the one that caused it," and her voice coarsened and she clenched her fist and hit the chair arm softly.

"But were you doing anything wrong because of this?"

"Yes."

"How did it make you feel? Can you tell us about it—were you tense or disturbed?"

"No, not about that incident. It's the over-all feeling I've had since I had electric shock. I believe in psychiatric treatment as the cause of anxiety. I believe that is what happened in Wisconsin. It's the same as an incident that happened. Electric shock did even that, and I believe that if I came to the hospital—I believe that by running from my father I tied this together and worked out what the cause of it was, my taking sick and losing my job."

"Did people have the wrong opinion of you after this incident occurred?"

"No, how could they, nothing actually happened."

"Did it make you feel anxious, though?"

"There must have been a cause for it," she said, looking straight ahead, not at Kovitz. "There must have been a cause. It was planned for the same reason. It has happened twice. And since nothing actually happened, Doctor—" She stopped, then went on, softly, "Something could have happened, Doctor, out at a sailing party, out on an island like that. But since nothing actually happened, so what am I to believe —that someone is out to corrupt me?"

"But who was it?"

"That's just it—who was it? I didn't know they were. But now I know they were. I believe he's been influential a lot of times in saying things and doing things in my younger years. Things have been said and done that I wouldn't approve of."

"Do you think boys want to cause you trouble?"

"No."

"Maybe he was just attracted by you."

"I'm not saying they weren't attracted by me," and she mentioned a former employer who she thought had been in love with her.

"Was it someone very important that was influencing you?"

"I believe that, yes. That's what caused the over-all difficulty. Whether they are responsible, or whether somebody where I work was responsible," she said, her voice getting harsh, her body rigid, "*somebody is responsible*."

She was upset. A certain fragility about her had gone; there was iron in her; she gestured hard and leaned forward tensely.

Kovitz said quietly, "Now they're trying to turn you into a wrong kind of girl."

Her voice steely, she said, "I believe it is impossible as long as I still have my mind."

"You have to fight against this corruption? Is that how you feel?" Kovitz asked gently.

"Yes."

"Does it seem like a pretty desperate struggle?"

"At times."

Kovitz asked if she was "the victim of persecution" and not sick. She agreed. "And you feel it isn't fair to lock you up here?"

"That's the way I feel, Doctor. I was a healthy normal girl, working, wanting the same things that every other attractive normal girl wants out of life. I was working, enjoying life. And then this happened. It isn't fair, it just isn't fair."

Kovitz looked at his watch. "I'm sorry," he said, standing, "but I have a meeting I have to go to. We'll talk some more—we'll be up to see you again. Thank you for talking to us."

She rose gracefully and smiled gravely and said, "Thank you, Dr. Kovitz." He unlocked and held the door and she walked ahead of him across the hall to the living room.

Downstairs in his bare little office which resembled a monk's cell, Dr. Kovitz sat at his desk and talked about Sally Bennett's case. "You see?" he said. "The peculiar way she has of reasoning about her life? She wants to think she's a perfectly normal healthy young girl. This is what you call a schizophrenic process of a certain kind. We didn't stir her feelings much today. She's calmer, cool and collected. But the feelings are there—they're just hidden. In the older textbooks you'll find it said that schizophrenics have inappropriate feelings, or even that they are incapable of feeling. But the feeling is there, and it's appropriate too—it's just that they've been trained from infancy to fear to show their feelings. They're very hard people to help, and that's one reason why—it's hard to know their feelings and to influence them."

We shall visit Sally Bennett again with Dr. Kovitz. But first let us see what we can learn of the disease afflicting her.

6.

Schizophrenia—that is the problem. Ask the superintendent of any mental hospital if he has a lot of schizophrenics and he'll sigh and say, as one did recently, "Lord, yes—who hasn't?" Another superintendent, gazing unhappily at a roomful of 250 naked deteriorated schizophrenic women standing jammed together, mindlessly facing the same direction like cattle before a rain, said, "Regressed schizophrenics—they're the bane of our existence. We don't know enough about the disease to prevent them from regressing."

It is believed that schizophrenia is world-wide and has always been, even in primitive societies, though it is most common where the tensions of Western technical civilization have overwhelmed primitive people. Dr. Manfred Bleuler of Switzerland recently estimated that one in every hundred people on earth today is afflicted with schizophrenia.

There are some 425,000 schizophrenics in American hospitals. Dr. Daniel Blain, of the American Psychiatric Association, told a House committee, "About one-half of mental hospital patients in this country have one form or another of schizophrenia—simple type, hebephrenic, catatonic or paranoid. Like cancer it is one of the great medical mysteries of our time, but unlike cancer, no comparable amount of time and effort has been spent to discover its etiology and possible forms of treatment. . . . Until schizophrenia can be better understood and treated there is little hope that the over-all mental hospital population in this country can be substantially reduced."

A psychiatrist doing research on schizophrenia at the enormous gleaming National Institute of Mental Health at Bethesda, Maryland, said, "I attended a meeting a while back and the discussion leader said he was going to write on the blackboard everything that was known with certainty about schizophrenia—everything that one of us could tell him was so and that none of the rest of us could say he knows wasn't so. At the end of an hour and a half he had an empty blackboard and a lot of angry psychiatrists. Thirty years ago or so the cure for schizophrenia was hydrotherapy—give 'em a good hot bath. But twenty years ago state hospital superintendents were telling relatives that when they put their cousin in the hospital with schizophrenia, they had better forget about him, he was as good as dead. For a while, when all the emphasis was on the organic, there was a theory of focal infection, and doctors were taking out tonsils in state hospitals right and left. That died away.

"Insulin shock came along, then electroshock, and for ten years shock was the answer. But by now there are some excellent hospitals that have given it up completely. Today we hear a lot of talk about the new drugs, especially Thorazine and Serpasil. But they have little to do with cure—they are useful in controlling patients, and will probably replace electric shock in a few years, but that's all. Today everybody is putting his chips on attitudes. Just a hundred years ago the superintendent of St. Elizabeths here in Washington wrote to Dr. Kirkbride and said that there seemed to be something about the character of the attendant that affected his schizophrenic patients. He said that sometimes after he put a new attendant on a disturbed ward it suddenly became a quiet ward. In the last few years a lot of doctors have remembered that. This is what is called total push. You throw the whole hospital into the effort to get a few patients out—more recreational therapy, occupational therapy, movies, dances, activities of all kinds; more psychotherapy, more drugs, more shock, more of everything. It gets some people out of the hospital but I don't know that it does much else. And it doesn't mean much—there aren't enough doctors and attendants in the world to give total push to everybody. Sometimes it gets hysterical—there's an emphasis on activities, everybody up and out, up and at 'em, the last one in is a bum. Of course, it's a good antidote to the attitude of the state hospital fogies who have basically given up. They feel a good deal of anxiety themselves because they can't treat schizophrenia, so they say, 'It's not my fault, he's just schizophrenic, he's a different species.' And in a way you can't blame them. Because total push or not, you come right back to where you started, so far as the knowledge of schizophrenia is concerned. We just don't know what causes it or how to treat it."

Psychiatrists have thus far not even been able to agree upon a definition of schizophrenia, let alone its cause. Indeed, they cannot even agree that schizophrenia is a disease entity, as is, for example, tuberculosis.

Some schizophrenics come from slum homes. But by no means all do. Again, some are poorly endowed physically by nature—one skinny young man with vacant stare and gaping jaw and wild long hair who looked like a caricature of all the mentally deficient on earth dragged himself to staff at Columbus Hospital a while back, admitted from a general hospital where he had been taken with congenital heart disease and where he abruptly made his schizophrenic break, crawling under the bed to eat cigarette butts and complaining that the water was poisoned; and a doctor watching him at staff murmured, "Poor protoplasm." It seemed as good a comment as any. But some patients, like Sally Bennett, come from "good" homes and are well endowed—they are just schizophrenic.

Eugen Bleuler, who coined the term "schizophrenia," seemed to think it had an organic basis, some anatomic or chemical disturbance of the brain, although the symptoms varied according to the personality of the patient.

Adolf Meyer and other American psychiatrists conceived schizophrenia as a way of reacting to life—a disorderly pattern of habits, a personality disorganization, and finally a withdrawal from reality, all resulting from an individual's faulty reaction to life's problems. Sometimes a physical illness, such as the flu, precipitates the psychotic break suddenly. Sometimes one of life's great crises precipitates it suddenly—adolescence, marriage, the death of one's mother. Sometimes it comes on insidiously, the patient failing to surmount one minor crisis after another and with each failure withdrawing more and more into himself, until one day his family realizes he is no longer dwelling among them but within himself.

Meyer argued that no physical basis for the disease could be proved, though he thought that an inferior constitution might pre-dispose an individual to it. The constitutional view has been urged by Ernst Kretschmer and, more recently, William Sheldon. Kretschmer observed that many schizophrenics before they made their psychotic break had what he called schizoid personalities—they were shy quiet seclusive shut-in people. (This is generally admitted today, though it is pointed out that probably a third of the schizophrenics do not have this sort of personality.) Sheldon, after studying the somatotypes, or body types, of thousands of individuals, has concluded that certain physiques appear to be clearly associated with certain temperaments and that the thin fragile ectomorphic type tends toward schizophrenia. Parallel to Kretschmer's and Sheldon's constitutional theories are those of the geneticists, such as Franz Josef Kallmann, who consider schizophrenia hereditary.

More recently the search for a cause of schizophrenia has turned to biochemistry and neurophysiology. Some researchers believe that the schizophrenic suffers from disturbances in metabolism. (And of this more later.)

The difficulty with the view that schizophrenia is of purely psychic origin is that the same psychological trauma may make one person schizophrenic, another neurotic, another an alcoholic, another a narcotics addict. Hence it is argued that to produce schizophrenia the psychological trauma must be inflicted upon a constitutional predisposition. In any case, the crucial explanation is missing. Most investigators seem to feel that no single "cause" for schizophrenia exists but that many things are involved. The general tendency today is to regard schizophrenia as of psychic origin, probably with some constitutional predisposition. Even the psychoanalysts hold this view. Franz Alexander wrote, "It seems highly probable that in the majority of cases of schizophrenia a constitutional element still undefined is of fundamental significance."

7.

The disorder called schizophrenia formerly was called dementia praecox. Dementia praecox means a disorder of the young which progresses to a demented state. Bleuler considered the term inaccurate— the disorder does not always appear during youth (though it frequently does) and it does not always progress to dementia (though again, it frequently does). Bleuler coined a new term, schizophrenia— split personality—because "in every case we are confronted with a more or less clear-cut splitting of the psychic functions."

This term has, however, resulted in a widespread misconception. Many people seem to think it describes a personality which is split down the middle, neatly, into two halves, so that the patient has two personalities and becomes, so to speak, one day a Dr. Jekyll, the next day a Mr. Hyde. This is wrong. The term refers to the fact that the psychic complexes—the ideas one holds that are loaded with emotion— no longer combine in a striving with a unified purpose, as in a normal person. Instead, "one set of complexes dominates the personality for a time, while other groups of ideas or drives are 'split off' and seem either partly or completely impotent," as Bleuler wrote. "Often ideas are only partially worked out, and fragments of ideas are connected in an illogical way to constitute a new idea." The association of ideas becomes bizarre. Often thinking stops in the middle of a thought. Affect, or emotion, may die, or seem to. For both association and affect are at the mercy of the warring complexes within the patient's mind. The schizophrenic personality is one that is split into many fragments. In the beginning a fissure appears in the normal whole personality. The fissure widens, and divides into other fissures, like a crack in a plaster wall; presently the personality is split into many fragments as the emotion-laden ideas, i.e., the complexes, war fiercely within; the personality, split and cracked in many places, disintegrates; finally it becomes deteriorated, sometimes unable to function even on the lowest physical level. This is the splitting process in schizophrenia. And it accounts for the peculiarly disorderly appearance of the schizophrenic's mind, his behavior and finally even his personal appearance. Disorderliness is a hallmark of schizophrenia.

The schizophrenic is deprived of one of the most valuable defenses a normal person possesses: the certainty that nobody else can know what is going on inside his head. The schizophrenic believes that the whole world knows what he is thinking. Like anybody else he sometimes thinks unworthy thoughts, thoughts of which he is ashamed. But unlike the rest of us, he believes the world knows he is thinking them. Not surprisingly, he concludes the world must be talking about him and accusing him of unworthiness. The world, the whole everyday world around him, accuses him and threatens him. He believes that articles in the morning newspaper refer to him alone, and so do radio and television announcers. (These are called "ideas of reference.") He cannot escape their threats. The most commonplace news items become very threatening to him. He reads a prediction in the paper that four hundred people will be killed over a holiday weekend, and although we understand that this is merely a statistical prediction, the schizophrenic believes the prediction refers to him, "they" are contriving his death, which because of his unworthy thoughts he so richly deserves. After a time the schizophrenic hears their accusing voices even when the radio and television are shut off, when there is no newspaper before him, when he is totally alone in his room. These are the hallucinated "voices" of schizophrenia. The patient has broken with reality. He feels he is no longer safe. "He may then," Abraham Myerson writes, "develop a 'delusion of influence,' a belief that somehow an influence of mysterious and potent nature is being used on him by others— The Others. For he is now an alien in the world." All this is by no means a full description of the schizophrenic process. But it does illustrate one way in which the fissure appears in the personality—the fissure that subdivides into innumerable fissures and splits the personality into myriad fragments and destroys it. It is an insidious and a deadly process.

In the disintegrated personality of the schizophrenic, the various fragments are incompatible feelings which the schizophrenic cannot harmonize. Some of these feelings are utterly repugnant to him. In the normal person, such hidden contradictions are expressed in dreams, in gestures, in feelings of tension. The schizophrenic cannot hide his disowned feelings; neither can he accept them. His experience then becomes confusing, dreamlike, fantastic, tortured.

To the man in the street, the schizophrenic's words and actions appear bizarre, disorderly, even senseless. They seem bizarre to the doctor too, until he begins to understand what is really going on inside the schizophrenic. The schizophrenic experiences things that really are himself, but do not feel like himself. They distort his picture of the world. The world becomes a threatening place. It is too much for him. He turns from it. It threatens him further. Threatened, he retreats, again and again. This is withdrawal—to mutism, sometimes. The voices still threaten: He lashes out. This is the homicidal tendency. He withdraws further, seeking to find a simpler order of life that he can cope with. He falls back to the furthest line of defense—babyhood. This is the naked incontinent patient in the back ward curled up in fetal position. Schizophrenia is an incomplete death in reverse.

Autism is the leading symptom of schizophrenia—the withdrawal into oneself, the break with reality, the way of thinking that is wholly subjective and unrelated to external reality. Thoughts arise from the unconscious, not from the outside world. One lives inside oneself only.

Though he wrote nearly thirty-five years ago, Ernst Kretschmer described the schizoid personality as eloquently as anyone. He wrote:*

Schizoid men have a surface and a depth. Cuttingly brutal, dull and sulky, bitingly sarcastic, or timidly retiring, like a mollusc without a shell— that is the surface. Or else the surface is just nothing; we see a man who stands in our way like a question mark, we feel that we are in contact with something flavourless, boring, and yet with a certain problematic quality about it. What is there in the deep under all these masks? Perhaps there is nothing, a dark, hollow-eyed nothing: affective anemia. Behind an ever-silent façade, which twitches uncertainly with every expiring whim— nothing but broken pieces, black rubbish heaps, yawning emotional emptiness, or the cold breath of an arctic soullessness. But from the façade we cannot see what lurks behind. Many schizoid folk are like Roman houses and villas, which have closed their shutters before the rays of the burning sun; perhaps in the subdued interior light there are festivities.

One cannot study the schizophrenic inner life in all its fulness from peasants. Kings and poets are good enough for that. There are schizoid men with whom we can live for ten years and yet not be able to say for certain that we know them. A shy girl, pious and lamblike, serves for months in the town; she is gentle and tractable with everyone. One morning the three children of the house lie murdered. The house is in flames. She has not lost her senses, she understands everything. She smiles uncertainly when she realizes her act. A young man dreams away the lovely days of his youth. He is so clumsy and loutish that one could shake him. If he is set

* In *Physique and Character*, translated by W. J. H. Sprott, published in 1951 by The Humanities Press, Inc., New York (London, Routledge & Kegan Paul Ltd.).

up on a horse he falls off at once. He smiles in an embarrassed way, rather ironically. He says nothing. One day there appears a volume of poetry that he has written, full of an exquisite feeling for nature, with every blow that some fat lout has given him as he passed by moulded into an inner tragedy, and the polished rhythms flowing on full of quiet.

That is what schizoid men are like. Bleuler calls it "Autism"—the living inside oneself. One cannot know what they feel; sometimes they don't know themselves, or only dimly. . . . But what their feeling is, whether it be a banality, a whim, an indecency, or a pearl of fairy lore, that is for no one—that is for them alone. . . .

Schizophrenic psychoses come in jerks. Something has got out of order in the inner structure. The whole structure may collapse inside, or perhaps only a few slanting cracks may appear. But in the majority of cases there remains something that never gets patched up. Where the attack has not been severe, we refer to a "post-psychotic personality," and in severe cases we speak of a schizophrenic idiocy—between the two no hard-and-fast line can be drawn. But we often are not aware whether the psychosis has disappeared or not. People who for years have performed the duties connected with their calling as merely eccentric or unfriendly personalities, may one day quite by chance disclose to us that the greater part of the time they carry the most fantastic illusions about with them—here, too, no boundaries can be drawn. . . .

He alone, however, has the key to the schizoid temperament who has clearly recognized that the majority of schizoids are not either over-sensitive or cold, but that they are over-sensitive and cold at the same time, and that in quite different relative proportions. Out of our schizoid material we can form a continuous series, beginning with what I call the "Hölderlin type"—those extremely sensitive, abnormally tender, constantly wounded, mimosa-like natures, who are "all nerves"—and winding up with those cold, numbed, almost lifeless ruins left by the ravages of a severe attack of dementia praecox, who hover like shades in a corner of the asylum, dull-witted as cows. And at the same time, even with the most gentle representative of that mimosa group of characteristics, we feel a light, intangible breath of aristocratic frigidity and distance, an autistic narrowing down of affective responses to a strictly limited circle of men and things, and occasionally we hear a harsh, loveless remark passed on men who lie outside this circle, and towards whose behaviour the affective resonance is damped. "There is a pane of glass between me and mankind," said such a schizoid recently—a remark of extraordinary significance. . . . The schizoid does not get on in a crowd. The pane of glass is always there.

8.

No cure is known for schizophrenia. Some patients get better spontaneously, of their own accord. Others progress steadily into deteriorated nothingness despite every treatment. In some, treatment seems to arrest the disease process and the patient leaves the hospital, better than when he came in but still far from well; it is likely he will come back. Bleuler included in his definition of schizophrenia the idea that it is a disease which "can stop or retrograde at any stage, but does not permit a full *restitutio ad integrum*"—that is, does not permit a complete restoration to the condition that prevailed before the patient became sick. It has been said that sometimes schizophrenia can be cured in the same sense that a gangrenous arm can be cured: The arm can be amputated, but the patient is not as he was before infection, for he has lost an arm. Most, perhaps all, schizophrenics, even those who make the best "social recoveries" upon leaving the hospital, are not as they were before. Most doctors believe that nobody is ever "cured" completely of schizophrenia. (Some add that nobody ever will be, and the only solution is to prevent their breeding.) A standard psychiatric text, by Henderson and Gillespie, says, "All medical men agree that the chief hope of success in treatment is earlier recognition of the disease. . . . We admit frankly that when cases have reached the stage of entering a mental hospital, the period of co-operation has usually passed, and the question then is much more one of treating symptoms."

Today schizophrenia is usually spoken of as though it were a single disease but Bleuler spoke of the "group of schizophrenias," and some authorities believe that what is today called schizophrenia is really a variety of disorders, each, perhaps, with its own cause or causes and cure, all as yet undiscovered. On the other hand, some authorities believe that not only schizophrenia but also manic-depressive psychosis and the other nonorganic psychoses are all one disease. Nobody knows.

And some believe that what we mean by schizophrenia—the three classic symptoms: autism, flattened affect and dissociative thinking— is a condition caused by hospitalization itself. It is indeed rare for a patient to arrive at the hospital with these three symptoms in severe form. Most schizophrenics upon arrival at hospital seem not too different from you or me. But after they have been there a while their symptoms bloom. And later they deteriorate. Why is this? Some believe the hospital produces what we call schizophrenia. Others say that the schizophrenic in the outside world struggles to maintain contact with reality, to preserve his personality, and that the hospital invites surrender, and so he ceases to struggle and his disease assumes command; as it does his behavior worsens, so he is ill treated by hospital attendants, and thus reality becomes more painful to him than ever, he retreats farther and farther, and he ends a "lifeless ruin," the hospital having abetted the disease.

9.

When Sally Bennett arrived at Columbus State, she looked fine. She talked well. Her emotions seemed appropriate and normal. ("Normal" people sometimes blow up and throw a clock at a window, as she had.) In fact, sitting in the nurse's office on Ward 13 and talking with her, one sometimes had to remind oneself that there was something terribly wrong with her. She heard voices when no one was there. She thought television announcers were talking about her. She thought The Others were trying to influence her, corrupt her, plot against her. Twice her illness had forced her to give up jobs she liked—schizophrenia is incapacitating, it interferes with one's life to the point where one cannot function.

What caused her sickness? No one knows. Doctors like Kovitz, confronted with a patient, are obliged to concentrate more on helping him than on studying him. Kovitz said, "Why is this girl schizophrenic? I don't know. Nobody really knows. She's just too afraid. Conditions like Sally Bennett's probably go back to very early in life. I suppose we all crowd children too much. I don't mean there is anything wrong with disciplining a child. The important thing is to accept the child, to help him understand he has a right to his own feelings. Schizophrenics have been made to feel as children that they don't dare express their emotions. So they bottle everything up. They are often outwardly well behaved, overinhibited. But sooner or later the denied feelings become too strong to control, and out they come.

"To the patient," Dr. Kovitz went on, "they may feel like a foreign invasion, like a force turning them into something evil. Sally wants to be good, but something—'he' or 'they'—won't let her. Her dread of people, her fear of being a woman and her need to be a woman were never fully part of her conscious life. Her conscious side shuts out all her unresolved problems. When they finally break in the open, she disowns them. They are felt as an imaginary man who controls her thoughts and interferes with her life. This experience of an uncontrollable something as *not yourself* is schizophrenia. A part of the personality breaks loose and is felt as an independent being, and after that everything has to be misinterpreted to explain it. If the television arouses an unacceptable impulse, it can't be *her*; it's the television influencing her. The voices are really part of her talking about herself, but she can't believe them. She can't stand to grow up, to face herself and her own emotions.

"The illness is a kind of compromise. She is committed, hook, line and sinker, to her delusional thinking. It gives her a measure of peace. She can't tolerate the tension that would be aroused by accepting her feelings. The delusions are her defense—they offer a kind of miserable truce in place of the peace she can never achieve.

"What can we do for her?" Kovitz said. "Psychotherapy would be difficult—it would threaten her delusional defenses, her system of security. EST might suppress the voices for a while, but she dreads it. And anyway she'd still be the same kind of girl six months later. So we'll give her Thorazine and Frenquel and get her out as soon as we can. We'd love to cure her with a pill. But we know darn well a pill isn't going to change her into a normal girl. The pills may make her more comfortable, able to carry on a more normal kind of life, but that's all."

10.

The second time Dr. Kovitz went upstairs to Ward 13 to see Sally Bennett he found her again stretched out on a bench in the living room. She went with him to the nurse's office and sat down on the edge of her chair and smoothed her dress on her lap. Kovitz said, "We wanted to talk to you some more, find out all we can about your difficulty, before starting on the medicine. How have you been feeling?"

She took a deep breath and drew herself up a little. "Well, Doctor, they still haven't cleared up."

"You're feeling about the same?"

"About the same. I'm wondering if I could go home, start taking my medicine at home. I don't think there's anything wrong with me and if there is it isn't much. I'd just as soon forget it, just forget about all of this. It's an illusion that's been presented to me, it's gone on for such a long time, it's something I can't seem to put my hands on, can't get hold of, something has been trying to make something out of me for a long time. I don't know, it's simply like an illusion, I don't want to bother with it, I feel I'd be better off at home." Her chin was up proudly, her expression almost haughty. "I'd just as soon forget it."

Kovitz said, "What do you mean by the word 'illusion'?"

"Well, it's like a skit. Something that happens to me. It's an over-all illusion. Like this incident that happened to me."

"Is that still being brought up? Is it being referred to by remarks that are being made?"

She looked down and gestured quickly. "Yes," she said.

"Are you being looked down on?"

"Well, probably so." She paused. Then, her voice harsh and hostile, she said, "Someone in my family is responsible or a close friend or the person involved in the incident, or maybe it's the hospital, I don't know who's responsible."

"What's the point to it all?"

"Maybe to make me grow up."

"How do you mean, 'grow up'? Grow up in what way?"

"Look at things in a more realistic way."

"But how? What things?"

She waited a long moment. Was she thinking about growing up to be a woman, with a man? If so she blocked the thought. She said only: "Don't jump to conclusions too much." She paused, then repeated, "Don't jump to conclusions too much. Be like other people who face their own problems."

Kovitz nodded and talked to her a moment about the need to face one's problems, and encouraged her to elaborate on this theme, but she would not. He returned to his former line: "You feel somebody has to be responsible for this. Do you feel lonely at times?"

"Since this has happened I don't feel that I'm part of anything, my family, anything, since that time I haven't been close to my family. I feel close to them but at the same time I feel more alone. I'm not close but I just don't trust people as much since this has happened. I used to more or less listen to what they'd say. But ever since this has happened it's made me cautious."

"When do you feel your troubles began?"

Her voice grew sharp, clear, louder, almost imperious. "Well, Doctor, what good is it going to do to go over it and over it when it's not there in the first place. I think it's best to forget something, that's the best way, and go get a job and forget all about it. It's been going on for years, I'd just as soon forget it, get a job and forget it, if it's not before me why should I worry about it?" She went on, demanding, "What is it supposed to mean, Doctor?" Her lipstick was bright red, her hair drawn back neatly, her face pale. Kovitz asked if it affected her even though she tried to ignore it. "I even overlook it," and she drew herself up tautly: "Let's say that I still think that I'm a single girl, I have my future before me and what I don't have before me I don't care about. An illusion of a person or a place or a thing is a waste of time. I want something I can hold onto, I don't want a figment of the imagination bothering me."

"What are your plans when you leave here?"

"I would get a job and have my own mind. I'd do as best I can. Be trying again and be content."

"But something keeps interfering? Things are being said or thought?"

"Yes," and she went on rapidly: "It's just like someone else is running my mind—someone is trying to influence me, someone is trying to boss me, someone is trying to love me," and she looked straight at him and waited for him to reply.

Kovitz uncrossed his legs and shifted his weight in his chair. "I have some thoughts about it. But first we need to know more about you. Can you tell us any more about how this makes you feel?"

She gathered herself once more. "It's like having your emotions drained from you. I had my emotions drained and I don't appreciate it. My emotions are mine. And when I meet someone I like I want to love them and marry them and have a home like any other normal human being. But this is like bothering with someone I don't like. Like having someone at times you don't like and listening to someone you don't like, it's like living with someone you don't like," this last in a low hard voice.

"Do you want to avoid it?"

"Yes."

"Is it a single personality?"

"It seems to be a single personality."

"Is it womanlike or more manlike?"

"Manlike."

"I see. Then it's a man and it seems he is interested in you and is interfering with you, attaching himself to your life, and to you this seems like an obstacle."

"I feel I want to stay young. I feel I'm twenty-three years old, I'm too young to like having someone forcing themselves on you and leading your life. It's like talking to *you* right now, you're forcing your opinions on me. And it can be any time, all the time. Say I'm drying dishes or in the library reading, it's like someone criticizing you."

"Does he make remarks *about* you? Or to you?"

"It's not like saying things directly. It's over your mind. Like talking *through* me to someone else. It's like you're forming an opinion and you'll be thinking something nice and he'll think something sarcastic."

"Does he ever talk to you directly?"

"Yes, sometimes."

"Is he friendly in tone, or not?"

"Friendly, at times." Then she burst out, "I don't know, I don't know what they're trying to do—that's what bothers me. What is it, Doctor? What are they trying to do?"

Kovitz said, "I have some thoughts about it. For instance, you may not believe this but other people go through it too."

"But what are they trying to accomplish? Is it that they're trying to teach you to get along with people? Is that it? Are they trying to see how personalities get that way—is that it?" and she cocked her head and looked at him quizzically. "Or are they teaching you to live with someone—is that what it's suppose to accomplish?"

"Is it like having to live with someone whether you like it or not?"

"M-hm."

"Does this mean growing up?"

"Yes."

"Do you ever see this person?"

"No."

"Then how does he get his thoughts into you?"

"I don't know. It's surely being directed at me and it's before me yet it isn't me," and she gestured gracefully.

Kovitz nodded. "It's not you. It's quite different from you. It's interfering with you. It's a man's personality and you're a woman."

She nodded, saying somewhat shyly, "You can like people when they're far off but you can't like them when they're too close."

"Does he express attitudes you're afraid to recognize, perhaps?"

"No," she said, then hesitated, said, "Well—" and stopped, then said, "I'm reacting differently at the time and it confuses me, because when I'm enjoying something, this other personality won't."

"For example?"

"Maybe he'll remark about somebody who I'm near. I'll say something nice but he'll say something sarcastic. They're just doing it to be devilish," and her voice hardened and rose: "I want to know how long is this going to go on and on and on."

"I can't tell you that."

"Well *why*, Doctor?" she demanded.

Kovitz said gently, "If I answered you now you wouldn't believe me."

"Is there a definite purpose behind it?"

"In a way," Kovitz said slowly, "there probably is. But I don't think you and I mean the same thing by the word 'purpose.' " She nodded but looked uncomprehending. Kovitz said, "Tell me, what kind of person do you feel yourself to be? What kind of girl have you tried to be as you were growing up?"

She said thoughtfully, "I've never given myself too much thought. To be healthy, to be active, to like people, try to get along with them, see their viewpoint as well as your own. You have to. I guess that's about all."

"What if you meet someone you don't like? What do you do?"

"If I don't like their silly habits," she said, a hint of iron in her voice, "I try to live with them, to ignore them."

"Do you have trouble saying 'no' to people? For example, if a salesman tries to sell you something, are you hard to sell?"

"I'm very headstrong," she said.

"You try very hard to be good?"

"Yes, Doctor."

"This other being wants you to be bad?"

"Yes."

"So this is a fight between the good and the bad, in a sense?"

She nodded.

"Does this other being remind you of anyone you ever knew?"

She paused long, then, "It could."

"Who?"

"I wouldn't want to say. I wouldn't want to involve anyone."

He asked if she had been shy, quiet, lonely, bashful as a child, and she nodded, agreeing, smiling at the words lonesome and bashful. Was she shy socially? She nodded. When had she been the most shy? "Oh, I imagine when I was growing up. In grade and high school. I was very shy then."

"Did you feel it was going to be hard to grow up—that adulthood would be hard to achieve?"

She said, "It still seems a long way off. I know it's here and yet it isn't here. I don't know how to explain it," and she made a gesture of futility with her long slender fingers. "I believe it's having security that helps people grow up, to improve, to be active, you have to have security to look forward to."

"Security," Kovitz said. "Did you have security?"

"Yes," she said definitely. "I had a good job, I liked my job, I liked the hours I was working, the pay, everything. I was happy with my family at home, I could go and come as I pleased. I felt that I was quite content at the time."

Kovitz said, "I think perhaps we mean two different things by security. There is a hint in what you've said about being shy and cautious that perhaps you didn't feel as secure as you say?"

"No, Doctor, what my goal in life was, was this: Someday I wanted to find someone that was very attractive to me and settle down and raise a family like every other normal human being. And I felt I had a good job, I was getting out more, meeting more people, and I thought I might meet someone. That was the only plan I had. It's funny, I don't look to other people, the people around me don't seem to mean much now, after this happened. When you like somebody." She stopped as though she had completed the sentence, and perhaps she thought she had.

"Did you like somebody?" Kovitz asked.

"Yes, Doctor, I did—and then, well, we broke up."

"Why?"

"Maybe I did it."

"When was this?"

"Over a year ago."

"It was after that that you had this trouble?"

"Yes. It seemed like something happened that kept me from writing to him, something was keeping us apart, there was something interfering, some*one* interfering," and once more her voice coarsened, "either *him* [meaning the other being, her phantom lover] or else a friend or my sister or someone that didn't want us to. At the time I figured my health was more important than any mere man, I figured there was always someone else you could learn to love."

"Your troubles began to be obvious as the problems of growing up became more difficult?"

"I always felt you should share with people. I had security and a good job and now I don't have that," and her voice grew weak and sad, she gestured wanly. "It just seemed like everything was lost and now I'm back in here and—" She stopped, pulled herself up, her voice grew stronger, "So I just feel like starting over again. I want to start anew and to get a job."

Kovitz said, "But we have to face this problem. This interference has really torn up your plans. You don't fully understand it, I think."

She said, "Yes, I do. I feel that, even though I did like someone. If I was interfered with I would be more than willing to oblige because my health is more important."

Kovitz agreed that it was. He told her that the interfering voices she heard were indeed an illusion, that they were what doctors call hallucinations, but he added that they were nonetheless not without some deeper meaning and it was this meaning that he and she must discover. She responded with another indignant demand to know who was responsible.

"Someone is interfering. Or else I without knowing it interfered with someone else," and the thought seemed to strike her forcibly. She leaned forward. "Did I interfere with someone else's love life? Did I? That has been said. That I stole someone else's boy friend. Did I, Doctor?" Her voice was tense.

Kovitz said quietly, "Well, I suppose there is always a chance we do that—we love someone and if he has a girl she gets hurt, and that's just too bad."

She rushed on, her voice taut: "But why do I have to come in here? I was happy on my job. I didn't write to him. If I interfered with him I did it unintentionally. Even though it would have never—it was there, I didn't know it at the time, I didn't do it intentionally, so why should I have to pay for it? When I could find someone else and be happy?"

"You feel it's very unfair, don't you?"

"That's what makes me mad. I was just going on being a normal human being, I didn't do anything intentionally. All I've got to do now is to get out of here. My health is more important—I can live alone the rest of my life and be happy."

"You feel if that's what having a boy friend can lead to, it isn't worth it."

"That's what I mean. Whether it was planned or not I don't know. It hasn't been too much fun."

"It's a very difficult situation for you and not one you can readily understand, isn't it?"

She said, "Is it forgetting a certain party, is that what it's meant to do? Am I supposed to forget him? I don't know what is expected of me," she said and repeated, "I don't know what is expected of me. Or am I to get along with someone? There has to be a reason."

Kovitz was silent a moment. He seemed to hesitate. He said, "You want answers. The trouble is that other people's attempts to explain won't satisfy you. And it's hard to help you find the explanation yourself. We don't even agree on our terms," and he smiled. "You mean one thing by security and I mean another. We don't agree on the meaning of 'purpose.' The hardest thing is to get agreement. But that's what we've got to try to do, if I'm to help you. Have you ever told anyone else this much about it before?"

She said shyly, "I've never discussed it with anyone else at all."

"And you feel you're not sick and you want to leave the hospital?"

"I don't want to be here the rest of my life," she said, resentfully. "It's like getting a record for nothing at all. I feel like I have a state hospital record when I'm a young girl—and for no reason at all. And I don't like it. I haven't committed any crime and to have this happen to me, it just isn't fair. That's the way I feel about it. I would have thought that would be obvious. I felt I could have done a lot of things, and if it wasn't for this force that's controlling me I could have, Doctor. I could have gotten a sales job."

"You could live if only the force would let you alone. Why doesn't it? Why is it doing this to you?"

"Yes, that's it, Doctor—why doesn't it come out in the open? I'm out in the open. Why isn't it?" and again she waited challengingly for his reply.

He began slowly, leaning forward and rubbing his hands together gently. "First of all, as to the reason you're here: Your experience is considered a form of illness. The things you ascribe to outside interference, we doctors ascribe to something coming from your illness. You have no enemies that we know of who would do such terrible things to you. Also we know of no earthly means by which they can interfere even if they wanted to." She looked somewhat impatient with him. He nodded. "I've told others this and they can't believe it either," he said. "If you could see it the way I see it, it would only make you more miserable. You feel it's not you—that there's nothing wrong with you.

You think you're all right." He paused. He was leaning forward, his elbows on his knees, hands together; she was sitting upright, and he was shorter than she anyway, so he was looking steeply up at her, his forehead wrinkled deeply. "This isn't a very nice thing to say to you and I wish I didn't have to say it—but you're really not all right. You're a very nice person—but a sick person with a sick personality who has maintained an illusion of being normal. And it hasn't worked." She shifted in her chair. She was sitting tensely upright. "The problems of growing up and getting along with men and getting married have produced tension in you, and what's interfering with you is a hidden side of your own personality. You have what people call a split personality. It's a very difficult condition to deal with, but we might as well face the truth. You're not the victim of enemies—only a part of yourself." He leaned back in his chair. "I don't feel very comfortable saying this to you," he said gently.

She had listened carefully. She had not moved but one felt she had drawn away from him. She said, speaking slowly and distinctly and carefully, "It's like having to live with a man under pressure, Doctor. It's not like choosing someone yourself. I felt like someone was choosing me for their mate."

Kovitz said, "It's terribly hard to help you understand this."

She said, her voice tense and rapid now, "It isn't so, Doctor, you're wrong, you'll never make me believe that. I know quite a bit. I know they have ways of influencing people, a lot of ways, like Roentgen rays. There is a way they can present illusions to people, I looked it up in Webster's dictionary, I *know* it," and her clenched fist struck the chair arm, "I learned it in a book."

Kovitz said quietly, "I knew you wouldn't believe me. We just don't agree—not yet, at least."

She said angrily, "Who is the one being mistreated—you or I? Who has the right to say—you or I?"

"You're suffering," he said gently. "You're ill."

She rushed on, "It's not an illusion. But everyone has the right to free speech, freedom of religion, freedom of the press, freedom of speech, and I have a right to believe or not, like any other sick person. I have a right to love when I want to, to agree with whom I want to." She was leaning forward, tense, her voice rising. "Everyone has different emotions, we're all different people. I have a right to do anything I want to try to do and I'm not a sick girl and I don't have to be here. It will hurt me to be here. It will hurt me to be in this place. This is a depressing environment. It will hurt me. I can live with anything, anything, if I know what is going on. I just don't like to be taken advantage of." She sat bolt upright as though about to go on but her mouth snapped shut.

Kovitz said, "It's only natural that we can't agree in a single interview. I can't force you to agree with me and I wouldn't want to if I could. I just want you to know how it looks to me."

"I'm not sick," she snapped. "What do I have to bother me? What am I saying that's so—" She broke off, veered sharply: "It's this other person—it isn't me. Is it a scientific form of experimentation?"

Kovitz said, "It's nature acting inside of you."

"Now you know it isn't nature in me! You're not going to make me believe that. You're a scientist and I'm a religious person and that's where we differ. I was brought up to believe there is a God. There *is* something more beautiful than this world and that's what keeps me going."

"You've got some faith," Kovitz murmured, nodding. "We need every bit we can get."

She was rushing on, "You say I'm unhealthy but I feel I'm being mistreated. It's just being here every day and every day and every day—it's awful," she burst out, "it makes me sick just being in here. Why can't I go home and start taking my medicine? Why can't I go home? Dr. Kovitz—why—can't—I—go—home?"

"I hope you can someday," he said.

"But when?"

"The staff has to agree that you are well enough."

"I don't think this is fair. This is twice in my lifetime this has happened to me and it isn't fair. Even when I was a little girl I used to walk by this place and I didn't like it," and she suddenly began to sob, though not uncontrollably. She sat a moment, daubing at her eyes with a balled handkerchief, smiling weakly. Kovitz waited, his brown eyes sympathetic. She said, "I never did like this place and I don't like the men here—the fact is, I don't like the whole state of Ohio. It's a horrible frightening place, all these sick people all around," and she gestured out toward the main hall of the ward, where other patients were pacing by. "How can a person live with this? Not to have anything to look forward to. After all I'm youthful, I don't like to live around dying aging people."

"They're sick," Kovitz said. "They can't help it."

She opened her mouth, hesitated, and her haughty look left her and she slumped a little. "They are," she said softly, nodding. "I know, Doctor," and she stopped. Then stiffened again and her voice hardened: "But why was I brought here to such a place? Oh, it's nice enough here, I eat three meals a day, I haven't slept too good, at times I find something to occupy myself, I've been helping out with the ward work, but that's about all. As far as looking out of the window goes and getting a little bit of sunlight, I'm doing that. But that's all."

Kovitz said, "We'd like to try you on some medicine. Will you take some medicine if we give it to you?"

Quietly she said, "Yes, I will, Doctor." But then she asked if she couldn't arrange to go home and take her medicine from the outpatient clinic.

Kovitz ignored that. "What effect did the medicine have on you?"

"I slept good and it relaxed me."

"But you didn't always take it and you didn't always come to see Dr. Dawson when you were supposed to."

"I will now, Doctor."

"Why didn't you before?"

She looked haughty again. "To me it was just a long bus trip, to have to track clear across town and come over here and talking about this over and over and over—you just keep building it up and building it up and building it up in my mind."

"You want to forget it and we force you to face it. Is that how you feel?"

"Yes, Doctor."

"Well, we may be wrong but some people feel if you really can understand what is going on you'd get over it. Your feeling is, though, that you'd like to forget about it and get out of here."

"I'm looking forward to Thanksgiving and Christmas and the sooner I can get out of here the better. I like to do something to get results. I wasn't accomplishing anything, just wasting car tickets, by coming here to the out-patient clinic last summer, riding the hot bus in the hot summer. I'd just as soon have a lemonade in the back yard," and she halted, almost sobbing again, then said more haughtily than ever, "I'd just as soon have a lemonade in the back yard or be working in a nice air-conditioned office earning a living. I wasn't getting anything out of it. And I'm not sick. And I never have been sick. This is wear and tear on me, living around this environment. I like to look at something bright and nice, not at scrub brushes and dirty old brooms and dirty old floors. You look around here and you wonder why a person is sick," and she waved her long fingers disdainfully. "When you don't have decent surroundings you're bound to be sick. I found someone I liked and after they left I was unhappy—that isn't sickness. That's what any other normal human being would do. There's no lying about it, Doctor," she said accusingly. "That is what has taken place, it's what has happened, I've been brought here and been branded a mental patient. I'd just as soon be home and seeing the doctor at home. I'll come and see *you*. I'll take the medicine if you'll promise me it'll help."

Kovitz said, "I can't promise you it'll help but I can promise you it won't do you any harm."

"I know the effect of electroshock, what it does to your eyes."

"We're not going to give you electroshock, don't worry about it."

"I've always been healthy, Doctor, and I am healthy now, and I want to go home."

Kovitz got up. He said, "We want you to go home too, just as soon as you're well enough. Don't worry about electroshock—we won't give it to you. I'll get some medicine for you and get you started on it. And I'll be up to see you again."

She too arose. "Thank you, Dr. Kovitz," she said gravely.

He watched her walk gracefully across the hall to the living room and sit gracefully in a rocking chair, choosing a chair off by itself, not close to other patients, and drawing her sweater a little more closely about her shoulders. Then Dr. Kovitz went out of the nurse's office and locked the door and walked quickly down the long ward, brushing past other patients who stretched out thin arms to him. He said, "Did you notice how hostile she became as soon as we threatened her security system, her delusions? Those beliefs are crucial to her security. She cannot see it the way everyone else does. To do so would rock her to her foundations."

He took out his keys and unlocked the ward door and stepped into a dark corridor leading to the next ward. He said, "Maybe you can see now from her what a tragically difficult problem we're dealing with." He looked worn-out. He said, "She's got to take refuge in Roentgen rays and all that nonsense. This is the schizophrenic break with reality. It's glaring in schizophrenia, but all of us have a definite limit to the amount of reality we can accept in our thinking. I'm not encouraged about her future. We'll try her on Thorazine and Frenquel. Frenquel is supposed to be specific for hallucinations and getting rid of her hallucinations might make her more comfortable. We'll hope to get her out someday but we'll never make her well, really well. We'll work out some sort of a compromise that helps her get along, helps her make the best of her crippled condition. Other people lose a leg or a lung or have a heart attack and have to make the best of it. She'll have to make the best of schizophrenia. Her potentialities will always be limited by her illness. There are physical limitations on some people, social limitations on others. The ills of society are many," he said, smiling a little. "They all restrict what life could really be."

5

A Psychiatrist's Day

■ A ward doctor's day at Columbus State began at 8 A.M., when he arrived to make the rounds of his wards. From then until he left at 5 P.M. he was a very busy man indeed, for at the time of our first visit to the hospital there were ten ward doctors to attend directly to the care of 2,700 mental patients. One of the busiest was Dr. Gordon L. Smith. He was taking care of the entire acute female service, four wards, containing three hundred patients. Let us spend a day with him to see how he managed, who he was, who his patients were and what he was able to do for them. And let us see who the other doctors were and what their lives were like.

Smith, a shaggy rumpled man of thirty-eight, spoke softly with a hint of a Western drawl. He was quiet. His head was large and he frequently needed a haircut. His suits usually needed pressing. He looked like an outdoor man; meeting him on the street one would more likely take him for an engineer than a doctor. He was a private general medical practitioner for nine years before he got interested in psychiatry and decided to specialize in it. He came to Columbus State in 1955 for residency training to prepare for examination by the Board of Neurology and Psychiatry and certification as a full-fledged psychiatrist. This was his first year as a resident. Like the other residents, at the same time he was taking residency training he also was paid as a staff doctor. After two years more of training and two of practice he would be eligible for Board certification.

Promptly at 8 A.M. he arrived at his office, a tiny monastic thick-walled cubicle like all the doctors' offices. In some hospitals the doctors' offices are scattered through the hospital, are on the wards with the patients, but not here—they are all together on this converted first-floor ward, and no patients are here with them. Smith's desk was piled high with patients' mail, patients' case histories, his own notes, books. He had been given charge of the acute female service in July of 1955; he had reorganized it. His wards lay one behind another, covering the entire second floor of the female wing of the hospital. Under his scheme new female patients were admitted to Ward 13, in the middle of the floor, unless they were so old they needed medical care, in which case they went downstairs to a medical ward, or were violently disturbed, in which case they went back to Smith's acute disturbed ward, 15. Ward 15 and Ward 13 were his electroshock treatment wards. If a patient improved on EST she was moved up forward to Ward 11, where she finished her course of EST and might be switched to one of the new tranquilizing drugs. If she continued to improve, she was moved up to the front ward, 9. Women went home from 9.

Of course not all patients followed this ideal course. Smith said, "Some of them go backward. We'll get them all the way up to 9 and just when they're about ready to go home they'll slip back and become disturbed. Then they have to start all over—15, then 13, then 11, then 9 again. It's no good to push a patient too fast." And some never did make it but continued to relapse and ultimately were moved off Smith's acute service—moved upstairs or out to the cottages where chronic patients go, many of them to end their days. Smith was not yet satisfied with the organization of his wards. "We've got a scattering of chronics all through that I futilely try to push on to the cottages. But the whole hospital's overcrowded." Nonetheless, his service was one of the best organized in the hospital. "But it's too much for one guy," he said. "I've got a grand total of three hundred patients and it's more than I can possibly take care of. There are some that are a complete blank to me—I don't know anything about 'em, they're just a name or not even that. And," he added in his quiet even voice, "that's too damn bad. This service should be split up between two doctors." (A little later it was.)

How did he keep track of his patients? "I've got a graduate nurse on every ward and on most of the wards I've got good experienced attendants. Every week I review the treatment list with the nurse, ask her how the patients are doing, and she tells me whether so and so is getting better or worse, whether she's hostile, negative, co-operative, friendly. I go by that. And by my personal observation. On Ward 9 I've got two social workers and they give me a line on when a patient is ready to go home and whether there's a home for her to go to. When they think one is all set, I interview the patient and if I agree I recommend her for trial visit"—that is, conditional release from the hospital, usually for a year, before final discharge. Dr. Smith's trial visit recommendation went to the superintendent's administrative assistant, Dr. Paul Kirch, one of the hospital's three certified psychiatrists; Kirch might approve the trial visit forthwith or might refer it to the full staff and Dr. Kovitz. Dr. Smith said with some pride, "I've got fifty-seven patients out since July and only three have bounced."

Today was Thursday, his easiest day. He gave no EST, had no staff meeting to attend and no interviews with patients' relatives. This was the only day in the week that he could spend entirely on his wards. Carrying a notebook and an armful of patients' records, he left his office. He stopped in the hall to ask Dr. Maria Madi if she had any vacancies on her third-floor chronic wards but she shook her head: "No vacancies today."

He went on. He wanted to visit Ward 15 first, at the rear of the second floor, and the most direct route to it lay through his front wards but if he went that way he'd never get to 15 because too many problems would crowd in upon him on the front wards; so he sneaked through other wards where the patients didn't know him and climbed a back stairs to 15.

2.

In the long bare dim-lit main hall a score of women were pacing to and fro or sitting on plain wooden benches; one was sprawled on the floor against the wall. Two approached while he still was locking the door behind him, but he brushed past them, saying, "Later, I have to attend to something," and he pushed past a half dozen more who stretched out their hands to him before he reached the door to the nurse's office, unlocked it and went inside.

The office was tiny, crowded with desk and cabinets; its ceiling was higher than its floor was wide, so it resembled a well. Instead of a window in the door there were two small openings covered with heavy wire mesh and reinforced with iron strips. The window in the outer wall was barred and screened. The nurse, a tall blonde young woman wearing the starched cap of a registered nurse, was drinking coffee and eating a doughnut at the desk. "How are things going?" Dr. Smith asked. "All right," she said, getting up. She asked if a patient might have the privilege of going outdoors. Smith knew her; she was a fighter at times. He asked, "What if she gets in serious trouble?"

"She doesn't get in trouble when she isn't kept on the ward all the time."

He considered, nodding. "Maybe that's the answer. Yeh, let's go ahead and try it," and the nurse handed him the doctor's order sheet from the patient's file and he wrote on it, and the nurse added the patient's name to a list on the wall. (Five patients on this ward had full grounds privilege and six more had full privileges "when good.") Another sheet on the wall listed thirteen patients who went to the hospital beauty parlor.

The nurse asked if another patient wasn't supposed to be getting Thorazine or Serpasil. She was, Dr. Smith said. When? "I don't know. I talked to Dr. Kovitz about her and he okayed her for hospital supply." (Many patients had to buy their own.) "I thought she was already getting it." The nurse said, no, no drugs ever had arrived for her. Smith picked up the phone and called the pharmacy and asked if Dr. Kovitz had approved drugs for her. He hadn't. Smith, hanging up, said, "I'll have to stir him up on that again," and made a note in his notebook. "I'm going to have to squawk to him too about patients who are sitting on 13 waiting for possible Frenquel or possible something else that never comes. I've got a lot of new patients here six weeks and still getting nothing. Everybody says at staff they ought to have it but the drug never arrives."

The nurse handed him the ward record of a new patient, saying, "She beat another patient up on Ward 5 last night and they brought her here. She's very combative."

Dr. Smith studied her record. She had been in the hospital since 1927. "She's been on EST—why don't we continue her on it if she's combative?" and the nurse nodded and made a note on her own records while Dr. Smith wrote on the order sheet.

A little Negro patient came into the office, and the nurse blocked her way: she tried to push past, her face stubborn. The nurse, writing, said, "Just a minute."

"I want to see the doctor."

"Just a minute."

Dr. Smith said, "What is it?"

She worked her way around the tall figure of the nurse and confronted him and said, "Am I on treatment tomorrow?"

"I don't know, I'll see. Why?"

"Well, I wondered why I have to have any more of them treatments."

Dr. Smith said to the nurse, "How has she been? Has there been any trouble?"

The nurse said hesitantly, "Well—"

Dr. Smith said, "I'll talk to you later," then to the patient, "I know you don't like treatment but we want to get you better."

The patient said resentfully, "Sometimes if you don't like somebody you make them take it."

"If you could learn to stay away from the other girls it would help."

"Would I be able to go back to 13?"

"Not so long as that other girl's there. But I could send you maybe to 11."

"What difference did that make?"

"It's something that isn't done. The law and society frown on open homosexual practices and that's what difference it makes."

"And just because of that!"

"Just because of that. It's the only thing I know of."

"When will I get off treatment?"

"I'll talk to the nurse. I'll have to look up and see how many you've had."

The nurse said, "She's had forty-five."

Surprised, Smith said, "In a row? In one course?"

"Yes."

"Why?"

"She was getting pretty sassy. Resistive. Slapping at people."

The patient said indignantly, "When did I slap anybody?"

"You slapped me."

"Maybe you slapped me first."

"I don't slap anyone."

Dr. Smith said, "Well, you go on now, and I'll see about it," and they turned away from her but she stood by the door, unwilling to leave. Dr. Smith said in a low voice, "I think we'd better leave her on a little longer, then give her a rest."

Another patient, a white woman with a sly furtive manner, glided into the room and clutched the nurse's shoulder and asked eagerly, "Did you get to ask him yet?" The nurse shook her head. "About my trial visit? You know—my trial visit." Dr. Smith recognized her and asked if she wanted to go home for a weekend. "No, for two weeks. I want to go home. I won't take the child, I promise I won't."

"Have you been home for a weekend yet?"

"Yes."

Dr. Smith hesitated, said, "You're doing real good now. You still tend to get excited."

She said rapidly, "But it's quiet out in the country, and peaceful, and you can sit there and relax better than here, when they throw things in here it's a madhouse," and she went on, pleading for at least a long weekend, and finally Dr. Smith consented, and she asked eagerly, "Be all right if I left today?"

Dr. Smith said, "Why not tomorrow—tomorrow's Friday?" Somewhat crestfallen, she agreed and left.

The little Negress tried to break in again but this time the nurse took her by the arm and firmly led her to the hall and locked the door.

The nurse told him she had had to put a patient in seclusion again for her own protection because "she's real high, she twists everything up, fiddles around and bothers everybody till they get ready to clobber her." The nurse wanted to give another patient EST, but she was elderly, and Dr. Smith took the precaution of first sending her to the medical ward for a physical checkup—"not that they'll find anything but if she should happen to conk out on us we'd feel better." (Last week a patient had died while he was giving her EST.) The nurse told him about a patient who, even though she was on Serpasil, had hit another patient. An old woman with bony face and stringy hair came to the door and peered through the wire mesh, clawing at it and muttering, "God damn this thing," then laughing and looking foolishly at the doctor. He paid no attention.

The nurse told him about a patient who "isn't too good." Dr. Smith nodded; he knew her. "Her family promised me they'd get Thorazine for her but they haven't done it. I'd better see about that. We'd better try EST before she gets worse."

The nurse said, laughing, "She's an awful big girl, especially when she stands up here like this and I'm looking up at her."

"I know. We'll certainly need a crowd to hold her down to give her EST. I tried to get Kovitz to put her on hospital supply of Thorazine and all he did is give me a few ampules but what good's that, it'll hold her for a few hours and that's all," and he made a note.

The nurse asked, "Do you think we ought to try Sarah on EST again? She's pretty bad, pretty combative."

Dr. Smith considered, then, "Oh, let's try and keep her off another week. She's already had forty ESTs."

The nurse said another nurse on an upstairs ward had told her she had some vacancies.

Dr. Smith said, "What kind of patients do they want?"

"I don't know."

"I'll see about it."

The nurse said, laughing, "All my patients say, 'Let me stay here. It's a combative ward and I like it.'"

Dr. Smith smiled and asked if that was all she had. It was.

He unlocked the door and went out, and a thin distraught woman fell into step beside him, wringing her hands and saying, "Dr. Smith, can't you send me back to 9?"

Walking on, he said, "I can't."

"Well, why not? I'm not insane. These people are cracked here."

Still walking and not looking at her he said, "I've tried and you get in too much trouble."

She protested, "I've never done anything. And I've got a church back of me."

He unlocked the door and, taking care to block it with his body, went through and locked it again, closing it in her face. "She's a paranoid schizophrenic, not deteriorated yet but very irritating to the other patients. She's been here a number of years. Several times I've tried her on better wards but she always gets in trouble. She's one that would do well on Thorazine but she has no relatives to buy it and there's no use in my trying to get her on hospital supply—she's a chronic, and I have trouble enough getting Thorazine for my acute patients. Though I'd like to see her have it."

3.

He walked down a long winding corridor and emerged onto the main hall of Ward 13, a quieter cleaner airier place. This was the ward where Dr. Kovitz had interviewed Sally Bennett. Smith sat at the nurse's desk and went through his notebook to see what problems he wanted to deal with here. This ward's problems differed from 15's.

This was the admitting ward, and Smith's task was to get to know the new patients and to get them started on the treatment recommended at staff meeting. Smith wanted to see one who had been here a week, diagnosed manic-depressive psychosis, manic type. Dr. Smith had wanted to put her on Serpasil at once but she had no money and the hospital supply was fully committed. So, Dr. Smith said, he proposed to "take the bull by the horns"—to write to her relatives. "I don't like to do it, to ask relatives to come in, then send them down to the business office and have them lop $12.50 off of them, but if I don't this woman will be here a month or more getting no treatment, nothing at all. In the past we'd have gone ahead and started her on EST but in the last month or so Kovitz has been saying no EST unless it's specifically indicated, and the staff recommended Serpasil for her— which is all fine, but we haven't got the drugs and patients are backing up on this ward getting nothing at all." He always interviewed a patient before asking her relatives for money for drugs so that if they asked how she was getting along he could answer honestly.

The attendant brought her in. She was a tall vivid black-haired olive-skinned woman in her forties. Dr. Smith rose and pointed to a chair, and she sat, leaning forward eagerly, wearing a bright billowing flowered dress. Dr. Smith introduced himself, and she said, "I'm glad to get to talk to you, Doctor."

He asked how long she'd been here.

"Since February tenth." (September 10 was correct.)

Why had she come here?

"Because my husband and I had a fight. He was out of work and refused to give me money for lunch and to run our car on." Speaking rapidly, her words tumbling over each other, ideas rushing by her too fast to formulate, she explained she hadn't been too happily married, she and her husband had had a farm, then a store, and the store burned, and she called the sheriff, but her husband thought she told the sheriff he had set the fire, but "I wouldn't do that, sir, not my own husband."

Quietly Dr. Smith asked about her children, and she answered one or two questions well but then soared off on another flight of ideas, as manics do. Gently Dr. Smith brought her back to the question of her illness, explained the need for drugs, told her how much they would cost, and said he proposed to write to her husband about it.

She said eagerly, "He'll be here Sunday."

Dr. Smith said, "The trouble is, I won't."

Not heeding, she rushed on, "I feel just fine, I slept fine last night, I haven't asked for no medicine or nothing, it's just one of those awful things, I asked for a divorce or separation, I called a lawyer," and she went on and on, irresistibly compelled to tell him all about everything all at once. Especially she wanted to know how soon she could leave, she was needed at the store—"It is very hard to find anyone to take my place"—proudly.

Dr. Smith said, "I know, but the important thing is to get you well. We want to get some medicine for you."

She interrupted to say she was taking medicine for a while on prescription but didn't take it regularly, and he began to explain how being here and taking medicine regularly would help, but she burst out, "I was overdoing!"

He managed to bring her back—was her husband able and willing to pay? Oh, this would present no problem. He said, "That's fine because the sooner we get you started on it the sooner you can get out."

She exclaimed, "Oh, I'm very anxious to get back to my job. I think that would be the thing to do. I don't want to give up the job. It's not good for me to give up things."

He said he regretted the hospital couldn't give her medicine free, and she was quick to tell him, "That's quite all right, Doctor." She left.

Dr. Smith consulted his notes, murmuring, "Let's see— who's next?" A woman of fifty was next, one suffering from involutional psychosis. The staff had recommended EST but Dr. Smith wasn't sure she could stand it. The attendant called her in, a gray neat little lady. She was not sure when she came here or why. She had had the flu and "terrible pains in my back," and her husband had found her down in the basement one day and she didn't remember much after that. Now she didn't feel well, couldn't sleep, was nervous. "It seems that pain is back of all my trouble. I've been to orthopedic specialists and they put weights on me, and to chiropractors too, but nothing helps. I used to ski a great deal. We went to New Hampshire, but I fell and hurt my back. Then I had a strep throat, and my little girl died, she was injured at birth and never walked or talked, and after that I got sick."

Dr. Smith asked, "How does your future look to you now?"

"Well, I think if I could get rid of this pain I'd be all right," putting one hand uncertainly on her back. "I'd love to go home. I have a nice

home. I think the world and all of my husband." Right now her worst
affliction was arthritis.

Dr. Smith nodded. "I know your arthritis is bothering you. I hesitate
to put you on cortisone but maybe we can find something else. I'll get
to work on it." She left. Dr. Smith made a note in his book, "Hypo-
chondriacal depression," but this was little help, and he looked worried.
He told the attendant to have her husband see him next time he
visited. "She's a problem. She ought to have EST, it's the only thing
really that'll hold. But yet her physical difficulties are in the way. Maybe
we ought to be hardhearted about it." He hesitated, sucking on his
fountain pen. "Let's go ahead. In the long run it's best." He put the
sheet away, saying, "It's the only thing to do," and picked up the next
file.

It was that of an eighty-five-year-old woman, and the attendant told
him, "She's real combative, fighting with the girls in the room. We had
to send her back to 15 today. Everybody's scared to death of her. She
tries to bite and everything. Everybody that goes by she yells at."

Dr. Smith said, "Why'd they send her here? She doesn't belong here.
Fifteen would be the place for her but they've got it all full of people
that've been there ten years and I can't get rid of them. This problem
of disturbed senile patients—"

The nurse said, "You want us to leave her on 15? They had to put
her in seclusion there."

"I guess so, for the time being anyway. What else have you got?"

She brought in two more patients. Once while he was studying the
folder of one, another patient came to the door and asked through
the screen, "Can I talk to you, Doctor?"

"No," he said, "I'm not interested in talking to you, I want to talk
to your daughter."

Her voice rising, she said, "I can't stand this life, it makes me so
nervous here. How soon can they let me go?"

"I can't give you any promises."

Clutching the wire mesh, she said, "Don't let me die, please let me
go out tomorrow."

He shook his head. She slid away slowly.

A tall young Negro woman took her place, saying rather foolishly,
"Guess what—I'm going home tomorrow."

"That so? Who you going to live with?"

"I don't know," and she grinned and left.

The other one came back: "Please, Doctor, how soon can I go home? How soon?" Smith turned away. This woman asked the same questions dozens of times a day. The attendant, weary of answering, had written "NO" on a piece of paper and given it to her and told her to read it every time she had a question.

It was 11:10 A.M. Out in the hall patients were eating lunch off trays in their laps. Somewhere a woman was wailing and screeching and sobbing, heart-breaking cries of "Oh, oh, oh, my God." The attendant said it was a patient who had just been returned from a family-care home, and she asked Dr. Smith to see her. He agreed.

There were twenty family-care homes to which Columbus State sent patients—private residences which boarded patients who were well enough to leave the hospital but had no suitable home of their own. The state paid the family-care operator sixty-five dollars a month per patient. He could not have more than four patients at one time. Social Service inspected the homes. The hospital had about forty-five patients out on family care, at least half of them old people.

This patient was a big woman of fifty, her gray hair neatly kept, her face big and red, wearing a flowered dress and white ankle socks and shoes with heels of medium height; and she came into the office sobbing and trembling and leaning heavily on the attendant, who kept patting her arm and saying, "There, there." She fell into a chair, and Dr. Smith, hitching a stool close to her, said, "What's the trouble?"

In a high wailing voice she cried, "Oh, she's so foul-mouthed, now she's in for it," and she raved on about the proprietor of the family-care home: "She wouldn't let me call a doctor, she made me go upstairs but it was nicer downstairs, and she was mean to me, I didn't like her brother's dad, I didn't like any of them," and she suddenly leaned forward and banged her head down onto her knees and wrapped her forearms around the back of her head and sobbed and screamed over and over, "Oh, my God, my God, my God."

Dr. Smith put his hand on her shoulder and raised her head. Her face was contorted with agony; tears were streaming, and she looked up at him open-mouthed, screaming, unseeing. He let go of her and turned to the attendant and said quietly, "I imagine we'd better send her to 15"—the disturbed ward.

The attendant tried once more: She lifted the woman's head and said, "Can't you talk to the doctor, Honey?"

But she stared back wildly, hung poised an instant, suddenly clawed at her own face, then flung her head back down to her knees and screamed in a strangled voice, her gingham dress stretched taut on her back, her back heaving. The attendant took her out. Dr. Smith sighed, made out a blue slip requesting medical clearance for EST—blood pressure and heart—then picked up his papers and left the ward.

4.

He went to 11, a quieter ward, soft-lit, with old varnished wooden pillars, furnished not only with the usual old high-backed rockers and straight chairs but also with wicker chairs and upholstered divans and flower pots and a piano and even a rug. It was of course crowded like all the wards—six beds in a room 10 by 15 feet, only ten inches between beds, no room at all for a chest of drawers, the patients' belongings kept in paper sacks lying on the beds by day and under the beds by night—but it was far more pleasant than most wards.

Though it was near lunchtime, Dr. Smith wanted to see one more patient, and the attendant fetched her. She was a fat woman with a round face and rimless glasses, neat in cardigan and dress and beaded moccasins. She had come here three years ago, brought by deputy sheriffs, a good wife and housekeeper who after many years of apparently happy married life one night had wakened her husband in the middle of the night and told him she was going crazy. She'd been right—a week later she was brought here a full-blown case of paranoid schizophrenia, suspicious of her husband, disoriented, listening to the voice of God. She soon had quieted and asked to do ward work; she had mopped a while but then had put the mop down, lain down on a bench, propped her feet up against the wall, and said, "That's enough of that for a while." Next day when her husband came to visit he had found her under the bed. She insisted he was the crazy one, not she.

Her progress had been erratic. EST would help her, and doctors would move her forward through the wards, then, when she seemed almost ready to go home, she would blow up and have to be put back on the disturbed ward. Right now Dr. Smith had worked her up from 15 through 13 to 11 and he felt she had reached another crucial point in her hospital career, where she might either go on to 9 and out or might slip back to 15; and he wanted to see what might be done for her.

She greeted him with a grave smile and when he asked, "How's everything going?" she said, "Real well, real fine, I went home for the weekend and I got along real good," but her voice was toneless.

He asked if she had seen only her husband. No, her mother-in-law and brother-in-law had been there. During the war she had worked and paid off the mortgage and made them move out but now they were back. She never had gotten along with them. "How do you get along with your husband?"

"Oh, fine. He wants me to come home, and I want to go too." She leaned forward and for the first time some warmth came into her voice: "Do you think I can go pretty soon? He'll need me at home pretty soon. It's getting cold and we have two coal stoves and I get up in the morning and get the fires going for him. He's got a hard job."

Dr. Smith asked, "How do you get along with your in-laws?"

She said, her face set, "They won't bother me again. I swear I won't *let* them bother me any more. I can't."

He asked her to tell him about them. She said her brother-in-law wouldn't work, drank a good deal, quarreled with her friends, and prowled the neighborhood half-dressed. "But," she added, "my husband says he's going to make them get out."

Dr. Smith said, "I think you could go home soon, you're getting along real good, but I wonder if we shouldn't put some pressure on your husband to get rid of these people first."

She looked worried. "Maybe you better not. He said come spring we won't have to see them. I feel sorry for his mother, though, even if I did get afraid of her. She didn't think he'd ever get married. I don't want to see them in any trouble, Doctor."

Dr. Smith said, "Well, I'd like to see you go home. But I don't like to see you go into a situation that won't work out for you. That drinking brother-in-law seems to be the main thing."

She said, "He could get a room uptown." She hesitated, then. "It's up to you. If you've got the courage to talk to my husband—"

Dr. Smith said, "It doesn't bother me. It's a question of what's the best thing to do for you. I hate to send you home to a mess like that."

"I know, but I've got to go soon. I'm afraid my husband will get the flu from my not being there to build the fires for him."

Smith looked at her records. She was on Thorazine, supplied by the hospital. He wanted her to stay on it after she left but so far none of her relatives had volunteered to buy it. He didn't want to worry her about it. He said, "Well, we'll see what we can do."

She arose and said, "Well, bless your heart. You get me out of here as fast as you can."

"We will," he said, and she left.

The attendant said, "What a mess," then, "Doctor, I've got everybody on the ward taking Thorazine today except one patient, and she put the money down last week. We've borrowed for some of them. If I could be sure they'd deposit the money—"

He frowned. "I hate to borrow for patients"—that is, to borrow drugs from the hospital supply with a promise that the patient's relatives would reimburse the hospital later. Then he said suddenly, "They've got plenty of money for beer but none for medicine." He went out of the office and out of the hospital and across the lawn to his home to lunch.

5.

Dr. Smith lived with his wife and three young children in half of a modest square brick double house owned by the state on the hospital grounds. It is one of the doctors' houses clustered on flat ground between Awl cottage and Broad Street behind the main hospital building.

Dr. Smith had grown up on the South Side of Chicago. After getting his A.B. degree at DePauw University, he had graduated from the University of Illinois Medical School in 1943, interned at Cook County Hospital, married a nurse, and gone to work for the Veterans' Administration. He hadn't liked it; the pay was low, and he was tired of Chicago. He and his wife had "got the Alaska bug—we climbed into our old car and headed west and ran out of money in Montana and stayed seven years." He had practiced general medicine in Eureka, Montana, a lumbering and cattle town of eleven hundred, the only doctor within fifty miles. He had liked his life there—he recalled nostalgically that "bears and moose used to come down in the back yard"—but he had gotten interested in psychiatry. "In my family practice there was a strong element of the psychosomatic at the root of a good share of their physical complaints. I did a lot of work on the Indian tribe we had and got interested in their psychology. For years I'd collected books on philosophy and anthropology. I decided I'd like to know more about psychiatry. So I got out an AMA residency manual and looked for the psychiatric residency that paid the most money and here I am."

As a resident at Columbus State he was paid five hundred dollars a month to start, "which is darn good." "And surprisingly enough it's a good residency—you usually hear that the ones that pay the most offer the poorest training." Actually, money hadn't been the only reason he had picked Columbus State. He'd wanted a hospital where residents spend a lot of time caring for patients, not a university hospital likely to emphasize formal study, which he considered better for a young man just out of medical school. He said, "I'm pretty old to still be taking training but heck, it's what I want to do."

Dr. Smith was often disheartened by his impossible case load but otherwise he liked Columbus State. In addition to his eight-hour day at the hospital he was on duty about one week end a month, and he sometimes saw patients' relatives week ends, though he tried not to— "Saturday afternoon and all day Sunday are my days with my kids." He owned a monkey and on Saturday mornings took it down to Hocking State Park to study it. He said, "Kovitz thinks it's crazy but I've got an idea that all the research work done on primates has been done on caged primates. If you let them out of their cages they change entirely. I've got a lot of theories that are different from Freud's about the basic endowment of animals and humans and I've proved them to my own satisfaction by doing some work on primitives and primates. This monkey is fairly friendly toward me but very hostile to other people. She bites so I can't keep her at home, I keep her at a veterinary's and take her to a remote place to work with her."

Smith wasn't sure whether he'd go into private practice or stay in state hospital practice after he completed his residency. He said, "If it was possible in private practice to charge a fairly moderate fee and still make a living I'd prefer that. But if not I'll probably stay in a state hospital. This business of trying to soothe a person's nerves while taking away most of his substance—I can't see that. For me treating the neuroses of the wealthy would be hard to do—I don't like to knuckle under to people, to be sort of a glorified servant of people of wealth. Here at the state hospital, they'll let you go ahead and do what you think's right. I've been around private sans and I know how they have to shilly-shally and it rubs me the wrong way. Not that I won't take orders—it's just a question of one's social philosophy. I suppose if you have dreams of getting wealthy you go into private practice, but that's no problem with me. Another thing, you almost have to practice psychiatry in a big city, and I don't like the city, I like to raise ornamental pheasants and go hunting with my boy. So all in all

I'll probably end up looking around for a state hospital somewhere out in the country."

6.

Smith was one of nine doctors who lived at the hospital. The superintendent had an elaborate apartment in the main building. Three doctors lived in smaller apartments in the main building and five, including Smith, all of whom had children, occupied houses. The other doctors lived in apartments or houses scattered around Columbus, some in suburban areas many miles from the hospital.

Until 1955 a doctor could live at the hospital cheap. For food, rent, laundry and utilities he paid only $35 a month for himself, $35 for his wife and $10 for each child. (Thus Smith, with three children, paid $100 a month for everything.) This was considered a sub-rosa means of increasing doctors' salaries. But a candidate for governor had charged that doctors were "living high on the hog," buying lobster tail and soda pop and other luxuries at stores in town and sending the bills to the state. So in 1955 the director of the Department of Mental Hygiene downtown stopped all maintenance and raised rents. Dr. Smith and others like him had to pay $90 a month for rent alone, instead of $100 for everything, and had to pay for their own food and laundry. At the same time, however, the legislature raised doctors' salaries, so most doctors were as well off as before or a little better. A first-year resident who formerly got $6,000 a year now got $6,900.

7.

The American Psychiatric Association, which establishes standards for state hospitals, said that, not counting administrative officers, Columbus State should have twenty-three psychiatrists instead of the ten it had in 1955. (And the APA would not have recognized the residents, but only the Board members and Board-eligible doctors.) When the APA surveyed Columbus it found one doctor for every 283 patients. APA standards called for a ratio of 1 to 94. The situation was much worse on particular wards. APA standards, for example, called for 1 doctor for every 30 patients on an acute ward, yet Dr. Smith was trying to take care of 300 acute patients. The APA found Columbus equally short of nurses and attendants. There was 1 nurse for every 141 patients but there should have been 1 for every 15; 1 attendant for every 9 patients instead of 1 for every 5. Columbus State in 1955 had roughly one doctor to every floor of the hospital—and there are four wards on every floor, with up to 110 patients in every ward. Dr. Kovitz wished he could have at least one doctor to every ward.

It takes a long time to train a psychiatrist. He must spend four years in an undergraduate college, then four years in medical school, then a year as a medical interne, then, to specialize in psychiatry, three years in psychiatric residency training in an approved hospital and two years in practice—fourteen years of schooling and training above high school. This, plus his two years in military service, make him about thirty-five years old before he becomes a full-fledged psychiatrist.

Young doctors in America do not wish to become psychiatrists. Bernard H. Hall of the Menninger Foundation investigating the attitudes of medical students toward psychiatry found that they didn't like it because it was "vague, ethereal and mystical," was practiced in institutions, was "irreligious" and "doesn't help anyone." Moreover, young doctors are repelled by psychotic patients for much the same reasons that everybody else is—they are afraid of them and can't understand them. And as doctors they do not know what to do for them. Dr. Hall wrote:

The resident has not been in psychiatry for many weeks before he longs for the specific treatments that he used in medicine and surgery. He recalls that it was easier to calculate, measure, and administer the required cat units of digitalis than he now finds to calculate, measure, and administer the appropriate amount of passive interest to show toward an assaultive, paranoid patient. He must decide what to do when there is no tumor to extirpate, or drug to measure, for the treatment of the withdrawn schizophrenic patient. . . . He is a physician, but none of his patients need the kind of treatment requiring scientific use of the stethoscope, the pharmacopoeia, or the scalpel. To further complicate matters, the patients are usually ambulatory and appear to be in excellent physical condition. This is a tremendous frustration for the newly trained physician; few of his skills, which he has worked so long and hard to acquire, are now of any use to him. . . . In psychiatry the new resident often finds himself alone with the patient with no armamentarium, nothing but himself. Gradually he learns that the scientific use of the self is the very essence of psychiatric treatment.

Psychiatrists are scarce. If every full-fledged psychiatrist in the United States were working in state hospitals, the hospitals still would be understaffed. Anyway, they aren't—most psychiatrists are in private office practice, in private hospitals or in other more attractive settings than state hospitals. State hospitals find it almost impossible to get full-fledged psychiatrists. They don't pay enough—a psychiatrist in private practice in a big city can earn twenty thousand dollars his first year. They are overcrowded and overload doctors hopelessly. They never have enough attendants, nurses, drugs, anything. Many are located out in the sticks; a good young psychiatrist fears he would rot there. One state hospital superintendent said recently, "It is almost impossible to get full-fledged certified psychiatrists to work here." Nearly every superintendent would agree.

As a consequence state hospital superintendents have had to take what they can get. Some staff their hospitals with older psychiatrists who long ago found a secure berth in the state hospital, where life is easier if less rewarding than in private practice, and if they are not inspired they are at least hospital-wise. Others staff their hospitals almost entirely with displaced persons from Europe who cannot get licenses to practice medicine in America any place except in state hospitals; although they may be highly trained and may have been eminent in Europe, frequently their language difficulties handicap them severely in dealing with American patients. Still others staff their hospitals almost entirely with residents, just out of medical school, others with retreaded family physicians like Dr. Smith who have decided to switch to psychiatry; and while the residents bring to the hospital an enthusiasm that old hospital hacks lack, they themselves lack experience. And, finally, some hospitals have on their staffs a sprinkling of doctors who could not earn a living elsewhere, usually because they are narcotics addicts or alcoholics.

In the main the mental hospitals of America are staffed by native-born residents, displaced persons and students from abroad here under a student exchange program. Some distinguished European doctors, forced to accept tasks beneath their skills, have returned disgusted to Communist satellite countries. It is a complicated question whether they are the victims of unfairly restrictive licensing practices or really ought not be licensed because their training was inferior—whether they have been shabbily treated in America or "are lucky to be here at all." But there can be little doubt that American state hospitals would be in much worse shape than they are were it not for the displaced persons and foreign students.

8.

Columbus State in 1955 had only three Board-certified psychiatrists. They were Dr. Kovitz, the clinical director; Dr. Kirch, the administrative assistant; and Dr. Tibor Agosten, a psychoanalyst. For the rest, it had on its staff no alcoholics or addicts (though once it had) but it did have all the rest—old hospital hacks, displaced persons and residents. And the backbone of the staff was the residents.

There were seven of them. Two were young men in their twenties, just out of medical school. The other five were older and had been general medical practitioners. The two young ones and two of the older ones probably would go into private practice when they left; the other three probably would stay in a state hospital. Unhappily, many residents left after two years, "just when they are becoming most valuable to us," as Superintendent Wedemeyer said, because they had to go elsewhere to get their third-year residency training— Columbus State was approved for only two of the required three years of residency.

By and large the residents considered the Columbus State residency a good one, though some missed the intellectual excitement of a university and felt oppressed by the musty state hospital atmosphere. They were particularly pleased that the staff included a full-fledged psychoanalyst, rare in a state hospital, and several of them hoped to undergo a training analysis with him while they were here. They were all greatly impressed with Dr. Kovitz, who directed the residency program.

Sometimes training conflicted with staff work, sometimes the other way around. The residents spent time at lectures when they should have been on their wards, and vice versa. Admittedly the system was a compromise. Every six months Dr. Kovitz shuffled the doctors— changed their ward assignments. He did this partly for training purposes —to give the residents experience on a variety of wards, chronic, acute, admission—and partly for the patients' sake, for a doctor who stays on one ward year after year may get interested in certain pet patients and overlook others. The system, however, had disadvantages. As one doctor said, "Just about the time you get to know your patients you get moved to another ward." And many patients benefited from having the same doctor continuously.

The doctors spent as much time on their wards as they could but on many days they were there only an hour or two. They had to attend staff meeting nearly every day, which they regarded as the most important part of their training; they had to attend administrative staff once a week, which they regarded as a waste of time. ("All we talk about is vacations, rent, job classifications.") They had to devote two hours two days a week to seeing patients' relatives. Each of them saw from three to six patients an hour a week for individual psychotherapy. They were supposed to write progress notes on all their patients periodically and case summaries on all they recommended for trial visit or discharge. They had to help plan the lives of patients ready to leave. Formerly social workers could interview trial visit patients who return for checkups but now that many patients were taking the new drugs after leaving, the doctors had to interview them in order to observe the drugs' effects and adjust the dosage or change drugs. Endlessly they had to deal with extraneous matters. They had to fill out innumerable insurance papers, for many patients owned hospitalization insurance which the state levied against, and insurance companies required detailed reports from doctors, not only on admission but periodically thereafter; this consumed an enormous amount of the doctors' time, and they resented it, and no wonder. They spent hours censoring patients' letters, confiscating those that were threatening or obscene.

Some hospitals have a stenographic force to cope with such matters; not this hospital: It had only four stenographers for the entire hospital, and only one dictating machine, so most doctors found themselves writing everything in longhand. Many a patient went years before a doctor ever wrote a progress note on him. One conscientious doctor complained, "When I left a ward a while back I dictated progress reports on a number of patients for the guidance of the new doctor and it was a month and a half before they got typed up and put into the patients' files. By that time some of the patients had already been discharged from the hospital. Some nurses and attendants never write anything on the ward records—and no wonder, they're overworked too, but it ought to be done, to give us doctors a line on how the patients are coming along." And another: "There's an awful lot of disorganization around here. Reports on blood specimens get delayed or lost. I'll start down the hall to the X-ray room and someone will come running up and ask me if John Doe, who went on trial visit last week, can have a driver's license, or any one of a thousand questions. You can't work effectively that way. Or when you're on the ward the patients keep coming up to you with their problems—there just aren't enough of us to handle their requests. I used to try to follow a fixed schedule—see this patient and this one today, that one and that one tomorrow. But it's hard to follow any schedule."

The system of keeping track of patients was sloppy, and frequently a doctor looking for a patient found he had left the hospital, though the event had not been recorded. Frequently doctors' orders did not get carried out or even transmitted. It was not unusual for a doctor to order a therapeutic measure for a patient only to discover some days later that nobody ever had heard of the order. Paper work and administration are not things that most doctors are good at; perhaps they need a lay office manager.

Usually there was no carbon paper on the wards so doctors wasted valuable time writing out in longhand two copies of a lengthy accident report. Attendants and nurses changed often; doctors spent hours making certain a new attendant, ignorant of routine and unfamiliar with the patients, didn't send the wrong patient to the diagnostic clinic or out to the grounds. Doctors might be willing to work all hours but if they wanted an attendant to help they were likely to be told, as one was, "I'd like to help you, Doctor, but it's two o'clock, time for me to be off, and I want to go to the races." There was an odd one-horse flavor about the hospital—nurses writing treatment rosters on laundry lists or ruling lines on a blank sheet of paper with a piece of cardboard; doctors writing letters to relatives in longhand; wards using old iceboxes instead of refrigerators; and attendants keeping extra syringes in cigar boxes.

At the same time the atmosphere of the hospital was rather pleasant and relaxed, at least for the doctors. Hierarchies and prerogatives were not rigidly fixed. The doctors chatted informally as equals in the halls and in the cafeteria, standing around a coffee wagon in the corridor, talking about patients and the hospital's problems, about the cost of renting a home in Columbus, about other doctors and their wives who used to be here and now have scattered over the country, about their younger days in medical school when they and their brides were carefree and poor. They talked of divorces and marriages and childbirths among the staff. Now and then a former doctor returned to visit and talk over old times, eager to learn how the old place had changed since he left (usually he concluded the hospital was not nearly so good as when he was here, though there was less work to be done and more pay for it). They talked of the hospital's problem patients— some who had been here for years and years, longer than any doctor, combative, dangerous, a tribulation to doctors and nurses alike. And they talked of each other's capabilities, older ones estimating closely the ability of each new resident, comparing this year's crop of residents with that of a few years ago. Of an evening the doctors went to medical meetings downtown together. Sometimes they and their wives or husbands saw each other socially. At Christmas time Dr. Kovitz and his wife held open house, and the young doctors played chess or gathered in groups to talk about psychiatry.

Thus in a sense the hospital was an organism, with a life of its own; thus in a sense the staff had some feeling of being a family—a family with shared troubles and hopes. It was for this reason that the hospital was so shocked when one day in 1955 one of the young residents was called out of staff meeting by the police; his wife had strangled their baby. She was schizophrenic. Dr. X—he has not been named in this book and will not be—was a nice-looking slender man in his thirties, well liked at the hospital, interested in his work, full of enthusiasm. He had married his wife ten years before. They had met in college. They had had three children, and Dr. X had gone into private general medical practice in a small town and prospered: "I was making a fortune at it and I liked it more than anything I've ever done." But his wife had wanted to move to Columbus, where her mother lived, so they had.

She had always been a shy quiet seclusive person, sometimes difficult to get along with, and their marriage had been rocky. For a long time her husband hadn't realized there was anything wrong with her —"I was as ignorant of mental disease as any other ordinary doctor." But about 1953 she had cracked up—neglected the children and her own appearance, withdrawn from neighbors and friends, become jealous of her husband, finally tried to kill herself with sleeping pills.

Her husband, who had become a resident in psychiatry at Columbus State (because, he now thinks, of her condition), persuaded her to go voluntarily to Columbus Receiving, for brief intensive treatment. She was there three times in 1954, sometimes leaving on trial visit, sometimes running away. While she was there she bore her fourth child, the one she later strangled. She received shock treatment and psychotherapy. Nothing helped. She kept trying to commit suicide.

Her husband was almost beside himself. He split the children up among relatives. She came home. The neighbors feared and shunned her. Her husband urged her to go back to the hospital. She refused. Her husband was reluctant to have her committed—he loved her, and her parents were opposed. She went home to her mother. She and her husband decided to get a divorce. "But when it came time to decide what to do with the kids," a friend has said, "they thought it wasn't fair to the kids to split up."

In 1955 she began visiting Columbus State's out-patient clinic. She seemed much better. She and her husband collected the children. They started house-hunting. They found a low rambling house by the river, where the kids could play. Her husband took his vacation and they moved in. Five days later he went back to work at the hospital feeling fine, telling friends about his new house and how he had taken his children fishing. That morning his wife wrote a note, saying she intended to kill herself. But apparently the baby, who was thirteen months old, cried and distracted her. She went upstairs and tried to strangle the baby with her hands. She couldn't. She strangled him with a belt from a dress. A court sent her to Lima State Hospital for the Criminally Insane.

The event shocked the hospital. The chaplain conducted funeral services for the baby. For a few days Dr. X's closest friend, young Dr. Dane, took care of the other children. But then Dr. X took them home with him. Dr. Dane said, "I'm worried about him. He's living in the house all alone with the kids now, trying to find a housekeeper to help. He's all mixed up in his feelings toward his wife. If he'd admit it he probably hates his wife's guts for doing this to him. And I guess there isn't much more you could do to a man, is there—break up his home, start divorce proceedings, decide not to, settle down, kill his son, ruin his career, expose him to all the unpleasant legal proceedings and publicity. It doesn't pay to try to live with a schizophrenic." Why had she done it? "Being left alone with the kids the other day was a major crisis for a psychotic person. I try not to let a homicidal or suicidal patient go home unless someone will be with them all the time. Of course it's easy in retrospect to say she should have been committed. But she never seemed irrational or out of contact, she knew she was ill, and they felt she ought to be able to work it out. Still, she did make several attempts at suicide, and that's not to be taken lightly, whether it succeeds or not. To kill yourself you have to have a desire to kill someone and you have to have a desire to die yourself. The successful suicides are those in whom the desire to kill oneself is foremost. The failures are primarily interested in killing *someone*."

Dr. X himself said wearily, "I really don't know what happened up there and I haven't seen her since it happened. Her diagnosis must be schizo-affective but I don't know what the dynamics of her case were, don't know what went wrong in her life, though I can guess. It doesn't matter anyway. It's obvious that I was guilty of a serious error in judgment in bringing them all back together, her and the kids. But I thought I was doing the right thing," and he sighed deeply, toying with a pencil on his desk. How did he feel about her now? He hesitated. "I don't know. The strain of the last two years has been too much for me. I couldn't help her. I don't see how she can ever get well now. I don't think *I* could, if I had done something like that, don't know how I could face myself again. I'm not able to think much about this whole thing, not yet anyway. I'm afraid I could have—" He stopped, then, musing, "But I don't know. I don't think I'll ever be able to do psychotherapy in a situation like this. As far as hating her goes, I don't. I do feel like she had the opportunity to get well and that's all. There is a certain amount of free will in this. One has to make his mind up. Why she did this I don't know, I don't understand it at all," and he looked up, his face almost empty of expression.

9.

After lunch on the Thursday when we were accompanying Dr. Smith on his rounds of his wards, he went back to the hospital at 1 P.M. to spend more time on Ward 11 and to visit Ward 9, which he had missed in the morning. In particular on Ward 11 he wanted to have a chat with Millicent Parker.

Now Millicent Parker is like thousands of young women both in and out of hospitals. Psychotic she certainly is; yet only rarely does she look or act like the popular idea of a crazy person. She seems merely an extremely unhappy and unfortunate young woman, a decent essentially good person with more troubles than she can bear.

She was born in 1920. Her parents had married late. Her father already had a son by a previous marriage. Millicent thought her father had married only to provide a home for his son and had not intended having more children. Millicent felt unwanted. She was very dependent upon her mother. Millicent felt unworthy. When she was sixteen, her father died of a stroke in her presence. During the war she married an older man, a fighter pilot. Overseas he had an affair and when he came home told her about it. She became depressed, developed a series of ailments, and began talking about evil influences at work on her. The probate court committed her to Columbus State Hospital in 1947. She told Dr. Kovitz her husband had wronged her, yet dropped to her knees to beseech Kovitz to send her husband to her that night. She clung to Kovitz and wept. She said if she had to stay here she might lose her mind. The staff diagnosed her manic-depressive, manic type, and ordered EST. After about a year her husband took her home, though the doctors thought her far from well.

Soon they were divorced. She was living alone in the rooming house. She worked a while, quit, got another job, quit that. She had no money. Finally she took to her bed and stayed there. A friend asked the assistant pastor of her church to visit Millicent, and he did and arranged for her to go voluntarily on November 29, 1954, to Columbus Receiving Hospital.

Columbus Receiving, located on the grounds of Ohio State University, was a part of the state hospital system but it took only patients in need of brief but intensive treatment. It was one of ten receiving hospitals Ohio built in the hope of relieving congestion in the mainline state hospitals. It hoped to treat and discharge large numbers of patients quickly, preventing them from disappearing into the mainline hospitals. But difficulties arose. The receiving hospitals were linked to universities. The state Department and the universities struggled for authority over them. The Department felt that Columbus Receiving was putting too much emphasis on training doctors and not enough on taking care of patients. The university replied that its main function was training and that the large mass of patients didn't belong in it. Doctors were far more numerous and care much better at Receiving than at Columbus State. But not many people could get in. Many authorities consider that a system of receiving hospitals tends to convert the mainline state hospitals into snake pits.

At Columbus Receiving Millicent Parker stayed in bed. She showed no interest in anything. She was afraid of EST. Columbus Receiving gave her carbon dioxide treatments and a doctor interviewed her three or four times a week. She became more and more accessible. After a month the doctors concluded she might benefit "from a long course of psychotherapy" but the time needed was too long for Columbus Receiving. So early in 1955 they sent her back to big old Columbus State, accompanied by her papers from Receiving which closed with this note: "Recommendations: It was felt that the patient may benefit from a long-term psychotherapy." This was probably true but sending her to Columbus State was a curious solution: Only 24 patients out of 2,700 there were receiving individual psychotherapy, so overloaded were the doctors. And the truth is that there was just no place in Ohio—nor for that matter in the United States today—where such a person as Millicent Parker could possibly get the treatment she needed. She could not afford private psychiatry; Columbus Receiving had not enough time for her; and Columbus State had not enough doctors. And there are thousands of people in America today in precisely her predicament.

She hated Columbus State: "This hospital ruined my whole life." The staff diagnosed her schizophrenic reaction, schizo-affective type. She was started on EST, two or three shocks a week for six months. Her ward doctor, Dr. Dane, then in his second year of residency training, became interested in her and took her on for individual psychotherapy. Like the other doctors at Columbus State, Dr. Dane saw a half-dozen patients for an hour each week in individual psychotherapy. What is psychotherapy, anyway?

In a sense any conversation with a patient is psychotherapy, since anything said may affect his mental state. But this is not what doctors mean by psychotherapy. To them psychotherapy is a conscious planned attempt to influence mental processes by mental means (not by such physical means as electroshock or brain surgery). At its fullest, psychotherapy is a full-scale formal psychoanalysis conducted along classical Freudian lines. This means a series of patient-doctor interviews, usually forty-five minutes to an hour each, in which the patient talks, associating freely; most of the time the analyst says little except, "Go on" or "And then," but sometimes he interprets and analyzes the material—dreams, memories, ideas, feelings—which the patient has produced, encouraging the patient to discover for himself the inner meaning of his experiences. Such an analysis is, strictly, conducted only by a psychoanalyst, that is, a certified psychiatrist who has taken additional training at the Institute for Psychoanalysis. There are only about seven hundred psychoanalysts in the United State. A full-dress psychoanalysis is just about unheard of in state hospitals. There is no time for it. Few state hospitals have analysts. And many doctors believe that psychoanalysis cannot help psychotics but only neurotics. Individual psychotherapy at Columbus State and at most state hospitals means a much more superficial therapy than analysis. Instead of attempting to help the patient unravel his whole personality and put it back together, the doctor merely tries to encourage and support him or to help him gain some insight into his condition. The doctor tries to help him to deal better with a particular problem in his life, to adjust to the world superficially. To shorten the process, the doctor guides the patient much more than in deep analysis. Dr. Tibor Agosten, of Columbus State, a full-fledged analyst, treats a few patients individually and once a week conducts group psychotherapy—collects eight or ten patients and for an hour leads their discussion of their problems. But he spends most of his time guiding the other doctors, reaching patients through them.

Dr. Kovitz, asked to explain psychotherapy, said, "It means encouraging a person to be himself, to come out with what's inside him, to discover what he really feels. Psychotic symptoms are like the surface rumblings before a volcanic eruption. All the while the volcano is bubbling away down deep inside, building up tremendous pressure. The doctor tries to help the patient find out what this pressure is all about. Sometimes just letting his true feelings come out helps tremendously. It reduces the pressure and helps him mobilize his resources. To the degree that he finds out what he really is, he gets some good out of psychotherapy. It isn't easy—everybody's trained from infancy not to be himself. You pay attention to what the patient says and to what he doesn't say. You try to learn what are the factors that interfere with his being free, what held him back from free natural contact with people."

Kovitz went on, "A great many people can't be cured of severe mental illness by psychotherapy. Of course, in a few private hospitals, such as Chestnut Lodge in Maryland—" which has about ninety patients and about twenty psychiatrists—"they can really apply psychotherapy because they have a controlled population and a manageable work load. Here we have to take everything that's sent us and the work load is heavy. Our psychotherapy here is a drop in the bucket but we can't help it. And at least it teaches the doctors things they can apply in their day-to-day contact with the patients on the wards.

And sometimes wonders seem to happen."

Dr. Dane kept Millicent Parker on EST while he saw her for psychotherapy. "Most of my own work with her was pretty much supportive. I tried to encourage her rather than to give her insight." Once when Dr. Dane gave her the privilege of being out on the grounds, another doctor found her down at the baseball diamond with a male patient and "warded" her—revoked her privilege and confined her to the ward. Dane soon restored the privilege. "She said she was just standing and talking to the male patient. I guess the doctor that warded her considers it a matter of control and—" smiling—"we do hate to have our girls get pregnant. But I feel that some men and women patients should get together more." After several months Dane didn't feel his interviews with her were accomplishing much. "She's too sick to be helped much by the amount of time I could give her. It amounts to spending three or four months getting to where she can even talk to you." She kept going up and down, behaving herself for a while then blowing up. When Dane was transferred to admissions, Dr. Smith took over Millicent's ward.

Dr. Smith took no particular interest in her. He stopped EST to see how she would get on without it. He talked to her only once or twice during the summer; he hoped Dane would continue seeing her. But Dane was busy. For a while nobody saw Millicent. She wanted to see Dane for psychotherapy but he felt he could help other patients more. Her condition worsened. She talked little, sat idle on the ward, refused to work, seemed unhappy and uninterested. Dr. Smith thought he'd better see her "to try and figure something out." And so on our Thursday he went to the ward and the attendant called her in.

She held her head high. She was a pretty woman, looking younger than she was. Her forearms were thin. She sat stiffly on a chair across the desk from Dr. Smith, her hands clasped tightly in her lap, leaning forward, peering at him somewhat tensely, a hint of pride in her bearing. Smith began in a quiet relaxed voice, "Let's see, you had your last EST in August, didn't you?" but she said sharply, "I wouldn't say that long ago."

He asked if she ever had taken any large orange pills (Thorazine). She hadn't. He asked how she was feeling. Pretty good. When had she come to the hospital?

"I understand it was last January—isn't that in my records?"

"What do you mean by 'understand'?"

"I mean I remember being at the University Hospital. I don't recall as to the exact date I came here."

"Why were you at the University Hospital? What was the trouble?"

She said, "No, I mean I can't explain, it seems to me that I went there for an operation. Did I? I mean I don't want to take up your time and I know you have a lot of patients but I would like to know. Why am I not—tell me, be honest with me—why am I not on full privilege?"

He said, "Probably partly because I haven't gotten around to talking to you."

"I'm on partial privilege now. I was taken off full privilege."

"When?"

"Quite some time ago. Then I talked to Dr. Dane about it. Do you realize that a lot of the ward doctors—we do not have the advice of a doctor. And after all a patient has to have confidence in her doctor."

Smith said, "You've had more contact with your ward doctor than many patients have."

She said skeptically, "I've seen *you* before?"

"Maybe you don't remember."

"I remember when you first came on the ward. I recall that. But I don't recall more than that."

"Have you been seeing Dr. Dane?"

"I—yes, I have."

"That's one reason you haven't seen me more."

"I realize that," somewhat sharply. "And I know I had confidence in Dr. Dane, in talking to him. And after all I don't know you."

He asked when she last had seen Dr. Dane. "Oh, about a week ago." She seemed to study him, then said, "I could not feel confidence in you. Because my husband was overseas to fight the Germans—" She stopped.

"What do I have to do with the Germans?"

"Aren't you of German descent?"

"No. I'm Welsh."

She looked disbelieving. She said, "I haven't the rest of my life to waste—" and trailed off.

He said, "You're doing a lot better," and asked if friends had visited lately. No. He said that Social Service would like to start making plans for her to leave the hospital.

She said, "I'd like to go as soon as possible," but she said it without enthusiasm. Then she asked about her past: "It's a terrible thing not to remember." He picked up her record and from it read the dates of her hospitalizations. She asked many questions and he went over the records with her patiently till she seemed satisfied. He said, "I'm glad you're doing better. In fact you're doing quite well. I do think medicine, Thorazine or Serpasil, would relieve your tension, and I'll speak to Dr. Kovitz about it."

She said, "I wish you would talk to Dr. Kovitz. I have confidence more in Dr. Kovitz. You might think I'm being very rude but I knew Dr. Kovitz before and when you came here I didn't know you. I don't think Dr. Kovitz would have me take any medicine that would hurt me in any way."

"I'm sure he wouldn't," Dr. Smith said. "He wants you to get well and so do I."

"That's what I want too. But what about this condition in my mouth?" And she went on about it. He promised to send her to the clinic (though no doubt it was an imaginary complaint).

She said, "The way I understand it now, I would rather know it and have it said right to me. Like the shock treatment—I didn't know they were going to do it. I'd rather know the truth. To be trusted like somebody has a little confidence in you," she ended resentfully.

"I don't tell my patients ahead of time because they may become tense and agitated about it."

"I disagree with you. How you treat anybody—that makes a lot of difference," and she thumped her knuckles hard on his desk.

He said quietly, "I don't intend to give you any more EST."

"But that's why I came back to the hospital. There have been times when I have been treated with the greatest consideration but there are other times when I don't think anybody should be treated the way I was. Well, thank you, Dr. Smith. I liked seeing you." She got up, smiled mechanically, and went out.

Watching her go, Dr. Smith said, "She's certainly a lot better than before. Of course, she still has some paranoid schizophrenic hostility. And she has a certain push of speech, indicating there's a manic side to her illness. She's schizo-affective—she combines the difficulties of schizophrenia and the affective difficulties of manic-depressive," and he smiled a little. "But she's a good one—she improved a lot with EST and now maybe Thorazine or Serpasil—if I can get it for her—

can help her make the additional jump and get her out. But even after we get her out, where can she go?"

10.

The attendant told Dr. Smith that five other patients wanted to see him. He saw two of them, one wanting a trial visit and another with a case of shingles. Somewhere a patient was calling in Spanish, and a radio was chattering quietly. There was the clatter of a chair as a patient got up suddenly. Every few minutes Dr. Smith was paged on the public address system, and he called the operator and did what was wanted. Watching him a nurse said, "He's the busiest man in the hospital."

He told the attendant, "I'm going to transfer some patients off of 9 today and I want you to find me some of yours who are off EST and good enough. I'll let you know later how many—probably a half-dozen or so."

The attendant, reaching for a box of filing cards, said, "I hate to lose some of our good workers."

Smith said, "Well you can hang on to any that you need real bad."

"I'd hate to lose Pauline—she's real good back in the clothes room."

She pulled out some cards, handing them to him, and he approved some for transfer and rejected others. She said, "If we send seven patients, we'll have thirteen vacancies here."

Smith smiled and said, "I've been getting 'em out of the hospital too fast. Don't worry though—I'll send you some good ones from 13."

"I hope you do, before somebody else sends us some bad ones."

He nodded, remarking, "We need more wards in this hospital for chronic disturbed untidy patients—they disrupt everything on 11 and 9, keep the other patients awake all night and everything. But all the other wards are overcrowded and it's hard to resist the pressure to put 'em here. Just when you think you've got your wards all sorted out, somebody sends you a bad one." He shut his notebook and told the attendant he'd try to complete the transfer quickly, so as not to interfere with her dinner, and hurried up to Ward 9.

It was one of the quietest in the hospital, soft-lit, neat, clean, nicely furnished. Women went home from here. Smith hadn't been here yet today. In the office the nurse told him, smiling, "We've got lots of troubles."

"What all?"

"Well, this one"—handing him a file—"just isn't doing anything, she lays around in bed all day, she's been on Serpasil a week and says she's all stiff and stinging over her body. Dr. Kovitz was up to see her this morning."

Smith, who was tiring, said, "I'm sick and tired of trying to do anything for that girl. Every time I try she runs to Kovitz or Kirch or Agosten. What else have you got?"

The nurse asked if another patient might go to an occupational therapy class. She might. She reported on the week-end visit of another patient. She told him two other patients were slipping and should go back on EST—one was confused and wouldn't eat, the other was back in a corner swinging an old mop at anyone who approached. Smith assented. She told him about another patient who was being difficult and he said, "If you think of anything sparkling to do with her, do it," and she laughed and said, "I don't know where to start."

"Neither do I. What else?"

She told him that a patient who had gone home on a week-end visit two weeks ago never had returned and asked if he wanted to change her official status to trial visit. He said, "She was ready for trial visit anyway but it makes you kind of uncomfortable when they take it in their own hands." He debated a moment; he could mark her either "trial visit" or "escape." He decided on "trial visit." This is customary; only if the patient is considered dangerous is he reported escaped and the police notified.

The nurse said, "Did you know we got two new patients? One has a broken hand."

"Oh, yes. That's all right. What about the other one? Is she over seventy-five?"

"No."

"You're lucky—they got an eighty-five-year-old one swinging from the chandelier back on 13. Who's yours anyway?"

She handed him the patient's record, saying, "She's all right but she's brand-new." He read the record. She had been admitted only yesterday. Smith said indignantly, "She hasn't even been staffed. I don't want patients up here that haven't been staffed. Those people down there on admissions—they'll send patients anywhere. This is a convalescent ward. She should have gone to 13 or 15. I'm going to have to talk to them." The nurse suggested that perhaps 13 and 15 were full. He nodded. "Probably. But I can fix that—I'll fill this ward off of 11 and fill 11 off of 13. This is supposed to be the best ward, and if I don't keep it full somebody else will send patients here who aren't ready to go home by any means."

He dealt with other problems, then said, "Before I make these transfers, let's review treatment. I haven't reviewed treatment on this ward for several weeks." She got out her records and hitched a chair up beside him and they went to work. She told him what medicine each patient was getting, how much, and how she was responding. Smith raised the dosage of some, cut others, and left others alone, particularly those he didn't know very well and whose dosage had been fixed on other wards by other doctors. He knew nearly all the patients well enough to discuss them without records.

Finished, he went to work on his transfer. He telephoned Wards 11, 13 and 15 to ascertain how many vacancies each had; he rechecked the vacancies here; he went over the patient roster here with the nurse, picking out patients who were slipping and had to go back to a worse ward. An attendant on one of the other wards called, all upset; she had agreed to work overtime on the transfer but the supervisor wouldn't let her, and if Dr. Smith wanted to complete the transfer today he'd have to hurry. He did. But other obstacles arose, and suppertime approached, and finally he gave up: "I guess we'll have to let the actual transfer go till tomorrow. We haven't got time to get the patients and their clothes together today. But a least we can finish the paper work today. Suppose you go ahead with that. I want to talk to Nancy Wilton a few minutes, then I'm going to call it a day." The nurse went to the hall and Dr. Smith slumped a little in his chair.

11.

Nancy Wilton was only twenty-one years old and she had been in the hospital only three months, diagnosed hebephrenic schizophrenia. She was one of ten children born to a man who had been variously a farmer, welder and handyman. Her father had been hit on the head years earlier and apparently had suffered a brain injury; he had become excitable, talkative, wrathful and had been twice admitted to Columbus State as a manic-depressive. One of the children once said, "We grew up in a home life of constant ranting and turmoil and in a very uncertain financial setup. . . . You can see we are all nervous."

An older sister had been committed to Columbus State several years earlier and diagnosed schizophrenia, catatonic type with hebephrenic features. Her family never had visited her. She had had about 148 ESTs and 79 insulin treatments with little improvement; a prefrontal lobotomy had been performed on her. She was still here, and recently had been improving on one of the new drugs.

Little was known of Nancy's own life—the family did not keep appointments to furnish information—but she apparently had been an honor student, taken a secretarial course and worked several years in an office. But she had become upset and had conceived the idea that people at work were trying to poison her. She had become tense, noisy, seclusive. She had laughed and wept for no apparent reason. She had quit her job and stayed in a hotel room for six months. The hotel had notified her family, and they had taken her home for a while, then had her committed.

Dr. Smith had admitted her. To him she had seemed neat and friendly but evasive and withdrawn. She had said she needed help but didn't want to stay in the hospital—all she needed was a rest. She had grinned broadly, her grin appearing and disappearing rapidly. Sometimes her voice had faded away. Her talk had rambled and been hard to follow. She would break off a thought in mid-sentence and interpolate a snatch of words from the song "Shake, Rattle and Roll." Once she had abruptly changed the subject and begun to describe nonexistent furniture in a faraway voice—a visual hallucination.

She had told Smith that at work other employees gossiped about her and blamed their errors on her—"She had seen the papers and they were not typed on her machine," Smith later had told the staff. This had led to trouble with her boss. Then one day while taking her customary walk in the park by the river she had discovered that her former boss was following her "and she reached an understanding with him that he was going to marry her." Or had the follower been an old friend she had not seen for years? Her former boss was dead —no, he wasn't. (Smith had been certain the whole experience was hallucinatory—her voice had trailed off in describing it, she couldn't repeat anything that was said in the park, she never saw her former boss anywhere else outside the office, he never took her dancing or to dinner.) Shortly thereafter she told her present boss he was not fit to be an executive, and she was fired or quit.

The staff had thought her "a classical case of hebephrenic type in the early stages." Dr.Kovitz had recommended Thorazine and Serpasil with individual psychotherapy, and Dr. Smith had begun seeing her for an hour a week. He had theorized that her ambition led her to attempt to exceed her endowment in the business world; she had dealt with the resulting frustration by the psychological mechanism called projection, attributing her own inadequacy to the hostility of others. At the same time she had fulfilled her need for a satisfactory sex life by hallucinating.

Smith said, "When she came in she was a terrifically psychotic girl. She was the sort that could expect to look forward to a lifetime of hospitalization. Her sister came here years ago in much the same condition and she's still here. There's little hope for her now. Nancy was luckier—we caught her fast, only a few months after her first psychotic break, and also we've got Thorazine and Serpasil now, which we didn't have then. They see each other, incidentally—her sister's on 15, and when she's good enough I give her a privilege and you see them walking the wards together."

Seeing Smith and taking Thorazine, Nancy had begun to improve almost at once—had seemed more relaxed and natural, had described pleasant dreams she was having. The Thorazine had relieved her tension; so, apparently, had "ventilating"—talking—to Smith. Like most psychotics she had disappointed her doctor occasionally. Once after a highly satisfactory therapeutic session with her, Smith had found her in the hall complaining loudly that her cigarettes were poisoned. He had taken her into his office, and she had dismissed this idea perfunctorily but gone on to say that "girls in red dresses" were pursuing and jostling her, and she thought they were connected with the office where she once worked; then she had wept and asked why she was in the hospital.

But after that she had seemed to make steady improvement. After several months Smith felt the time was near when she could leave the hospital, provided she would continue to take drugs. He wanted to get her out as soon as possible. He experimented with her drug dosage. Originally he had given her large doses of Thorazine but they had made her rigid and tremulous, symptoms akin to those of Parkinson's Disease. He had cut her Thorazine and added Serpasil. Now before eliminating Thorazine entirely he wanted to see how she was getting along on the reduced dose. As soon as possible he wanted to get her down to a minimum maintenance dose of Serpasil. When he found out what that was he would send her home on trial visit. He could keep her on hospital supply at her present dose for about two months after she left but if he could cut it in half the supply would last four months, which would give her more time to find a job so she could buy her own drugs. His problem was to strike a delicate balance between the minimum dosage she could get by on and her small budget for costly medicine. Such are the undramatic but extremely important problems that confront state hospital psychiatrists constantly. "We are walking a pretty tight wire here," Smith said, smiling, as the nurse brought her in.

She was a young pretty girl with a somewhat foolish half-smile. She was wearing a billowing green flowered skirt and a pale blue blouse. Her hair was neat. She sat, at ease, and he asked how she felt, and she said, "I'm fine."

The phone rang, it was for him, she waited patiently, her hands folded loosely in her lap.

He turned back to her. "We haven't talked for quite a long time."

She said, "I wasn't worried."

"Did you go home last week end?"

"Yes, I did."

"What did you do?"

"Oh, I worked a little and watched television and went to a movie and led a normal life."

"Who was home?"

"My mother and four of my brothers and sisters."

"How are you getting along here?"

"Just fine. All the girls seem to like me and I like them."

"Have you been working?"

"Yes, in the Recreation Department. I take patients off the wards and bring them to the Recreation Department and give them paper work and try to get them interested."

"Have you been typing any?"

"I haven't had a chance yet but I'd like to. To brush up."

"You ought to. Is that what you want to do when you go home?"

"Yes, it is," and she smiled a little more broadly. "My mother's fixing up my room. She thinks I'll be home soon."

Dr. Smith said, "I think so too."

She said, "The only thing I know how to do is office work. I had four years of high school. I can't do secretarial work because I don't know shorthand, but I can type and file."

"Where do you think you'll look for work?"

"I thought here in Columbus."

For a few minutes they chatted; they might be casual friends met by chance. He glanced at his watch; it was time for her supper. He said, "Well. Do you feel that anybody here is trying to cause you trouble?"

"Oh, no. They've all been so nice to me."

"Haven't had any more trouble with those girls in red dresses?"

She laughed sheepishly and said, "No, Doctor."

"Do you remember that?"

"Yes, vaguely, but it doesn't bother me any more."

"Do you feel people on the outside may try to cause you difficulty?"

"No, I don't. Because it hasn't happened on week ends. Most people know I've been here and they all treat me fine."

"You don't expect to have any trouble at all."

"No, Doctor. I'm very happy and I know where I'm at and I know where I'm going."

He said, "I think you're about ready to go home."

She said hesitantly, "I suppose I'll have to go to staff meeting."

"I don't know. I'll send your papers to Dr. Kirch and if he decides it's okay you won't have to go to staff at all, you'll just go home. If you still feel as good as you do now I don't think there'll be much question about it." He paused a moment, then said, "And for heaven's sake if you have any trouble in the future, come for help quick."

She said quietly, "I will, Doctor. I'm not afraid to come here now. I had a fear of it at the time but I don't feel that way now."

"You've been a good patient."

"I try to be."

He hesitated, deciding whether to discuss with her today the dosage of her medicine and its cost; he decided to wait a week, see how she did on Serpasil alone, then, if she still seemed ready to leave, to have a final interview with her. He said, "I guess that's all."

She said, as though she'd read his mind, "What about my medicine —are you going to take me off of it?"

"No, I don't think so, not right away. We'll keep you on it for six months or so. It's better to keep going too long than to stop too soon."

"Okay. I'm glad I talked to you," and she smiled more broadly at him and got up and went out.

The nurse said, "You should have seen her when she came in here. She doesn't seem like the same girl."

Dr. Smith said, "I guess we'll call it a day," and somewhat wearily he got up. As he walked down the ward three or four patients stepped out from corners or little rooms and said, "Dr. Smith, Dr. Smith, can I see you for a minute, Dr. Smith, can I talk to you soon?" But to them all he shook his head and said, "I'm kind of talked out now. I'll see you pretty soon." He unlocked the door and went to his office and, after gazing at his correspondence a while, went home.

6

Disturbed Ward

■ At six o'clock on a September morning in Columbus, the sky was just getting light, but already for the patients and attendants on Ward 8 deep inside Columbus State the day had begun. About 5 A.M. the lone attendant who had spent the night there had aroused most of the patients, seen that they dressed, sent them out to the porch, and supervised patients making the beds. Now at 6 A.M. the registered nurse, Constance Novak, and four male attendants came on duty. While in the kitchen a great banging and clatter commenced, and while in the tiny office the nurse prepared medicines, the attendant in charge, Walter Stratton, a tall rangy man in white, and another attendant went back to the annex to check the seclusion rooms.

The annex is at one end of the long main hall, a large dim rectangular room with tile walls and terrazzo floor off of which open the nine seclusion rooms. They are all alike, bare little cell-like cubicles. The door to each is of thick solid wood, with a slanting peephole at eye level. Some of the doors, broken over the years by violent patients, are reinforced with steel strips. The room is little more than twice the size of a bed. The walls are tan tile, the floor terrazzo. The light bulb is recessed in the high ceiling and guarded with heavy wire mesh; the switch is outside the door. The small window is protected by iron bars and heavy wire mesh. There is nothing in the room but a bed.

The patients locked in seclusion had not been awakened by the night attendant, for no attendant alone may open a seclusion room door. Stratton would arouse them. With his partner, Foster Cooley, a cheerful chunky man, standing by, Stratton went to the door of one room and looked through the peephole. He did so a trifle warily, not pressing his eye against the hole but keeping back a few inches; patients have been known to tear a bed apart and jab a piece of it through the peephole. He opened the door.

A naked elongated Negro was lying on the bed, his head propped up. He did not move, made no sign he was awake, stared unseeing at Stratton. Stratton said, "Come get your breakfast." He shook his head. Cooley brought in an aluminum partitioned tray of food—oats, beans, coffee, bread—and put it on the bed but the Negro did not move. Stratton, closing and locking the door, remarked, "He won't touch it till you leave. He's been here for years. We let him go till he gets so we can't handle him, then give him shock. He's untidy, destructive, combative."

He unlocked the next room. The patient, a middle-aged man in his underwear with a gray stubble of beard and his hair awry, was standing in a corner, looking fearfully at the door. His bed was wet. Stratton said reprovingly, "What's that on your bed?"

The patient mumbled, "They didn't put no pot in here. Didn't let me out last night. I pounded on the door."

"Did you?" Stratton said and gave him a tray and shut the door.

In the next locked room the patient was pounding on the door and yelling, "Let me out of here, let me out of here."

Cooley, the attendant, remarked, "That's all day."

Stratton opened the door. The room was filthy—the bed sodden and torn up, the walls and bed smeared with excrement. It smelled horribly. The man inside, a thin gray man with spindly legs, Sam Adams, said, "Let me out of here."

Stratton said, "After a while, Adams."

"Give me a cigarette."

"You can't smoke in here, you know that."

"Can I have some breakfast?"

"Not just yet," Stratton said, locking the door, then, to Cooley, "We'll have to change his room." Immediately the door closed Adams began to hammer on it. Adams was due to get electroshock treatment this morning and would get no breakfast.

Stratton and Cooley checked the other seclusion patients, then went back to the middle of the main ward hall and stood at the entrance to the kitchen beside Miss Novak. She had a tray filled with little paper cups containing medicine, each marked with a patient's name —Dilantin or Mebarol for convulsive states, Serpasil or Thorazine for certain psychotic states, vitamins, sedatives. Down a cross corridor from the porch came the patients, a long straggling line of men, many in blue jeans, some walking smartly, others shambling and shuffling along, some alert of eye, others looking as though a veil had been drawn over their eyes. Most of those due to get medicine knew it and halted beside Miss Novak; she had to call to a few. The others swirled on around her and passed through the cluttered little kitchen and out onto a porch used as a dining room. They found their accustomed places and sat, close-packed at long tin-topped tables on which their trays already had been placed. Three attendants followed them in and stood watching. Always in the crowded dining room a sudden blow-up can cause turmoil, just as in a prison. The patients who helped with the ward work ate in the kitchen. Flies were everywhere. A faucet dripped into the old tin sink. The light was dim. Through the wire mesh on the windows could be glimpsed trees and grass and sidewalks, damp from last night's rain; leaves were coming down now in the fall; but all that seemed a long way off.

Ward 8 is one of twenty-eight wards in the main building at Columbus State. Let us see what goes on here in an ordinary day— what the patients do, what the attendants do for them. Let us see who the attendants are. And, since this is a treatment ward, let us watch electroshock.

2.

Ward 8 contained on the day of our visit seventy-eight patients in space that the American Psychiatric Association said was suitable for sixty-seven. "This place is like all the others—overcrowded," said an attendant. Forty-five of the patients slept in two big dormitories off the cross corridor, their beds shoved close together. Thirteen slept locked in the fifteen single rooms on the cross corridor because they were likely to wander around at night. Fourteen slept in nine open rooms off the main hall. And six slept in seclusion. The patients used their beds only at night; during the day they were up and about the ward.

Ward 8 was a busy ward, busy all day long. Life here was not the unending corrosive gray round of existence for patients and attendants alike that one found on the chronic wards—mopping and sitting and eating, mopping and sitting and eating, with now and then a blow-up. Ward 8 was a disturbed ward. Disturbed means screaming, pounding the floor, tearing up things, beating out window panes, hurting someone, attempting suicide. Nearly all mental patients become temporarily disturbed at one time or another. And a few are chronically disturbed, through years of life in the hospital. Ward 8 was intended for disturbed patients in an acute stage of their illness, patients who arrived at the hospital disturbed. Ideally it should contain no one else. But like all the other wards in this or nearly any state mental hospital in America, its condition was not ideal. On the day of our visit less than half its patients, thirty, were new acute patients—had been in the hospital only a year or less. Among the rest were nine who had been in the hospital more than ten years and one who had been here since 1922. Some of the long-term patients had been sent down here for electroshock treatment when they became disturbed on chronic wards upstairs; others had been sent from chronic wards to the medical ward for treatment of a physical disorder and, becoming disturbed there, had been hustled back here. Some of the long-term patients here were not disturbed at all—they were ward workers, kept on this ward because they were needed here. The man who had been here since 1922, for example, took care of the seclusion patients' clothes; he never left the annex except to sleep. "You couldn't run a ward without patients to do the work," said an attendant, and it's true, just as you can't run a prison without the co-operation of the convicts. The attendants gave actual physical care only to patients too severely disturbed to dress or feed themselves; other than that they served as straw bosses over the sixteen patients who did the ward's mopping, bed-making, scullery, who carried laundry, brought food from the main hospital kitchen, took care of the clothes room. Thus, really, the patients cared for themselves and each other. The ward workers were not paid but they were rewarded in other small but important ways. They got their ration of the scarce free tobacco first. During the day they were allowed to roam the main ward hall, not made to sit on the crowded porch, and so they had more privacy and freedom. They got their food and medicine first. And at night they were allowed to sleep in the unlocked private rooms off the main hall, where they might even have space for a tiny night table in which to keep their things—comb, toothbrush, a spare handkerchief, tobacco —a luxury enjoyed by almost no other patients in the hospital, for a chest of drawers was virtually unheard of, and most patients carried toothbrush and everything else they owned in their pockets or in a paper bag.

Most of the patients on Ward 8 were young or middle-aged men. But seven were past sixty, and one was fifteen. The records of twenty-seven were marked "homicidal" or "suicidal" or both. (This meant that they had actually attempted suicide or homicide; many more here were potentially one or both.) Nearly half the patients were diagnosed schizophrenic (just as about half the total hospital population of 2,700 was schizophrenic). A score were suffering from organic brain disorder—cerebral arteriosclerosis, chronic alcoholism, paresis. A half-dozen were manic-depressives, another half-dozen were psychotic with mental deficiency, one was severely psychoneurotic, and the diagnoses of the rest were scattered or unknown. By far the most common occupation was that of laborer—twenty-two of those with known occupations. The occupation of fourteen was "none" or "unknown." Five were farmers; two were carpenters, two were retired men, two were railroad workers; and there was one baker, radio technician, truck driver, mechanic, glass worker, factory worker, dishwasher, cab driver, manufacturer, coal miner, engineer, plumber, molder and livestock buyer.

The ward these men inhabited is located on the ground floor at the rear of the north wing of the big old brick hospital. To reach it one walks from the administration offices through three other wards. Ward 8 is a complex of corridors and rooms and cubbyholes, the whole roughly in the shape of a T. The main hall is a long dim-lit cavernous place, 128 feet long and 18 wide, with a ceiling 15 feet high, tiny light bulbs high in the ceiling casting but a dim light to the terrazzo floor. The unadorned walls are painted an old fading dirty ivory; the paint is peeling. Along the walls are ranged eight benches, eight or ten chairs, a television set and three potted plants. On the walls hang a clock and a firehose and two loudspeakers. This is all; there are no other decorations or furnishings. The doorways to the sleeping rooms are high and narrow, rounded at the top, and the walls are more than two feet thick. The whole place seems massive and old, in some ways almost medieval. Off the main hall open the kitchen, the clothes room, the attendants' office, shower room and toilet. (There are also two toilet bowls on the porch, making a total of four toilets for seventy-eight patients.)

From the main hall a long cross corridor runs out to the porch. This section is newer than the rest. Dormitories and sleeping rooms open off the cross corridor. At its end is the porch. Three walls of the porch are glazed with heavy glass and steel detention sash, the fourth is tiled, and along the walls are fifteen benches, a rocking chair, two straight chairs, two tables for a radio and magazines, a ping-pong table, tin cans for cigarette butts. At one end are a toilet, a shower room and a barber chair.

To care for all these patients there were in 1955 four attendants and a nurse on the morning shift, three attendants from 2 to 10 P.M., and one attendant the rest of the night. A doctor visited the ward every day for anywhere from fifteen minutes to an hour.

Patients new to the hospital were brought to this ward if they were disturbed. Here they received treatment. If they improved after a few months, they moved forward to Ward 6 or Ward 4. If they failed to improve they were moved upstairs to a chronic ward where they might stay for years, perhaps for the rest of their lives. Dr. Robert H. Felix, director of the National Institute of Mental Health, estimates that if you enter an American mental hospital your chance of leaving —alive—in the first year is about 50-50; if you fail and stay two years the odds against you jump to 16 to 1; and if you stay over five years the odds against you are worse than 99 to 1. ("The odds after five years," he says, "are so bad you wouldn't risk any money on it.") The first year, then, indeed the first few months, of a man's hospitalization are perhaps the most critical period in his entire life. This is the time when treatment is most likely to benefit him. At Columbus State in 1955, if he was a disturbed new admission, Ward 8 was where he spent these critical months.

But although this ward was the acute male treatment ward, at the time of our visit fewer than a third of the patients on it were getting treatment. Five were on Thorazine and five on reserpine, the new tranquilizing drugs. Ten were getting electroshock. Two were receiving individual psychotherapy for an hour a week. In addition, seven were getting sedatives and three going to the occupational therapy shop. And that was all. (A nurse added that forty-nine others were receiving "recreational therapy," but the ward doctor said this must include everybody who ever went to a movie or read a magazine.)

Why are so few getting treatment? The ward doctor would have liked to have had more patients on the new drugs but the hospital had no money for them. The doctor had no time to give individual psychotherapy to more patients—she took care of three wards, 209 patients. She gave electroshock to all she thought would benefit. There is no other therapy.

3.

Electroshock was given three days a week, and our visit being on a shock day, a Wednesday, the attendants began getting ready for it right after breakfast. Breakfast took only fifteen minutes. Most of the patients filed back down the corridor to the porch, where they would spend the day. A few stayed in the kitchen, cleaning up. A dozen began mopping and sweeping the halls and rooms. They worked industriously and very seriously, one, an enormous globular man, talking loudly the while. The tall charge attendant, Stratton, and two others, Cooley and Clinton Wyatt, went back to the annex to deal with the patients still in seclusion.

Years ago the keepers of lunatic asylums, as we have seen, kept their patients chained up all the time. Patients were cast into dungeons, and the strait jacket and camisole were routine. Indeed, the single rooms in Columbus State originally were designed like prison cells. But by 1955 in most hospitals, including Columbus State, only those patients who were suicidal, dangerously assaultive or violently destructive were secluded in bare locked rooms or restrained with leather cuffs that bind the wrists to the abdomen. (Sometimes a patient was both restrained and secluded—put in a seclusion room and bound down to the bed.) A hospital rule at Columbus State provided that seclusion or restraint might be used only on a doctor's order, but in practice the overworked doctors left standing orders to seclude or restrain troublesome patients, and so discretion often rested with the attendant. Dr. Kovitz said, "There's a real place for seclusion. Some patients can't stand the excitement of others. A good attendant who knows his patients can tell when a patient is going to become disturbed and can put him in seclusion and give him a chance to calm down, rather than waiting till he can't stand the pressure and breaks loose. Of course it's an entirely different matter if it's done for punishment by a sadistic attendant."

Last night six patients had slept in seclusion on Ward 8, and now the attendants took two of them out to the porch, leaving the other four in the seclusion rooms, where they would get electroshock. Sam Adams was still slapping the walls. As they unlocked his door, he stopped and turned to look at them, his hand still raised. "Let's go take a bath, Adams," Stratton said. Adams shuffled forward and, walking between Stratton and Cooley, crossed the annex and went down the hall to the shower, nudged once or twice by the attendants. While they bathed him, two patients mopped and scrubbed his room and removed the dirty linen. When he came out of the shower he stopped in the main hall, a thin man in underwear, and said, "I'm all right now."

Stratton said, "Yes, you're all right now."

Adams stretched one hand high over his head as though grasping for something. "Can't I go out on the porch? I can't reach 'em here."

"What you reaching for, Adams?" Cooley said.

"My nerves. I'm reaching for my nerves."

"Try down here," one of the attendants said, reaching toward the floor. Adams squatted and reached toward the floor but shook his head, straightened and reached up again. "Let me stay here," he said.

The attendants, tiring of the charade, took his elbows, one saying, "Come on, Adams," and led him back to his seclusion room. The young attendant Wyatt, locking the door and leaving him, remarked, "The other day I didn't eat my lunch, I gave it to him. He said he didn't have any. He keeps reaching for his nerves all the time. He keeps saying, 'I got to stop this, I don't know what I'm doing.' I ask him every day what 32 and 32 is. Usually he says 48."

Behind him, locked in, Adams was shouting loudly, "I'll get 'em," and beginning to slap the locked door with his hands. Another patient in seclusion began to shout too, "It's a tree over there by the courthouse." Adams was yelling now. Wyatt yelled through the peephole, "Hey, Adams! Adams! When you going to lay down? Lay down on the bed, Adams." Adams stopped slapping the wall. He said, "A little later on." But as soon as Wyatt left he began to slap the wall and yell again, "O my God, I'll get 'em, I'll get 'em, hurry up, hurry up, I'll get 'em," and the sound of his hands beating on the walls of his room reverberated down the long echoing corridor. The annex was full of flies. Cooley, walking down the hall to the office, observed, "Can't afford a man just to stand there and talk to Adams all day."

4.

In the office Stratton was hunched over a desk, making out his daily report on the condition of the patients in his care. Most, he reported, were "good." A few were "fair." He worked laboriously, tall, sprawled in his chair, his long legs in white duck pants stretching far under the desk, his shirt collar open and his little black bow tie dangling. When he applied for this job two years ago his application form said he could not read. He was forty-seven years old, from Kentucky. Formerly he had been a construction worker but he had contracted tuberculosis and while he was sick his wife had got a job as an attendant here, and later he had come to work here and so had his father and stepmother. On Stratton's desk were the ward records—a list of narcotics on hand, laboratory reports, a list of medications given, the daily report. One cabinet was filled with medicines, another with thermometers, blood pressure apparatus, enema can, an emergency tray. The narrow window was barred, and on the window ledge was a cigar box containing spare syringes. Pasted to the wall were various lists—the thirteen privileged patients, the ten patients visiting their homes, bed charts, patients' money on deposit in the front office— and various orders from the supervisor's office: patients must be inside the hospital by 7 P.M., attendants must keep a record of all razors, blades, scissors and knives. (Such instruments are kept in a locked drawer, as are narcotics.) One list showed the ward doctor's standing prescriptions for a cold, gastric upset, athlete's foot, cough, headache, body and head lice, diarrhea, constipation. On the wall hung a calendar bearing a picture of a wilderness stream and a ruddy fisherman.

The nurse was giving a patient a shot, saying to him as she swabbed his arm, "I'd like to go someplace where I could catch some nice catfish," and he said, "They got a nice lake down there." From the annex came the echoing racket of Adams' pounding, and from the kitchen came a clatter of dishwashing, and in the hall patients were banging scrub buckets about. Another patient waiting for a shot, an old man, complained, "There's so much racket here I can't hear nothin'." (He was trying to listen to the voices.) A man with a swollen infected elbow—he arrived that way from jail a few days ago—asked for tobacco. The nurse gave him a sack. Stratton, watching, said, "That's one thing—I wish we could get more tobacco somehow. We only get thirty-four sacks a week for seventy-five or eighty patients.

Very few patients have their own cigarettes. The rest just go without."

A hulking low-browed defective farmer came in to ask, "Hey, boy, you couldn't let me out for a while could you, boy?"

Stratton without looking up said, "Not for fifteen minutes." He was a privileged patient and wanted to go outdoors to sit on a bench.

An odd-looking short-legged little man with a bundle of magazines stuck inside his shirt bustled in and complained loudly that his room had not been cleaned. The nurse looked at Stratton, who said it had been—"I know it has because we're going to use it for EST."

The patient, Theobald Tuttle, a former schoolteacher, said, "You're a liar. You're the biggest liar this side of hell."

Stratton just looked at him. Tuttle went out and sat on a bench in the hall, saying loudly to another patient, "He's the biggest liar in the world and he's about to get it too, buddy," then walked swiftly toward the porch, saying, "You'll get your head blowed off some day, boy."

Stratton remarked mildly, "He's the biggest griper on the ward."

The door from Ward 6 opened and a gray-haired nurse brought in six patients from that ward who were to receive EST here. It was 7:45 A.M. The doctor was due at eight to give EST. Stratton took them to the cross hall and put them into private rooms. Attendants Cooley and Wyatt were doing the same with the seven patients from this ward who were to get EST. They put one man in each room; they fastened long straps of heavy cloth to the bed. A skinny red-faced old man said, as Stratton led him toward his room, "My heart isn't good enough for that treatment," and hung back, but Stratton gently pulled him. He said, "Don't lock that door," and Stratton didn't.

Walking down the hall, the young good-looking attendant Wyatt nodded toward a patient in one room and said, "He jumped on me in the kitchen the other day. He blows his stack every seven or eight days." Nurse Novak passed by, and the attendant Cooley told her he'd already put the straps on the beds in the seclusion room. She said, "Are you sure the patients can't get them loose?" She was afraid one might hang himself. "Not my patients," he said, grinning, "I got confidence in my patients," but he went back to the annex to keep an eye on them.

The other attendants went back to the office to wait for Dr. Esther Handcock to arrive and give the shock treatments. The main hall was deserted. The ward was quiet now. The EST machine had arrived. It stood in the hall outside the office, a small brown box on a cart resembling a teacart. The box was about ten by twenty inches, rectangular. Dials on its black face regulated the amount of electrical current and the duration of the shock. On the cart too was an emergency tray and a tank of oxygen to revive a patient if he failed to regain consciousness after shock. At 8:15 the phone rang: It was Dr. Handcock, she wouldn't be here till 8:30.

5.

"EST is still our mainstay," said Superintendent Wedemeyer in 1955. EST was given three times a week on the male wards and every day on the female wards. Patients got it once, twice or three times a week, and in a few exceptional cases oftener. Eighteen men and ninety-nine women were getting it—a total of 117 patients, far fewer than formerly. In 1952, for example, 800 women and 195 men had been on EST, and a total of 14,275 individual treatments had been given that year. In 1948, 18,137 treatments had been given. The new drugs cut the use of EST. They tranquilized disturbed patients; EST had often been used for the same purpose.

EST seems to work best on manic-depressives in an acute depressed state and on patients suffering from involutional melancholia. Dr. Kovitz said, "In the old days the involutional melancholic used to go into old age in a rut, habituated, rigid, fixed, monotonous, preoccupied, like a broken organ playing only one tune, almost a kind of schizophrenia. With EST this is broken, and the patient can go back home in a few months." In some cases doctors view EST as a lifesaver—it can break the tension that drives an acute depressed patient to suicide, or the tension that drives an acute excited catatonic into a frenzy that may end in death from exhaustion.

EST is, essentially, a method of treating psychosis by inducing epileptic-like convulsions. It was introduced in 1937. Four years earlier Manfred Sakel had produced convulsions with insulin injections and a Budapest doctor had produced them with Metrazol injections. By 1955 Metrazol was little used, and the use of insulin was declining. EST is easier and cheaper than either. The apparatus is more portable. EST requires less nursing than insulin. It is less frightening than Metrazol—it produces immediate unconsciousness but Metrazol does not. Finally, EST is considered safer than other convulsive methods.

One year at Columbus State, when eighteen thousand ESTs were given, there were eleven hip and vertebrae fractures, twenty-one loosened teeth, seven dislocated jaws and one dislocated shoulder. About once in every two thousand treatments a patient dies. One had died at Columbus State a few days before our visit to Ward 8—had failed to resume breathing after convulsing and could not be revived. She had been on Thorazine. Since her relatives refused permission for an autopsy, the cause of death was unknown. The accident upset the doctors. They wondered whether EST and Thorazine was a dangerous combination. Thorazine was a new drug, and a good deal remained to be learned about it. They quit giving EST to patients who were on Thorazine.

Nobody knows why EST works. Some doctors deny that it does work. Some private sanitariums refuse to use it. The head of one, a psychoanalytically oriented institution, has observed, "I personally don't like shock. I don't feel it has any theoretical justification. I have to admit that every now and then someone we've worked with a long time without results will go someplace else and get shock and get better at once. But I still prefer to use Serpasil and Thorazine if we have to use something—they're less traumatizing." (His institution charges a patient about sixteen hundred dollars a month.)

Some doctors regard electroshock as little but torture—a treatment so painful and terrifying that it drives patients out of the hospital. But Dr. Kovitz has said, "Terrorizing treatments were used for centuries and they didn't do the work that EST does. EST does something to the brain activities that maintain tension in psychotic people. It doesn't cure anybody. It calms patients down, helps in their management, and it does more—like any other treatment, it helps the patient mobilize his own resources. When the sick side is dominating but the healthy side is trying to push back into control, EST helps give that push. A doctor can't give EST mechanically like so much penicillin for pneumonia. One or two treatments at the right moment will do more good than twenty at other times. Once in a while a doctor spots an old chronic patient who has been here a long time and who suddenly begins to show considerable tension; he gives a few ESTs, and the patient goes home. When I was a boy in medical school I wrote a thesis on insulin therapy—it was a novelty then. Then EST came along, and we were all excited, maybe it was a cure-all. But then its limitations became apparent. We saw acute patients respond to

EST but then relapse. We had to give more and more EST to a point of diminishing returns. It didn't hold. The patients feared it. They became confused. It interfered with their memory. We know now that EST isn't the answer, not by a good deal." The commonest criticism of EST arises from its overuse. EST is used principally for two purposes: as intensive treatment of acute new patients to get them out of the hospital quickly, and as a means of managing difficult chronic patients who have been here for years.

It is this last use—called euphemistically "maintenance shock"— that is criticized. A patient would blow up and break furniture and hit people; shock quieted him down. Another patient wanted to die and wouldn't eat; he was shocked back to life. Another wouldn't keep her clothes on and was resistive to every suggestion; shocks "brought her in line." But this was not really therapy; it was control. And as the years passed in a chronic patient's life, he might receive an enormous amount of EST. One patient at Columbus had received no fewer than 427 shocks. And three hundred was not uncommon. Everybody deplored this; but it was done. Nobody set out to give a patient three hundred shocks, of course—a patient might get a course of twenty or forty shocks when he arrived, then a year later another course from a different doctor, then another a year later when he became disturbed, and so on, until one day a doctor reviewing his case realized what had happened. Too much EST can produce epilepsy, according to a standard textbook. At its worst, EST was used as punishment. Many patients so regarded it—punishment for misbehavior. And this was not surprising, for many got it after misbehaving and, more, some attendants threatened to "put you on EST if you don't behave." Nobody condoned this either; but it happened. All too often it was the attendant, not the doctor, who really decided who got EST. It once was axiomatic that "if you antagonize the attendant you go on the shock list."

Most doctors don't seem to like EST any better than the patients do. One at Columbus State said, "It is a pretty terrible thing to do to a person, throw him into an epileptic convulsion, when you don't even know why you're doing it." And Dr. Kovitz said, "I think we'll all be happier when it can be superseded." Patients fear EST because in the state hospitals they have seen or heard other patients getting it, and EST is not pleasant. Most doctors and patients agree that EST is not painful if properly given—the patient loses consciousness too quickly to feel pain at the time and afterward he usually cannot remember anything about the treatment. At some hospitals the patient is given Amytal before treatment to calm him or curare to reduce the muscular movement. Neither was given at Columbus State in 1955 except rarely. The authors of a standard psychiatric text, Henderson and Gillespie, say they discontinue EST after a series of twelve treatments if no improvement results. A series was likely to be much longer at Columbus, and at most state hospitals, though the number was not fixed. The common practice at Columbus seemed to be to give a moderately depressed patient from six to ten treatments, manics ten or a dozen, and as many as thirty or forty to schizophrenics, in the hope of preventing relapse.

At Columbus State, after the staff recommended EST the patient's ward doctor wrote an order for treatment on the doctor's green order sheet in the ward office. It was then up to the nurse to get the patient to the treatment ward on the next treatment day. There an EST machine, a doctor, and nurses trained in giving EST were waiting. But the doctor who gave the treatment—the one who actually pushed the button—was not the patient's own ward doctor: He was simply the doctor assigned to give EST. This system was more efficient and cheaper than letting each ward doctor treat his own patients but it did have disadvantages. One ward doctor complained, "An attendant stops you in the hall and says, 'So and so is cutting up again, he needs EST,' so you say okay and order it—but what you don't know is that the guy nearly died on EST the last time he had it two weeks ago. The doctor who gave the EST knows it and he meant to tell you but he didn't happen to see you in the hall that morning and he forgets it, he's got too many other things to think about. The ward doctor has to order treatment without ever knowing the patient's reaction to it. And the doctor giving treatment has to push the button on somebody else's patient without knowing anything about him—very often not even his name and diagnosis, let alone his history." Moreover, there are many variations in the amount and kind of shock, some more severe than others, and a ward doctor might prescribe a particular kind, but the patient didn't always get it. Here again information just didn't get through from one doctor to another. And finally, since a patient's ward file did not show how many ESTs he'd had, the ward doctor, importuned by an attendant to give EST to a patient new on the ward, might order it only to discover by checking at the EST supervisor's office, as one did, that the patient had had ninety-six ESTs in a row on a succession of wards. The textbooks speak of giving EST judiciously, of watching EST patients carefully, of following treatment with intensive psychotherapy; but at Columbus State and most state hospitals this is a dream.

Some doctors consider EST a perversion of the principle of insulin shock, which was discovered earlier. They believe insulin shock to be grounded soundly in biochemistry but EST to be without rationale —shock for the sake of shock. Some studies have indicated insulin shock is more effective than EST. But other psychiatrists feel that this is so—if it is so—only because patients on insulin get more attention. In any case insulin is more expensive and requires more nursing. At Columbus State, and at most public hospitals, the use of insulin declined as the use of EST rose. At one time at Columbus State forty-eight patients were on insulin but by 1955 it had been abandoned, and the insulin rooms on the cross corridor on Ward 8 were used for sleeping rooms by night, for EST rooms by day.

6.

On the morning of our visit to Ward 8, the doctor giving EST, Dr. Handcock, arrived at 8:30 carrying a notebook and wearing a long white starched coat. Dr. Handcock was a small thin gray woman. She had been a ward doctor here fifteen years. She had come here after several years as a general medical practitioner and a year and a half at Logansport, Indiana, State Hospital with the intention of training for her Board examinations. "But I never did anything about taking my Boards," she said, "and I doubt now that I ever will." She lived at the hospital in a top-floor apartment alone. She was a somewhat seclusive person, keeping apart from the young residents, seldom even attending staff meeting. She took care of three chronic male wards.

As she greeted Nurse Novak now on Ward 8, she had a set smile on her face and it never left her throughout the time she gave shock treatment. An attendant plugged the electric cord of the machine into a wall socket and with the nurse pushed the little wheeled cart down the cross corridor, the long black electric cord unwinding, Dr. Handcock following. The other attendants were busy with the EST patients in the rooms, tying ankles to iron bedsteads, fastening strips of cloth to wrists, tying wide belts loosely across bellies. The cart halted in the hall at a doorway. Stretched out on his back in the bed, his head

toward the door, was a thin man of twenty-one, a catatonic schizophrenic laborer. He rolled his eyeballs upward to look at the doctor
but he said nothing. The three male attendants went into his room and
sat down on the edge of his bed. Nurse Novak smeared some paste on
the electrodes on the ends of two wires attached to the EST machine.
Dr. Handcock bent over the machine, her sharp features intent, her
teeth bared in the fixed smile. She set the dials—300 milliamperes
and two-tenths of a second. The nurse, who was wearing gloves, bent
over the patient and pressed the electrodes to his temples; the attendant Cooley seized his legs at the knee, Wyatt held one wrist, and
Stratton held the other and also held a gag in his mouth. The nurse,
waiting, looked up at Dr. Handcock. Dr. Handcock pushed a button
but nothing happened, and she looked quizzically at the nurse, then
back at the machine. She said, "Oh," and flipped a switch, then pushed
the button again, and instantly the patient stiffened, his toes straightened out, the cords in his ankles went taut, then his legs locked like
iron, then his whole body locked, until his arms were stretched tight
and his head thrown back and the cords in his neck were taut. The
machine's timer ticked away, then ceased. He lay like that for seconds,
quivering, then he began to spit foam from his mouth and suddenly
he jumped convulsively, rocking the attendants, then, moaning and
howling in muffled tone through the gag, he leaped convulsively again
and again, his knees and elbows jerking up, then out, his back arching,
while the attendants held down on him with all their strength.
Gradually the convulsions subsided. He had stopped breathing for
perhaps half a minute but now began again, his breath coming in blowing gasps through the foam on his lips; and soon he was sleeping deeply
and breathing normally, snoring. The attendants tightened the straps
across his belly and around his wrists, then got up and came out into
the hall and went to the next room, while the nurse pushed the cart
to the next doorway and swabbed the electrodes.

They went from room to room that way. Cooley, opening the door
of one, said, "Good morning, Miller," and the tall dark good-looking
young man on the bed gazed at him fixedly, and the nurse said, "This
is your treatment, Miller," and he said, "I'm cold today," and they
seized him and the nurse put the electrodes to his head and said,
"Okay," and Dr. Handcock pushed the button and, watching him
convulse, remarked, "It *is* kind of cold in this room today."

While holding a patient the attendants did not look at him; rather, they looked at each other, or at the machine, or at the wall; sometimes they seemed frightened; once when a patient convulsed hard, one of them, straining to hold him, said, "Wow." In the office the phone was ringing, and from the porch came radio music and the sound of a ping-pong ball hitting a paddle. One patient, as they took hold of him, mumbled some question, and Stratton said, "Shock treatment," and as Handcock pushed the button he groaned deeply, "Oh, oh, oh," and kept groaning a little during his convulsion as though in terrible struggle, then his breathing became irregular and, watching, Dr. Handcock asked, "Is he all right?" The nurse bent and looked at him closely and nodded; they wheeled the cart on. The attendants worked methodically and skillfully; usually it was less than half a minute from the time they opened a patient's door until the doctor pushed the button.

Earlier Stratton had left the door open on one fearful old man, and now as they worked on a patient across the hall, he raised up in bed and said, "Please, Doctor, I wouldn't like to have a treatment, my heart isn't good enough." She smiled and went on with her work. His face was red, he was trembling violently. He said, "Please let me out." Nobody paid heed; they moved on down the hall, and in a moment the old man slipped out of his room and fled unnoticed to the main hall and disappeared. They were busy with another patient; when Dr. Handcock pushed the button nothing happened. "Was there enough goo on the electrodes?" she asked, and the nurse said, "Yes, I just put some on." The doctor said, "We'll give him a stronger dosage but let's wait till we're through with all the others." She was fiddling with the machine, pushing various buttons. "Something is not working," she said; "I'm sorry." She pushed some more buttons. "There were instructions somewhere, they used to be in the cart, but I don't think they're there any more. I wonder where those instructions are," and she pushed another button, while one of the attendants watched her fearfully. "There!" she said. "It's all right now," and they moved on to another patient.

Attendant Cooley, glancing into the old man's room, said he was gone, and went to the main hall and brought him back, a thin frail trembling middle-aged man, his tousled white hair awry. They were ready for him now. He sat on the bed, saying, "But my heart isn't good enough."

Dr. Handcock said, "You always say that."

"But listen to it, please listen to it," he pleaded, and the nurse said, "Maybe you could listen to his heart, Doctor—it makes him feel better," and Dr. Handcock, with a resigned air, took up her stethoscope and listened gravely to his heart.

Cooley told Stratton, "I told you if we didn't lock him in we'd have to chase him down. He gets all excited."

The old man was saying, "My heart just seems like it jerks, doctor." Dr. Handcock straightened and removed her stethoscope. "It's perfectly normal and regular so if I were you I'd just forget it, it's just nervousness."

"Well, give me the lightest you can, will you?"

"All right, we'll give you the lightest, now please lie down," and he did, slowly, still saying, "Don't give me too much. My heart is jumping right now," and the attendants secured the straps and took hold of him as he said, "It's pounding to beat hell right now," and the nurse put the electrodes to his temples and Dr. Handcock pushed the button. He shuddered. But nothing happened—the nurse looked up and said, "Something isn't working," and Dr. Handcock said, "Isn't it working?" She looked the machine over carefully, with deliberation, while the nurse, holding the electrodes to the old man's temples, looked up at her, impatient. "I guess I didn't throw it onto 'treatment,'" and she slipped another switch, then pushed the button, and this time it worked: He shuddered, then convulsed, then slept; and they moved on.

As they worked, another patient in a room across the hall sat up in bed and watched, and the nurse, seeing him, said, "Lie down." He said, "I've already had shock, ain't it?" "Just lay down. There's nothing to worry about. You don't have to look over here." He said, "Doctor, can I ask you something?" One of the attendants closed his door. Already Miller was up, wandering slowly down the corridor, dazed after treatment, his expression vaguely troubled, a lost look in his eyes.

They went back to the annex to treat the four patients in seclusion. When they unlocked a door, the patient was standing in a corner, wearing a rumpled bathrobe. Stratton said, "Lay down, Harrison." He didn't move. Wyatt slapped his shoulder lightly. "Lay down." He sat on the edge of the bed, and they laid him down on his back and strapped him down. Stratton asked, "Did you tie that, Harrison?" pointing to a knot in the strap, and he smiled, and Stratton said, "You did a good job," and the electricity hit, and he reared up almost to a sitting position, loose from their grasp, and one muttered, "Damn," for he had thrown off the electrodes, they would have to do it again. They laid him down, and the nurse lubricated the electrodes and pressed them firmly against his temples, and the attendants seized him hard, and again he heaved mightily in convulsion, an awful animalistic outcry coming from his throat, and this time they held him. His eyes rolled wildly, Stratton grabbed his head and looked directly into his eyes. He was all right.

They moved on to another patient, then another, then to Sam Adams, and as they opened Adams' door, he drew back into the far corner and huddled there, a scrawny little man in BVDs, his knobby knees pressed together, his thin arms crossed on his breast, fingers touching his shoulders, and he said, "Don't bother me, please don't bother me." The attendants went into his room, and he crouched, saying, "You aren't going to kill me, are you?"

The nurse said, "Come on, Mr. Adams, lay down."

Cooley, gripping one of his wrists, said, "You get your breakfast, Adams?"

He said, "Don't bother me," and Stratton, pulling him gently to the bed, said, "No breakfast, Adams?" and the nurse: "Would you like some orange juice, Mr. Adams, would you like a cigarette? You can have them after your treatment," and Stratton, laying him down, "It'll make you better, Adams."

But Adams, struggling weakly, yelled, "It'll make me worse."

"Now, Mr. Adams," the nurse said, "don't you worry," and Stratton, forcing him onto his back and fastening the strap, said, "How you doing, Adams?" The nurse put the electrodes on. He screamed, "Don't kill me, please don't kill me," and strained to get free, but the attendants were holding him, and the nurse nodded to Dr. Handcock; "click" went the button, and the timer ticked away, and Sam Adams' legs, thin as a child's, stiffened and in a moment jackknifed in convulsion.

Outside through the iron bars in the window the dying leaves of the trees rustled in the wind. Dr. Handcock said, "Is he all right?" and the nurse, feeling his pulse, murmured, "M-hm"; he snored raucously, and they covered him with a sheet and left him. Shock was over for the day. Thirteen patients had received it.

7.

Now Sam Adams' was a somewhat curious case. When you asked the ward doctor, Mary Lou Hippert, about him, she said, "Poor Mr. Adams," and nearly everyone felt that way: He looked so unhappy. Sam Adams had been brought to the hospital in 1949 because he had tried to kill himself. He had been forty-nine years old then, single, living alone on a farm. He always had been "very quiet and timid" his sister said. In 1948 he became depressed, couldn't sleep or eat, lost weight, became irritable and forgetful, neglected the livestock, refused to leave the farm, felt "a shade nervous" and said his forehead hurt. Sometimes he would say, "My mind's gone, it's gone completely, it's blank." He didn't care how he looked. Early in 1949 he slashed his wrists with a razor blade, in the spring he tried to hang himself, and his brother took him to a doctor in Columbus, who put him in a private hospital and gave him EST. He soon improved and went home. But a couple of months later he cut his throat and was brought to Columbus State as a voluntary patient.

He said he had been depressed because his sister was trying to get his farm away from him. "I know it was wrong to attempt suicide, but when I get like this, so depressed and everything, I get so terribly afraid of mental disease." He never smiled. His mood was deep melancholy. He suffered greatly. He said, "I feel so bad this morning."

Dr. Kovitz diagnosed him manic-depressive psychosis, depressive type, sent him to Ward 8 because he was suicidal, and ordered EST. At first it seemed to help him, and he was moved to Ward 4 then to Ward 6, presumably on the way out. But he slipped back, needed more EST. During the ensuing five years Adams received 183 ESTs. And during that time he was bounced to and fro from one ward to another, usually among 4, 6 and 8, with occasional stops at a chronic ward like 16 or the chronic disturbed ward, 24. Always the story was the same; EST improved him temporarily, made him as rational and clear as anybody, but it never "held," he became noisy and destructive, pounding on the walls and reaching in the air for "my nerves," and he had to go back to Ward 8 for more seclusion and EST. His depression simply was not yielding to EST, as depressions in manic-depressives should.

In 1952, a court summons for him arrived at the hospital: His sister had sued him, asking that the farm they had inherited jointly be partitioned. A mix-up ensued. There is no way to be sure Adams actually was served personally with a copy of the summons. As a voluntary patient, he could have left the hospital to defend the suit. But he did not leave, so far as hospital records show. More than a year later the state, trying to collect from Adams' relatives for his hospitalization, was told Adams was penniless as a consequence of complicated litigation; and the downtown office asked the hospital superintendent to see if Adams himself could shed any light on the whole matter. But he found Adams disoriented, "very confused, and totally unable to participate in understandable conversation." And there the matter rested. And Adams went on his weary way.

He was considered a disrupting influence and a nuisance. He annoyed other patients, and they beat him up. On April 5, 1955, Dr. Handcock wrote a "progress note" on him, the first "progress note" that any doctor had written on him in his six years here. She wrote, ". . . noisy, agitated and depressed. . . . Is the noisest patient on 16 intermittently and even when in seclusion can be heard exclaiming, 'O my God, my God!' 'I don't know how to reach up there. You're not going to beat me to death are you? Are you?'" Dr. Handcock wrote that Adams had just finished a course of thirty ESTs without improvement and that he had been given one of the new tranquilizing drugs but it had not helped either. Dr. Handcock concluded that the only solution, everything else having failed, might be psychosurgery —prefrontal lobotomy, topectomy or some other brain operation—and that same day she made out a form asking for a psychosurgery consultation.

Adams' case apparently was not considered at a formal staff meeting but, rather, was discussed informally that same day when the doctors met to talk over their problems, as they frequently did on Tuesdays. One doctor was astonished that Adams was being proposed for psychosurgery. "I'd seen him shortly after he was admitted and I wasn't even sure he was psychotic. He seemed clear and oriented—just a lost soul. Since then he has gone in and out of this peculiar schizoid depression. But I'd never thought of him as a candidate for lobotomy." Dr. Kovitz is inclined to doubt today that Adams is a good candidate for lobotomy. Nonetheless, the conference apparently approved Dr. Handcock's request that he be considered further for lobotomy, for she wrote, "Should be considered for psychotherapy." She says today this was a slip of the pen—that she meant psychosurgery, not psychotherapy. Her written request was forwarded to the hospital's neurology clinic, where a resident, doubtless confused by Dr. Handcock's slip of the pen, noted on it, "You figure it out." Ten days later somebody hit Adams in the eye.

Nothing further happened for nearly three weeks. Then on May 5 Dr. Handcock wrote on a blue referral slip to the neurology clinic: "Is psychosurgery being considered? Is being very difficult. Blank was sent you some time ago."

This slip came back from the neurology clinic marked, "Patient must be seen at staff before decision by Dr. Secrest"—the consultant neurosurgeon.

Dr. Handcock immediately wrote on the slip, "Was. See file and blank sent you. E. Handcock."

Matters rested there another two weeks, then on May 23 Dr. Handcock sent another blue referral slip to the neurology clinic: "Reminding you that he is a very difficult noisy patient. Do you plan to operate, and if so when?"

This produced some action. On June 7 the case was referred to Social Service, for somebody had discovered that Adams was still a voluntary patient and so could not be operated on without permission from his relatives. (Indeed, it is customary to get permission to perform surgery so drastic on any patient.) Promptly a social worker telephoned the person whom he regarded as the proper one: the same sister whom Adams had accused of trying to get his farm away from him. The social worker asked the sister to have Adams committed to the hospital by the probate court.

But nothing happened. Dr. Handcock sent another blue referral slip to the neurology clinic: "Is surgery going to be done? Urgent. Very trying to the ward." She underlined "urgent" and "very" three times. And, apparently despairing of getting anything done quickly, she also transferred Adams to the disturbed ward, Ward 8, where he was secluded and given EST.

The social worker called in the sister, had her sign a permit for psychosurgery, took her down to the probate court and had Sam Adams committed. All was in readiness for his operation.

But the operation never was performed. Perhaps this was because Adams, being on Ward 8, was no longer the patient of Dr. Handcock, the chief advocate of psychosurgery for him. Possibly other doctors felt it inadvisable. Most likely it was because at about this time the hospital virtually ceased to perform such operations, for reasons we shall discuss later on.

Looking back at Sam Adams' career in the hospital, nobody seems very happy about it. Several doctors and social workers entertain a vague feeling that he has not been well dealt with. They wonder: Did the hospital fully protect his legal rights? And, if drastic surgery would have benefited him, why was it not done expeditiously? And, if it would not, why was he pushed to the brink of surgery and rescued only by chance? And, is it not possible that the blows the hospital itself dealt Adams have aggravated his illness? They are unsettling questions, the sort that arise in nearly every state hospital, rather than questions of intentional brutality which laymen expect.

Adams has worn calluses on his hands by clenching them so tensely for so many years. "All his human energy goes into reaching up in the air for his nerves," said Dr. Kirch. Once he had a quiet period: A medical student on vacation helping out at the hospital took him out for a walk every now and then, and it made a profound difference in him. Dr. Hippert felt sorry for Adams. "He seems so miserable, so unhappy, and it seems as though there ought to be something we could do for him." But nobody knew what.

8.

Now at 10 A.M. after EST the main hall of Ward 8 was deserted but for one or two patients wandering to and fro. An attendant was straightening the clothes room, a big closet crammed with bins full of patients' clothing. The state furnished heavy work shoes, green khaki or gray moleskin pants, and blue work shirts. Everything had to be washable, which in part accounted for the patients' bedraggled appearance. (Somehow, women patients always seemed to look better than men.) In another clothes room hung the "good clothes" that the patients had worn on arrival, awaiting the day they left—business suits, neckties, leather jackets, hats.

Attendant Stratton was bathing a patient. All patients were bathed twice a week and given a change of clothes. The other attendants, aided by patients, were washing the seclusion rooms and arousing the patients in them and taking them out to the porch. In the dim half-light of the annex the soft jangle of keys could be heard all the time. The old man who had helped out in the annex for years was puttering around. The nurse came for him: There was a bug in her office, and she wanted him to get it out, and he shuffled off dutifully. The library cart arrived and stopped in the hall; it contained a few worn books and magazines; only two or three patients strolled up to it.

In the office the nurse was working on her records. Theobald Tuttle, the tousle-headed busybody, hurried in and said, "I'd like to speak to Dr. Hippert when she comes. I had a partial privilege and she took it away from me."

The nurse, without looking up from her writing, said, "Why did she do that?"

"Because there was an attendant on this ward at the time who was against me. You're cooped up here all the time, it isn't good for you."

"Wasn't there some other reason?"

"Oh, I got in an argument but that didn't amount to anything." He bustled out. He was a gnarled, short-legged little man, his face bright red. He had been in and out of mental hospitals for twenty-five years. Originally he had been a college teacher. After each siege of illness, he had descended to a simpler social level—high school teacher, then factory worker, then gardener. Each time he had managed to get along for a few years, but he always had returned. He was a problem. Most of the time he was a nuisance, not a menace. He was constantly in and out of the office. Five minutes ago he had asked about his privilege; here he was again, wanting the nurse to take the wax out of his ears, he'd complained of it a dozen times but nobody in this place ever did anything about anything. Moreover (kneeling before the nurse), "My folks are coming and I want to see them out on the lawn, you're penned up in here for a couple of months and it's very difficult. Then somebody tells a lie and it's over, you're back in here again. We've got more than our share of liars and crooks on our staff, unfortunately."

The phone rang and the nurse answered and Tuttle left. The nurse called an attendant and told him a patient was going to have a special visit from his wife—"She's got a check for him to sign or something"—and the attendant brought the patient to the office, a tall thin worried Negro. He waited uneasily. Presently the ward door opened and an attendant let a Negro woman in. She had a check she wanted him to sign. It was for $2,100, apparently representing his total wealth, and when the attendants saw it they were astonished. He said, "I'm not going do it."

His wife said, "But I've got to make a payment on the furniture or they'll take the furniture."

He shook his head determinedly.

Stratton said to him, "She's your guardian, see."

He laughed. "How can she be my guardian? She's my wife."

Stratton explained that the court had appointed her his guardian. He had the vague expression of a psychotic but he understood this money matter and on it he was determined. He turned to the nurse and said, "All she want to do is get the check in her hand. She might skip town, car and all."

Theobald Tuttle was striding busily up and down. The Negro's wife tried to hand her husband a pen but he put his hands behind his back and shook his head and said, "If the court says she's my guardian, let her go to the court to get the check signed. I won't sign it."

Stratton looked at the wife helplessly. "If he don't want to sign it I can't make him."

Annoyed, she said, "But what can I do?"

"Tell you what—you go to Social Service. They'll take care of you," and he directed her to the Social Service office in the administration building, and she left.

Nothing needed doing at the moment, so Stratton and Wiley took time out for sandwiches they had brought with them. By now the privileged patients had gone out. Only twelve were allowed to go unattended. Only half chose to leave, for there was little to do—go to the commissary and buy candy, or wander around the grounds and talk to friends, or just sit on the benches—"making little sticks out of big sticks," as one doctor said, "watching the cars go by on Broad Street." Only three from this ward went to the occupational therapy shop, where they made things out of wood and leather.

Occupational therapy (OT) at this hospital was woefully inadequate. Psychiatrists believe that performing a simple task with the hands, such as weaving, carpentry, ceramics, often restores a patient's contact with reality, and enables him to commence functioning again at a simpler level after he has retreated from the complexities of everyday living. In theory, when a doctor at Columbus thought a patient would benefit from such work, he prescribed OT, and the patient went to the OT shop. But in practice only sixty or seventy patients in the entire hospital—out of 2,700—went regularly, and many of those had been going for years and probably benefited little.

Why wasn't OT used more? There were not enough attendants to take patients to the shop. And there was only one occupational therapist. In some hospitals OT workers visit every ward daily, taking

sewing or other materials to patients too sick to leave the wards, and
the wards are busy places, with every patient who is able participating
in some activity; but at Columbus State in 1955 this was almost never
done. Some hospitals use volunteers to overcome the shortage of help;
but at Columbus State there was little but talk of this. The superintendent considered OT seriously weak.

So was recreational therapy. At some hospitals activities are almost
constant—dances, games, movies, roller skating, bowling, gardening.
(Indeed, some psychiatrists deplore "mere busy-ness" and argue that
both occupational and recreational therapy must be carefully supervised and prescribed only by doctors for particular patients in particular conditions. But most state hospital superintendents would be
grateful for enough employees to create "busy-ness.") At Columbus
State, although the recreation department issued an impressive annual
report in 1955 stating that "individual therapy has been applied to
530 patients with a total of 2,674 contacts" and "recreational group
therapy, by verbal assignment, was applied for 922 patients with a
total of 4,243 contacts," the department's program was not adequate,
and the large number of "contacts" evidently included everybody who
was even taken to a ball game or shown a movie. About once a week
privileged patients went to the clubroom to shoot pool or talk or play
cards or checkers. Occasionally there was a dance or a ward party.
"But there aren't enough employees to provide a consistent program
of daily activities," said Dr. Kovitz, "and they can only take them in
dribbles. Day in day out they just sit on the wards."

Right now late in the morning on Ward 8 nearly all the patients
were sitting on the porch. They sat there all day, all but the privileged
patients and the ward workers. There were a radio and a ping-pong
table on the porch but most of the patients just sat, a husky attendant
in the center of the room keeping watch over them to prevent trouble.
Dr. Hippert felt it would be far better to permit them to move around
more freely as patients did on other wards, but this would have
required more attendants, since being disturbed patients they could
not be left unguarded, and on the porch a single attendant could
watch a hundred men. Dr. Hippert said, "Probably at least half these
patients could go outdoors if there were attendants to take them. But
there aren't. So they sit on the porch. They get out two or three times
a year, to a picnic and a couple of ball games and that's all." Dr.
Kovitz said, "We know it isn't good but we're forced to do it. The

place is an architectural monstrosity—it became overloaded so they built additions onto the wards and created massive wards for patients who need small wards. It's still overloaded and the only way we can handle it safely with a limited number of attendants is to cram them onto porches and keep them in sight all the time. In some hospitals they use hydrotherapy and allow the patients more freedom, but we don't have hydrotherapy any more." The hydrotherapy tubs and showers were still standing on Ward 8, unused for years. Doctors prescribing EST and insulin had got out of the habit of using them. The space they took up was needed for beds. It had become increasingly difficult to hire a trained hydrotherapist. The equipment had aged and replacing it was prohibitively expensive.

Recently the new drugs had calmed many patients so they might be allowed to leave the porch but another consideration had arisen: An attendant said, "I've found that if you've got ten or fifteen patients who don't do anything but just sit around in the main hall waiting for meals, your kitchen crew resents it, they figure, 'These guys don't have to work so why should we?' " Nobody liked the porch; being allowed to leave it was a reward for working. When the kitchen crew wasn't busy they could sit in the main hall, only a dozen of them in the big hall instead of nearly a hundred crammed onto the porch; and in the hall was a television set, while on the porch was only a radio. Little things mean a great deal in a hospital, as in a prison, where laborers and manufacturers, flunkies and scientists, are equal.

9.

Now at 10:30 A.M. Dr. Hippert arrived for her daily visit to the ward. She is an attractive blonde woman in her late thirties, married, formerly a nurse. She originally was from Armstrong's Mills, Ohio, but she had grown up in Cincinnati and finished nurse's training in 1938. While nursing she had got her M.D. at the University of Cincinnati and gone into private general practice. She had become interested in psychiatry "because such a large proportion of patients I saw in general practice were really psychiatric or psychosomatic problems." Deciding to specialize in psychiatry, she had come to Columbus State in 1954 for residency training. She had thought to go into private psychiatric practice after taking her Board examination but since being here thought she might stay on. She liked everything about it except the patient load—"I'm taking care of 209 patients and it's pretty frustrating sometimes."

Now as she came on the ward, having already visited her other two wards, 4 and 6, she found a patient waiting for her at the office door. He was young, slender, with wavy hair and sensitive features, and he said rapidly, "Can I speak to you a minute, Dr. Hippert? Can you give me a partial privilege? Can you transfer me to Ward 6? I want to continue my schoolwork, I've got all my materials but there's no place to keep them here and it's so noisy I can't study, and I'd appreciate it very much if you could transfer me."

Dr. Hippert regarded him silently a moment, then said, "We'll see, wait till I get through here," and she went into the office and asked the nurse, "How's he doing?"

Pretty well, the nurse said. He had come here three years earlier when he was twenty-one. A spoiled baby, a puny child who stuttered badly, he had begun to show signs of serious mental troubles at fourteen, when he had skipped school, quit church, begun to have temper tantrums, invented boastful tales about himself, and bought expensive cameras and sold them at a loss. He had liked guns. At seventeen he had had a serious love affair; the girl had become pregnant and he had married her. Later, after his psychotic break, he had blamed it all on "someone" at a dance who must have given him "Spanish fly," a supposed aphrodisiac, and thus enticed him into sexual relations. The child had been born; the marriage had been miserable; he had accused his wife of infidelity; she had been afraid of him; he had got deeply in debt, become increasingly nervous, and drunk heavily. He had kept a gun under his pillow. Often he had talked to it. He had taken deer rifles outside and shot them off at night. His wife had sued for divorce. He had thought the Chicago police wanted him for manslaughter. He had thought the door of his house was broken open by enemies. He had said, "The whole town thought I should have my head examined. I was at a friend's house and in walked the sheriff." At the hospital he had been diagnosed schizophrenic, paranoid type, and given insulin shock; he had recovered quickly and gone home on trial visit, but soon the police had brought him back to the hospital: He was threatening to kill his wife. On Ward 8 he had improved on EST in the last few weeks, and now the nurse said he hadn't been upset for some time. He came to the office, bringing a sheaf of blueprints, and, his hands trembling, showed them to Dr. Hippert, saying eagerly, "This is the material, Dr. Hippert. It's real interesting," and he rattled on, pointing to things on the blueprints. Dr. Hippert listened patiently and told him she'd transfer him to Ward 6 so he could continue his studies, then, saying he'd have to excuse her now, turned away; and he left reluctantly like a disappointed child.

She asked the nurse, "How did treatment go this morning?"

"Pretty good."

Dr. Hippert looked over the list of patients who received EST. "I think we ought to stop Adams now. It isn't doing him any good," and she wrote on the green order sheet. Glancing at her notes she said, "Why hasn't John been going to OT?"

The nurse said, "I didn't know he was supposed to. I didn't know anybody went on OT from here."

Dr. Hippert said, "Well, two or three are supposed to."

The nurse said she'd send him.

Dr. Hippert said, "Who was that I saw in the hall just now? He seems quite disturbed and hostile."

"He's very hostile," the nurse said and handed her a letter the patient had written. He was a young homicidal laborer who had been here only a few days. Addressed to the superintendent, the letter said:

"Upon receipt of this letter I wish to be released immediately. I didn't sign myself in here and as far as I know, no one else did. I had an epileptic seizure and as you and I know there is nothing you can do for me. I have my own medicine at home and this confinement doesn't do me any good. . . .

P.S. If you'd teach your attendants not to try and strong arm a patient they may get better results."

Dr. Hippert put the letter in her pocket. The patient was being committed by the court today. Nobody knew what was the matter with him. He looked normal, and the electroencephalogram was normal, indicating he did not have epilepsy. Dr. Hippert suspected a "posttraumatic episode with psychomotor equivalents," basing this theory on the fact that he had been hit on the head with a meat cleaver in a fight a couple of years previously; but at present he was classified as an emotionally unstable personality, and if further tests and observations confirmed the diagnosis he'd be released in a month as not psychotic.

The nurse said, "Theobald Tuttle wants a partial privilege."

"Is he up or down?"

"He's been better. He wants to visit his sister outdoors."

"All right, put him on the list."

The nurse made a note, then said, "This patient," handing her a file, "was in seclusion all night and this morning he had loose stools and it looked like blood in them so I sent him to 2"—the medical ward.

Dr. Hippert nodded and asked, "Who else was in seclusion?" The nurse told her, adding, "They're all out now except Harrison and he'll be out after a while. He usually sleeps two hours after EST. He's so confused he don't eat or anything else."

"I'll go see him. Who's that in the hall?" and she nodded. A patient was sitting with his head in his hands. He'd said he felt "groggy," the nurse reported, and couldn't eat breakfast. He had epilepsy and had felt like he was going to have a seizure, so the nurse was keeping him in the hall where she could watch him.

Dr. Hippert walked down the hall to the annex. The attendant Wyatt went with her. Theobald Tuttle stopped her to demand a partial privilege; she said she'd already ordered it. Then he demanded to be released. She told him he wasn't well enough. He said, "What do you expect of me?"

"It isn't a matter of expecting anything, Mr. Tuttle. It would take quite a while to explain it to you better and I'll try to arrange to talk to you soon in my office." She went on back to the annex. Near its door a big young powerful Negro lay stretched out on a pile of mattresses. Dr. Hippert stopped in surprise. "Why, George Wilson. What's the matter?" He raised his head but said nothing. She repeated it. He looked at Wyatt. Wyatt stiffened. Wilson, nearly twice Wyatt's size, sneered and turned his head to the wall. Wilson, a psychotic mental defective, had been here only a few months and had been getting along so well that Dr. Hippert had been thinking of sending him home; she had talked to his mother, a charwoman, who had said she could arrange to get a job cleaning offices evenings and could take George with her so she could keep an eye on him; but somebody had told George that he was going to be released last Friday, and when Friday passed and he was still here, he had run through the door when an attendant opened it and had escaped into Ward 6, and the pursuing attendants from Ward 8 had been obliged to carry him back, fighting and screaming, to Ward 8 right through a cluster of visitors. Now he turned his face to the wall.

Dr. Hippert went to a seclusion room and Wyatt unlocked it. Sidney Harrison was inside, a lumpy man of forty-five in dirty underwear sitting on the floor. He stared at the doctor unseeing. He first had come to the hospital eight years earlier and had gone home several times, sometimes on trial visits, sometimes escaping. Recently he had been brought back, dangerous and combative, saying, "I will fight any time. Everyone abuses me. I want to fight." The admitting doctor had reported, "His ideas centered around the thought that there was a mouth disease sweeping the country which made everybody run off the mouth. This disease apparently was brought to this country by a soldier serving in the First World War. He relates that this soldier told him the following story: The soldier was lying on the battlefield and got his hand wet with dew and the dew and gunpowder mixed and the poison spread through his system and he developed this mouth disease which he brought back to this country. This disease, he stated, has some relation to cancer, either causing it or caused by it. Many people are fleeing the country because of this disease."

So now here he was in seclusion, and Dr. Hippert said to him, "How do you feel?" No answer. "What happened?" He raised his gaze up to hers and mumbled something about "the pier." He was fooling with a strip of cloth. "What's that?" she asked.

He said, "It's just a mess of—" but his voice trailed off as though he had lost interest in what he was saying; he walked backward to the barred window and turned his back on the doctor and stood there gazing out through the bars, sunlight streaming in strongly on his graying hair.

Dr. Hippert, about to leave the annex, caught sight of Miller, who had received EST earlier. He was a tall young man with long slender fingers, sitting on the cot in a seclusion room, his elbows on his knees, his face buried in his hands. He always had maintained that when he had been put in an army neuropsychiatric hospital, a sergeant had "bashed his head against the wall." She sat down beside him on the cot. He did not move. She said, "What's the trouble?" He did not answer. She touched his shoulder. "Won't you tell me?" He did not move or speak. "Won't you talk to me, Mr. Miller?" He did not move or speak; he just sat. She sat too for another minute. Then she got up and left him. He had been improving on EST; now suddenly he had slipped. Dr. Hippert looked disappointed.

She walked down the hall, and a stocky sneering young man fell into step beside her and, looking up at her, his head twisted to one side, said, "You doctors are all alike. They transferred me here from

Cleveland Receiving Hospital and now they won't let my sister visit me. This place stinks, you doctors are all alike, you're a bunch of fools." He had been here a year and a half, a wanderer whose schizophrenia had begun insidiously a long time ago. EST had done him no good; now he was on Sandril, one of the new drugs. Dr. Hippert paid no attention to him, she had heard all this before, and he dropped away, sneering at her. At the office door was the young man with the roll of blueprints, and he asked, "Would it be all right if I went to Ward 6 right now?" She told him, "A little later," and he thanked her eagerly and hurried away. She asked the nurse about a couple of other patients, ordered one sent to Ward 4 for some tests, and hurried off to an administrative staff meeting, having been on the ward half an hour.

10.

It was 11 A.M., and the nurse was getting medications ready to distribute at lunch. On the door of the office was a sign: "NO PATIENTS ALLOWED IN THIS OFFICE UNLESS CALLED FOR. THIS MEANS EVERYONE." The admonition was futile. The excited young man who had talked to Dr. Hippert about working on his blueprints now came in again to ask if he could move to Ward 6 at once. "Just wait," the attendant Stratton told him. Nine men were sitting in the hall, one leafing through a magazine dispiritedly, one the epileptic with head in hands, the others just waiting for lunch. Two or three more came in, privileged patients. Theobald Tuttle hurried in, carrying a scrub bucket and complaining bitterly: He had scrubbed the porch clean and a patient had thrown a bucket of dirty water onto it. "You can't have anything around this place," Tuttle said. An attendant went halfway down the cross hall and called "Lunch" toward the porch, and in a moment the patients streamed down the cross hall, one as he emerged halting in front of Wiley and saluting stiffly at attention and refusing to move on until Wiley returned the salute; the patient was mumbling military titles.

Lunch was beef, potatoes, tomatoes, and gravy, served on partitioned tin trays, eaten quickly to the accompaniment of the screech of chair legs moving on the terrazzo floors.

After it the patients went back to the porch.

Wyatt brought a new patient to the office and asked Stratton where to put him. On the porch, Stratton said. The patient, a talkative little man with his pockets stuffed with magazines and documents, didn't want to go. Stratton said, "Maybe you can play some ping-pong or cards or something," and Wyatt took him out.

Theobald Tuttle bustled in demanding to know when Dr. Hippert was coming.

Cooley said, "She's already been here."

"When?"

"Forty minutes or so ago."

"I wanted to see her."

"She said you could have your partial privilege."

"Oh, she did. Well, I wanted to see her about something else."

"She was here."

"She wasn't here forty minutes ago because I was here myself then."

No one answered. He had seen her and had forgotten. He looked from one to the other then stalked out, muttering indignantly.

Stratton grinned at Cooley, saying, "He called you a liar—why didn't you hit him?"

"I can't hit a man because he calls me a liar—in here. I would on the outside."

"Sometimes you feel like it in here."

From the kitchen came a great banging and clattering. An old man came in to ask that somebody get him a plug of tobacco from the commissary, and Cooley made a note on a list of other patients' requests. Presently a studious-looking patient with sandy hair and glasses, wearing a neatly knotted necktie, with several pencils and pens clipped to his shirt pocket, strolled in, and Cooley handed him the list and let him out to go to the commissary. Stratton finished working on a record book and went out to lunch at the commissary himself.

The World Series started today but only one patient was watching it on television. The nurse was making out her EST report. A patient came in to talk to her, he couldn't make out what the voices were saying. The nurse got rid of him, remarking after he'd gone, "Too much paper work, you can't see the patients. It'll be worse when the student nurses start." (The hospital soon would start a training course for nurses.) Another patient came in, he wanted to write a letter home, he needed a stamp and paper and envelope and didn't remember his home address. The nurse looked up his address and gave him paper and pencil and told him the doctor would mail his letter. The hospital furnished one stamp a week. Theobald Tuttle came in to get some shoe polish; he'd have liked to rummage through the cabinet drawers looking

for it but the nurse got it for him. Another patient came in to take his
medicine.

Cooley put a folding screen across the hall between the office and
the door leading to the next ward; it was 1 P.M., time for visitors. The
telephone rang, and the nurse, answering, then hanging up, told
Stratton, "Cyrus Thatcher is going to have company," and Stratton
said to Theobald Tuttle, who was hanging around the doorway, "Go
tell Thatcher he's going to have company."

The telephone rang. A big simple-looking man came in and rumbled,
as he had done after breakfast, "You couldn't let me out for a little
while, could you?"

Stratton, answering the phone, said, "Is it one o'clock yet?"

"Yes."

"I've got ten till one. Wait till one." He left, muttering something;
he was a powerful lad with beetling brows, and people were afraid
of him; he had been sent home on Serpasil but had lasted only four
days before he had threatened a neighbor. Right now he was angry
with the hospital because his aged mother had broken her hip and he
felt he ought to go home to help her but the hospital wouldn't let
him, and this morning he had written a letter. "Hello Mother, I am
getting awful mad at this hospital."

Stratton finished with the phone call. The other patient who had
wanted to write a letter brought it to the office to be mailed. It said:

DEAR WIFE,
How are you doing. I don't sleep very good yet but if I don't improve
some pretty soon I will see about coming home. Do you see Joe any more?
Do I have a job any more when I come back if I ever make it? I feel a
little better than when you were here last. Then I didn't know where I
was or anything.
P.S. I got weighed today weighed 163 pounds.

The nurse took the letter, and he asked, "May I have permission
to go up and watch the ball game?"

She nodded. Eight men were watching now.

A patient came in to talk to her: "Insulin is busting up my body so
I won't bother women any more," and he rambled on and on while
she worked.

A tiny shriveled old man waltzed in and in a high-pitched squeaky
voice said to the nurse, "Hello, sweetie."

She said, "Hello, sweetie, how are you?"

"Sick in bed. Can I have some tobacco?"

She gave it to him and went back to making out her report.

She telephoned for penicillin. Theobald Tuttle came in and asked her, "Did you say I was going to go to the clinic at one o'clock? It's one o'clock now."

"A little later," she said.

The phone rang; a patient was coming down from a chronic ward, 12, where he had been causing trouble and was considered an escape risk. Stratton said, "That'll leave 12 with a vacancy, won't it?"

The nurse telephoned Ward 12 to ask if they'd have a vacancy. They would. "Don't let anybody take it," she said and hung up, and she and Stratton looked over their roster to decide whom to send from here to 12. Stratton suggested a couple of names but she shook her head: "It's Ward 12, it'll have to be a good one. He'll have to be able to walk to the dining room too." She telephoned Dr. Hippert to consult her about the transfer.

An attendant arrived to take patients to the clinic, and when he heard Theobald Tuttle was to be one of his charges, he smirked: Evidently Tuttle was known all over the hospital. A woman came in and gave Stratton a slip of paper: Cyrus Thatcher's visitor, and she sat behind the screen, and in a moment Thatcher arrived, fetched by Theobald Tuttle. "Visitor," Stratton told Thatcher. He was the thin old man who had been afraid to have EST because of his bad heart, and he hurried eagerly past the screen to sit with his wife.

The new patient from 12 arrived, an attendant in charge of him. He was a young tense little man and he bounced into the office laughing and chattering, "Hello, what's the story, what's cookin'?"

Stratton, eying him, said, "How are you?"

"Well as could be expected. I've got a new toothbrush. I brush my teeth three times a day with my feet. Don't mind my swearin', it's just shorthand."

He had a new toothbrush sticking out of his shirt pocket, and his sweater was bulging with a bundle of belongings, mostly newspapers and magazines and dirty rolled-up sheafs of paper covered with penciled writings.

Stratton asked the attendant from Ward 12, "What's the matter with him?"

"He wants to run off all the time. He's just a damn nuisance and he torments the nurse to death."

Stratton nodded and told the new patient, "Go out in the hall and have a seat for a little while."

He did, but was back in a few minutes, asking, "How soon can I get out of here? I got a job, fifty dollars a week and room and board, I don't have to be with this class of people, I got money to spend, I wish I had the money I'm supposed to have, I got ten thousand dollars coming to me, I can buy a car and keep a car. That's what I should a done," and he laughed rapidly. "I had the money but I got finagled out of it. Is that shorthand you're writin'? I know shorthand. I only need to brush up my shorthand and I can get the $750 I need."

Stratton waved him away and he went.

The nurse and other attendants had left to attend a class. Stratton was alone on the ward. The studious man in the blue sweater brought in a paper bag full of purchases from the commissary and gravely gave it to Stratton. After he left Stratton mused, "There's a man that was a law student when he came in here. Now he runs errands to the commissary for the other patients."

Chris Haverford had been a brilliant law student, clerking in a law office, when he made his psychotic break. He took his bar examination and afterward remarked that he felt "as if somebody threw a tomato up against the wall and it broke." He wired his parents and brother, "Her name is Judy and she loves me." There was no Judy. He quit his job. He had severe headaches that summer. He would suddenly become angry and scold his parents violently, demanding, "Are you clean?" and pointing a finger at them accusingly. His parents tried to quiet him; he threw a pan at them. They tried to get him to go to bed; he ordered his mother to bed. One day he dug a big hole in the back yard for no apparent reason.

His parents took him to a private sanitarium in Columbus and after eleven ESTs he was sent home. But next spring he broke again. He thought a girl singing on the radio was making advances to him. "I don't think she was a good girl." His mother once recalled, "He has always felt girls were immoral." He always had been aloof, secretive, bookish, religious. He went to the sheriff and insisted he get him a hat. He pushed the sheriff. The sheriff brought him to Columbus State and the next day he was committed.

He was sent to Ward 8. Resistive, he had to be tube-fed. He sat on the porch, not talking. Suddenly he would sing hymns very loudly or stand up and salute. Sometimes he smiled secretly. When he answered questions it was in the pseudo-scholarly manner used by many educated schizophrenics. But asked about hearing voices he shouted angrily, "What do you mean, voices?" The staff diagnosed him schizophrenia, paranoid type.

On insulin shock he lost his delusions and soon he was playing chess on Ward 6 and going regularly to the OT shop. He was sent home to his parents on trial visit. Two members of his former law firm called on the superintendent to ask whether giving him his old job back would be in his best interests; he had asked for it. The superintendent feared he was still too unstable but said they could try. Haverford came to the hospital for a checkup. He was totally without insight into his condition, stating that he had come to the hospital originally "to study mental illness." His thinking was schizophrenic. The doctor felt that Haverford would soon be back in the hospital but with misgivings, urged him to apply himself to the law. He also told Haverford he would be discharged from the hospital, hoping this would increase the "push" on Haverford. The doctor wrote, "All these steps would not be taken in a routine case, but they are to be tried here because of this man's outstanding education and the feeling that so much is to be gained in his case."

All failed. Less than six months later he was brought back. He had quit his job. One day he had ordered his mother to prepare dinner, had stood over her while she did so, then, when she put the meal on the table, had turned the table upside down and ordered, "Get down on your knees and clean it up." He had locked the doors. He had ordered his mother to chop up the table. She wouldn't, so he did, with a hatchet. His father had tried to get in. Haverford had pushed him away. His father had called the sheriff.

He was diagnosed catatonic schizophrenic. On the ward he sat. One day he attacked an attendant and it took three men to hold him. The hospital gave him intensive treatment—EST, insulin, work on the ward, work in the recreational department. Dr. Kovitz attempted psychotherapy with him and he went home for a while but soon he returned, this time voluntarily. He was in good contact with reality, said nothing bizarre. But several times he had gone through what Kovitz thought were brief catatonic episodes—once he slapped a man on the street because he was puffing a cigar in a way that Haverford suddenly found intolerable—and he had returned as a voluntary patient to discover the reason for his tension and impulsiveness.

He was given EST—he had one hundred ESTs between 1947 and 1951—and insulin shock. He got worse. He broke an attendant's nose and blacked his eye "for no reason at all." He began having convulsive seizures. He made no progress. After three years of this the chief psychologist, Dr. J. T. Carter, took him in hand for psychotherapy, one hour a week. It did little good. After two years Dr. Carter felt his relationship with Haverford was still tenuous.

In 1954 the hospital conducted its first experiment with the new drugs, Thorazine and Serpasil, and Haverford was one of the patients who received Serpasil. It calmed him; his outbursts ceased. He went to OT. He was interested in baseball. He read. He wrote for the hospital newspaper. But he spent a good deal of time sitting on the ward, doing nothing. Dr. Carter suggested to Dr. Hippert that she do nothing more about him until Haverford approached her. So far, he had not.

11.

Now at 2 p.m. the afternoon shift attendants came to work, and Stratton went home. There were three of them—Delmar McClaskey, a tall slender clean-cut good-looking young man with black wavy hair; Alphas Shafer, a burly loud good-natured man standing six foot two and weighing 230 pounds; and Robert Rurode, a smaller quieter younger man. They were joking about whom to send up to Ward 12. "We could send them this fellow," McClaskey said, holding up a card.

"Sure," said Shafer, laughing, "send him—he's a good man."

"A little disgusting at times."

"And this is one of the times." They called Dr. Hippert, and she told them whom to send.

Changing shifts, the nurse and McClaskey counted the medicines, particularly the narcotics, and recorded the amounts on hand; then she left.

McClaskey and Shafer made up the evening medications. Patients kept coming in and out of the office, wanting things. Shafer, big and burly, spoke to them gruffly, demanding, "What do you want?" in an almost menacing tone but they seemed to know he meant well and was kind underneath, was all bark and no bite, and they did not resent it, they even seemed to enjoy it. The new man with the toothbrush came in and asked, "Any chance of getting out so I can get a job on the outside?" and McClaskey told him seriously, "I don't think so, tonight," and he left. In the hall three or four patients were talking to visitors, only half-concealed behind the folding screen. This was a busy time of day. At three o'clock the loudspeaker boomed. "It is three o'clock, visiting hours are over."

Shafer waited a few minutes. Not all the visitors had left. He went to the screen and said, "Time to go, folks," and waited. Three Negro women got up and the patient they had been visiting shuffled back to the porch. The old man who had been afraid his heart could not stand EST, Cyrus Thatcher, got up and so did his wife. Shafer opened the door to the outside and the Negroes left. Thatcher kissed his wife and as she reached the door he called, "Watch crossing the street," then stood and watched the door close behind her; he looked happy.

Shafer went into the kitchen. It was 3:20. He unlocked and raised a little panel in the wall. It opened into a dumb waiter shaft. He pulled a chair in front of it and tilted back on two legs and planted himself there, remarking, "Otherwise they'd crawl down and get out. A fellow did that once." A patient who worked in the kitchen asked, "How's it going?"

Shafer, big and comfortable, said, "Won't do no good to complain. How much bread we got?" Six loaves, said the patient, counting. "We better get some more." Shafer poked his head into the dumb waiter shaft and listened. Presently he heard a sound below and hollered down for more bread. He bantered with a friend down there. Four or five patients were clustered around him, enjoying it.

McClaskey came in and Shafer said they'd better get one of their good kitchen workers back from another ward, they had one man here who didn't do much. A patient gave the attendants coffee. The light in the kitchen was dim, only a single unshaded bulb dangling by a cord. The rope in the dumb waiter shaft trembled and with a clatter the food came up—trays of bread and chocolate cake, battered tin canisters of beans and coleslaw and meat balls. Shafer slammed and locked the panel and all fell to work, attendants and patients alike, McClaskey bringing utensils from the office, Rurode cutting cake and Shafer bread with sharp knives, patients ladling out the food and filling the compartmented trays, other patients carrying the trays to the dining room; the assembly line worked smoothly.

Shafer and Rurode went out to the porch and took a large Negro by the arms and led him to a seclusion room. Shafer put him in a corner facing the wall, reached around his waist, expertly unfastened his pants and unbuttoned his shirt, told him to step out of his pants when they fell to the floor, removed his shirt while leading him to sit on the bed, took off his shoes and, while Rurode was stretching him out on the bed, tossed his clothes in a heap to the door, where the ancient patient who helped here gathered them up in a bundle and took them to a closet; it was all done in a trice. Shafer and Rurode locked the door and walked back to the porch. They seemed unhurried but nothing took them long. On the porch a patient was pacing, another was reading a magazine, another was listening to the radio, most were just sitting. They beckoned to Sidney Harrison. He was sweating profusely. He did not move. They took his elbows and lifted gently and he got up, and they propelled him forward, and he staggered limply, and they half-supported, half-dragged him down the long corridor to the seclusion room where they put him to bed and locked him in. They got the others, the same six that had been locked in last night. The old shuffling Austrian put their clothes away. He never got the clothes mixed up. He had full privileges but nobody could get him to leave the ward. He had been here over thirty years.

Shafer went to the office and got the tray of pills. Most of the men due for medication were already there, waiting, and he gave it to them. Then he went halfway down the cross corridor and bellowed, "Let's go," and they were seated and eating at 3:55. As they sat at table they looked, above all, disheveled and young. The attendants moved among them; they took trays to the seclusion rooms; they moved expertly, men who knew what they were about. It all seemed familiar and ordered and sensible and somehow remarkably safe.

They had finished eating by 4:10. Shafer left ahead of them. He went halfway down the cross hall and planted himself, remarking, "The ones that go prowling around at night, shutting doors, opening doors, getting in other patients' beds, we put them to bed right after supper so they won't get hurt," and as the line of men came down the hall heading for the porch he plucked five patients from it and led them into five single rooms here in the cross hall and bade them undress. McClaskey helped. They took the new man out of line, and he wanted to know where they were taking him and Shafer told him, "Here's your room," and pushed him gently to it, and he went, a trifle reluctantly, saying, "That's a lobectomy of the respiratory system," and Shafer said, "I don't know about that but take your clothes off and pile 'em in the hall."

Finished, he and McClaskey went back to the office for a breather. It had been a busy two hours and a half. Shafer remarked, "We put new patients that we don't know anything about either there or in the annex—not in the dormitory. If you don't they may get hurt and the accident report comes back on you. This ward here, you got a lot of combative people right off the street that think they're getting gypped being put here. This new medication is controlling a lot of guys. It's even getting some out of here for a while. Whether they'll stay I don't know but it's something."

The new man came in: "Say, s'pose I could have some sheets?"

"Aren't there none?"

"Yeah, but they're filthy and dirty."

"Okay, I'll get you some."

The kitchen crew was hard at work. Shafer said, "You've got to run the ward any way you can. We get along pretty good because we've worked together quite a while. If the attendants quarrel among themselves, the patients know it and fight 'em." He was filing the end off a glass ampule and filling a syringe. It is clear why often the ward records on individual patients are sparse: Attendants have little time. The sneering man from Cleveland came in, and Shafer gave him a shot of Sandril.

Out in the hall an enormous globular patient, childlike, a simple schizophrenic who has been here for years, was hollering and yelling. McClaskey laughed. "Jimmie Fisher's raising the devil. He does it all the time. He'll do it at the door and you ask what he said and he'll say, 'Oh, nothing, dear soul, I was just talking to myself.' He runs off every once in a while, gets homesick. He used to wring his hands a lot. One time he was getting everybody upset doing it and Shafer and I decided to put him in a room. Remember?" Shafer, weighing 230 pounds, grinned. "He wrung his hands so hard he bounced both of us against the wall. He didn't mean to fight. He takes spells rubbing his ears, or hitting them," probably because the voices bother him, "and he's rubbed great big cauliflowers onto them."

Shafer went back to the seclusion rooms, checked the patients, and picked up their trays. Returning, he passed Jimmie Fisher, a giant walking up and down with a simple serious look on his fat face, saying, "He's Jim E. Fisher, yes sir, that's who he is, he's Jim E. Fisher," but saying something else too, unintelligible. He first came here in 1932. He had been going with a girl and wanted to marry her but she had refused until he got a job and the only job he could find didn't pay enough to support a wife—only a dollar a day, and three-fourths of that went to chiropractors, for he had pains in his back. A chiropractor told him not to marry for at least eight months "because he was too weak sexually"; this worried him, as sex always had worried him, and he became depressed and wept and pulled the buttons off his clothes and finally came to the hospital, diagnosed "psychoneurosis, neurasthenia and feeble-minded." When he got out he married his girl; she bore a child but it died after two days; she divorced Jimmie, and soon he was back, and he had been here or at another hospital most of the time since. Once a doctor had noted on his records, after a dozen years of hospitalization, "There is no record of any treatment and there is no mental improvement." Almost surely he would die here. Now he followed Shafer into the office and knelt on the floor and talked a while, then left, for it was time for him to go to work: He had a job scrubbing at Awl cottage, one of the few patients on this ward with a paid job; he got two dollars a month, and it worked out well, except that some nights he forgot to come in but sat down on a big boulder out on the lawn, and Shafer had to yell at him from a window at lights-out time.

12.

McClaskey and Shafer fell to talking about their work. Although this was a disturbed ward it was rare to have as many as ten seriously disturbed patients at one time. "A lot depends on how well you know the patients," McClaskey said. "Sometimes the only way you can run the ward is by strength. But the biggest majority of the time, if you stay on one ward you get to know the patients well enough so you can see if they're going to have to be locked up, you can see it coming on several hours or a day ahead of time, and you can head it off. They'll start talking to themselves, or start fussing with their clothes; they'll get up and walk, or take their clothes off, or won't eat, or will hog their food down."

Shafer said, "One patient, when he sits with his hands over his eyes, you want to watch him."

McClaskey nodded, saying, "And if one fellow blows up pretty soon the whole ward'll be in an uproar. But if you can spot him and put him in a room, the whole place stays quiet. We used to have more leeway—nowadays the nurses don't want you to put a patient in till you have to, and sometimes you get in trouble. We three are here all the time and we've got it worked out pretty well. Three men can handle it real nice."

The kitchen work was done, the kitchen workers were in the hall watching television, and a few patients from the porch drifted in. The hospital does not censor television. Patients never react violently to violent programs. They do not react to many things as do the sane. Some patients refuse to watch television, thinking it controls their minds. In psychotic delusions in recent years television has replaced high-tension wires as the agency of evil influence. Television in mental hospitals is used to some extent as a substitute for occupational therapy and recreational therapy. It does give patients something to do, or, rather, something to look at. But many doctors consider it so passive that it is harmful.

McClaskey, standing in the doorway watching them, said, "We seldom have to restrain a man here. We had one the other night we had to, a new admission. He was having seizures on 2 and rolled off the bed and they brought him back here and we put him in a seclusion room and put cuffs and a bed belt on him."

Shafer said, "They had a patient killed on 24 like that once. He was fastened by one hand and one foot and somehow he killed himself."

McClaskey said, "We don't use restraint enough here sometimes. We had one old fellow that wouldn't lie in bed, he'd lie on the floor, which was okay, but one time he scooted around and around on the floor till he got floor burns that amounted to second- or third-degree burns. His wife was very upset about that, and she thought an attendant had hurt him."

Shafer said, "If you want to lose your job, just punch a patient. You're allowed to handle them but as far as knocking them down and punching them, that's out. There's no chance of getting by with it. You have to make out an accident blank on every injury, no matter how little it is."

McClaskey said, "A few years ago these places were snake pits. Attendants beat hell out of a patient if he didn't do what they wanted. Now we're getting so much treatment and medicine that we're beginning to counteract it. I've seen some wonderful recoveries on this ward. I could name a dozen patients admitted to this hospital in the last fourteen months—and I mean in bad shape, locked up in seclusion rooms—and by God they're back on the street today. And if a person can see recoveries like that—"

Shafer said, "We had one guy, he was bad, we cuffed him, he busted the door, he lay on his back and kicked us; well, he got treatment and in less than a week we had him working in the kitchen, and he's home now, a salesman right here in Columbus. It's a funny thing about this place. The wilder they come in, the quicker they recover."

McClaskey said, "When I see a patient coming through that door, I like to see him coming through fighting, tearing the hell out of this place."

The old Negro who had refused to sign the check for his wife came to the door and asked anxiously what had happened about the check. These attendants didn't know anything about it; it had happened on the earlier shift, and Social Service hadn't notified the ward what it had done. They told him to ask the doctor tomorrow.

It was time to take patients to the movie. Rurode went to the porch and rounded up eight or ten; any could go who wished for they would be under lock all the way but no more wanted to go; Shafer counted them and Rurode took them out, picking up other patients from Ward 4 and Ward 6 as he went.

McClaskey said, "That's another thing—the patients should have more recreation. Last Saturday night a Lutheran church group came in and brought pie and coffee and had a party for one or two wards in the clubroom. If we could get more groups like that to come in it would help a lot. But people are afraid to be around mental patients. It's silly, but they are."

Shafer said, "Here's another thing. If we could get 'em off these wards. I'd like to see a fence built so we could let 'em out to exercise around. We had a few patients that sat on that porch and didn't want to do nothing, didn't know beans from apple butter, and we'd get to talking to them, get 'em to the kitchen to work, to the OT shop, and they're gone now, gone home. Sure they may come back. But at least they're out for a while."

McClaskey said, "I do think the hospital does a wonderful job with what it has. But it could do more. The commissary ought to be enlarged and set up next to Broad Street, so outsiders could stop and buy stuff."

Shafer said, "They wouldn't come in. People are afraid of these places. We have open house every year when we let the public come in but we ought to do more with it. I don't mean show 'em just the best wards, but the whole thing—get people to go through and see what we're trying to do here. If they only knew, I think they'd help. These places are not the best places in the world to be. But you got to have 'em. And it takes somebody to run 'em. And a little entertainment helps."

13.

Shafer, a burly man of thirty-nine who walks with head thrust forward, was a farmer and a laborer before he became a mental hospital attendant. He has a high school education. He got married and got out of the army in 1947, took veterans' farm training and bought a little farm near Gallipolis, an Ohio River town where the chief industry is a state mental hospital. "I spent all I could rake and scrape trying to make a living," he said, "and when I was out of training the stock was paid for but the farm wasn't, so I came to Columbus to get a job." Like many men who come up from Gallipolis, he looked naturally to the state hospital for a job. In 1955 he was paid fifty dollars a week. He had three children and paid fifty-five dollars a month rent for a three-room apartment in town. "You have to stretch your money," he said. Shafer was considered a good steady attendant and it seemed likely he would stay at the hospital. He said, "You get aggravated and feel like quitting sometimes but I've seen lots quit and come back. This work gets under your skin. Somebody has got to work these places, and if you like it you better stick."

McClaskey was several years younger and had worked here only since August of 1954 but already he was considered an outstanding attendant and one with a future, probably as a supervisor. He too came from Gallipolis—"I was born and raised in a country town out of Gallipolis and my father was a farmer and drove the school bus"—and indeed he worked a year at the state hospital there. He had a service station for a while but it was not successful and he sold it when he got a chance. "My wife was bound to go to work, so I said, 'Hell, we'll go up to the nuthouse and go to work.'" They both became attendants. At first they had lived in an apartment on the third floor of the hospital and were able to save two hundred dollars a month, the earnings of one of them, for the hospital charged them only forty dollars a month for room and board and laundry. But "the food got rotten" and he and his wife had to share a bath with about twenty-five other attendants and their wives, so they moved out. McClaskey liked the work, though not the pay, and intended to make a career of it.

The 1955 legislature raised the pay of doctors but not of attendants; a good many attendants quit. Their pay started at $200 a month and went up to $240 after five years. Charge attendants, who had charge of a ward, got up to $264. Many men worked here and at the same time held down a job in a factory or another hospital. One attendant worked the afternoon shift at St. Anthony's Hospital, got off at 10:30 P.M., hurried out here, reported for duty at 11 P.M. and worked till 7 A.M. This does not conduce to efficiency. Attendants here worked forty-four hours a week. Many quit to take higher-paid jobs in industry. Some left to become guards at the Ohio State Penitentiary downtown, where the pay was slightly higher. The turnover of attendants was high—about 90 per cent in a year.

An attendant can make or break a ward. A poor attendant can undo the best efforts of a good psychiatrist. The doctor may prescribe but it is the attendant who performs. The doctor is on the ward for a half-hour a day; an attendant is there twenty-four hours. In a very real sense, everything an attendant does is psychotherapy—it may be good for the patient or bad for him but it affects his psyche. Yet the attendants were untrained people. Most were farmers or laborers. This work has advantages over common labor—is steadier, is done indoors, has a retirement plan. Many attendants come here from southern Ohio, Kentucky and West Virginia—worn-out coal mining and farming country. Many have worked at other state hospitals, especially Gallipolis. Sometimes state hospital work runs in the family—a man gravitates to this work because his father did it. Some apply because their friends work here, some are drifters who wander in, some are elderly farmers for whom farm work is too heavy, some are young men out of school waiting for another job to open up, and some are mentally ill persons themselves, afraid to seek hospitalization but hoping to get help indirectly. In 1955 there were 248 attendants for three shifts on the 40 wards in the entire institution—two per ward per shift. More than half were women. (No men worked on the female side of the hospital; 21 women worked on the male side.) The hospital also employed 28 registered nurses.

Ideally, perhaps, all attendants would be nurses but there are only 11,000 nurses in the United States (and, according to the American Hospital Association's average daily census of 1957, there were 722,001 patients in mental hospitals and 633,791 patients in other hospitals). The shortage of psychiatric nurses is frequently called more serious than the shortage of psychiatrists. Attendants often are called "lay attendants" who "assist" the nurses, but actually in most state hospitals the attendants run the wards, even in such hospitals as Columbus State, where registered nurses technically have authority over them.

Since attendants' pay was low and the work repels many people, the hospital could not establish high qualifications for applicants. Indeed, it had no set requirements except that an attendant had to be a citizen of the United States, a resident of Ohio and between the ages of eighteen and seventy. He needed no special prior experience, no minimum education and, unlike some states, no political sponsorship. The superintendent said, "We want them to be able to read and write—" though not all could—"and we make them fill out the application blanks themselves, right in front of us." The hospital had at least one ex-convict as an attendant (in fact, he had been hired while on parole from a five-to-thirty-year sentence for burglary at Ohio State Penitentiary, his second conviction). Psychologists gave applicants a test designed to estimate whether they were likely to make good attendants.

What makes a good attendant? One psychiatrist has said that good attendants are people who long for passive care and affection from others and can therefore identify with a sick person and can help themselves by sublimating their own need in helping him. The doctors at Columbus State feel that a good attendant is not exceptionally intelligent or educated—if he is he will not follow doctors' orders but will initiate treatment himself—nor on the other hand is he so downright dull-witted that he is incapable of following orders. Dr. Kovitz has said, "If he has problems of his own he is more likely to be interested in the patients and their problems, and if he can handle his own problems successfully he can probably help them." Patients respond to an attendant who is firm but is kind and interested in them. McClaskey has said, "If you're mean to these patients they'll hate your guts but if you're firm but good to 'em they'll do anything in the world for you. I've been attacked in the hall by a patient and had a half-dozen other patients jump in to help me." Usually an attendant who fails is afraid of the patients. Being afraid, he is likely to mistreat them, and even if he doesn't he can't help them. To overcome this and other common attitudes the hospital requires its attendants to go through a training course. It is valuable in a formal way—teaches attendants how to handle violent patients without hurting them, reassures them that mental illness is not contagious and that by no means all mental patients are dangerous—but it can't do much more: There is no substitute for experience.

The work is probably not so dangerous as most people think. Hospital employees are injured at the rate of about 10.5 injuries in each million man-hours of exposure. This is roughly one-third the rate for coal miners but three times the rate for auto workers. Once the night supervisor at Columbus State was sitting in the office on Ward 14 when a patient hit him on the head from behind with the headrest from a barber chair. Whenever a patient anywhere in the hospital becomes unmanageable, a call for help goes to Ward 8. Once, answering such a call, McClaskey found a patient wielding a table leg and daring anyone to approach; with other attendants he picked up a bedspring and advanced and they subdued the patient, but not before he had clubbed one of them on the head. Once Shafer and a three-hundred-pound attendant, called to a woman's ward to deal with a little one-legged woman, talked her into going to her room but when they turned to leave she knocked the bigger man down, jumped on him and beat him severely. On an average day four or five injury reports come to the superintendent's office—an attendant bruised a knee in a fall, one cut her hand on a can opener, one was hit in the nose by a patient he was weighing, one was hurt while chasing a patient who dived through a screen door to escape, one was hit on the head with a flowerpot, one was knocked down and kicked in the ribs and had her hair pulled out by a patient, one trying to separate two fighting women was herself knocked down and kicked in the stomach.

The work is more likely to be unpleasant than dangerous. One morning McClaskey opening the seclusion room of a new patient, found that during the night he had disrobed and smeared feces all over his body. McClaskey and two other attendants, using towels, grabbed him and started to take him to the shower. But his body was slippery and he broke loose. "I mean he really went wild," McClaskey has recalled. "There was nothing to do but grab him, so I did, and we rolled on the floor together. I managed to hold onto him and the others got hold of him and we slid him onto a sheet and dragged him to the shower and rolled him under it. We all had to take a shower. Once in a while you do get into messes around here. He got EST and was transferred to another ward and he's getting along real fine now."

Superintendent Wedemeyer said in 1955, "It has been a long time since I fired anyone for mistreating a patient, though I won't say it hasn't happened without my knowing it." Some years ago beatings had not been uncommon. Now the safeguards against them were numerous. The ward doctor had to approve all accident reports, examine the patient, and send a copy of the report to the superintendent. If an attendant beat a patient and did not make out an accident report, the injury might be observed and reported by the ward doctor, the nurse, the attendants' supervisor, or the chaplain or assistant superintendent, both of whom visited the wards regularly. Several attendants had been fired or had quit under pressure for other reasons—one for drinking at the hospital, another for taking a female patient out of the hospital without authorization (he was discovered when she wouldn't return and he had to call the police).

14.

A little before 7 P.M. McClaskey and Shafer left the office and walked around the ward. In the dim-lit dormitory six or seven patients had already gone to bed. "They think their day's over," McClaskey remarked. Out on the porch about fifteen men were rocking or talking or staring out the window at the night. The kitchen and dining room were scrubbed, everything put away neatly. "You never have to be in here—the crew goes right ahead," McClaskey said. He unlocked the ancient wooden icebox and, reaching behind the penicillin, got milk and cake for himself and Shafer and they stood there munching it and talking about their ward workers.

McClaskey said, "They'd rather be in the kitchen than sitting around on the porch not doing anything. It's better for them too. It helps some as much as treatment. Keeps their interest up." Dr. Kovitz, the clinical director, agrees, adding, "Ward work is good for some patients provided the right spirit is kindled and it isn't just enforced drudgery." Dr. Hippert has said, "We couldn't run a ward without patient help. That's the main reason that about a third of the patients on 8 are chronic—the personnel has to depend on patients to help with the work, and acute disturbed patients can't help much. Of course it's good for some patients to have something to do—but some of these people have been doing the same thing for years and I don't think they're getting much of a therapeutic nature out of it. Some doctors think that willingness to work indicates something to build on in a therapeutic sense. But I don't think the reverse is true—that a patient who doesn't want to work on the ward has a poor prognosis. I don't think I'd want to wash dishes in this place if I were a patient here."

At 6:55 P.M. a buzzer rang, and Shafer unlocked the back door and the privileged patients filed in and headed for the porch. They were due in at seven. They were all here. "They usually come in," McClaskey said. Did any ever try to escape? "Hardly ever from inside here. Of course, if three or four took a notion to go out of here you couldn't stop 'em. They could gang you, take your keys, take you back to a seclusion room and lock you in, and you could pound and holler till you was blue and nobody'd hear you. That's why at night, when there's nobody much around, we check in with the operator every hour. One time seven of 'em planned to kill the night attendant with an iron pipe and escape when he made bed check. Another patient tipped off the attendant and he called in help and shook the place down. He found the pipe all right—two feet long."

In the hall now about twenty men were watching television. Shafer gave an evening paper he had sent out for to one of them. He took it without a word. He'd pass it on to the others. Another, a husky young man in a plaid shirt, got up and slouched out to the porch. He had had EST this morning. His eyes looked vague. Shafer, watching him go, said, "There's a rough one when he gets upset. He'll walk by you and knock you from here to there for nothin'. When you see them pants of his drop down low and his shirt tail come out, you better watch him." On his file in the front office was pasted a large red star, a warning used some years ago that a man was very dangerous. He had been red-starred in 1952, after he had attempted to attack his mother sexually while home on trial visit and, returned to the hospital, had attempted to attack a female patient. Shortly after he had been lobotomized. He was now on drugs and maintenance EST and though not combative or destructive of late, he was being handled warily.

About 7:45 P.M. a patient came to the office for a shot of penicillin, another for a shot of insulin for diabetes. A patient complained that another patient on the porch was throwing the ping-pong balls and paddles out the window; the attendants put the culprit in a seclusion room. The new man, still wandering around, tagged along after them and back at the office talked to them about his knowledge of shorthand, about how he used to be a teacher (he never had been), "but I should of got married, I'd be better off, it's not so good to go to the opera," and he rambled on and on until Shafer, tired of listening to him, said loudly, "I thought you wanted some sheets." "I do." "Well, there they are," and pointed to them on the desk where he had put them a couple of hours ago. The patient took them and left.

A patient wanted a razor blade to trim his corns; they refused. An old man came in and picked up a cigar off the desk and left without a word. Every day at the commissary he bought cigarettes, which he gave away, and five cigars, which he gave to the attendants for safekeeping; out of cigarettes by night-fall, he retrieved the cigars and broke them up and smoked them in his pipe. One patient was always sending to the store for garters; he never wore them, just unraveled them.

The sneering little man from Cleveland came in to insult the attendants for a while. They ignored him. After he left McClaskey observed, "He's gotten to be a pest since he's been on Sandril."

The elderly Negro who had been worried about the check wondered if he could get a job working in the kitchen, he used to be a good worker on Ward 4. Shafer said, "That's right—the attendant there told me about you."

McClaskey said, "Let's give him a job."

Shafer asked, "You want a job?"

"Sure. I'd rather be workin' than settin' around."

"Come up tomorrow night, we'll give you a job."

He left, pleased.

Every few minutes a patient would step in with a cigarette in his mouth; McClaskey or Shafer would light it, and he would leave without speaking. At eight o'clock McClaskey called the telephone operator to report all well. (If he didn't she would send help.) Soon the patients returned from the movie. Some went to the porch, some watched television. McClaskey said, "We never bother the patients, never fool with 'em, unless they start trouble. They'd rather be among themselves," smiling, "just like us—we're not sorry to see the doctor leave." McClaskey liked his work and he liked this ward. "I go through the ward and I don't feel a bit different than I do walking on Broad Street. In fact I'd rather be on this ward than in Lazarus' store downtown when it's crowded—there you never know who's going to try to slip your wallet out of your pocket. Here I can go around among the patients and it don't bother me a bit. Some people can't do it. It gets on their nerves. But this ward here, if a person wants to learn anything about the hospital, he can learn it on this ward—medications, shots, treatments, seclusion, anything, we have more of it than anybody in the hospital. That's why I like this ward. And you're doing something for the patients. The big thing is not to make them afraid. I talked to a former patient once and he was telling me that when a patient first comes here he's afraid of the hospital. Well, if he's beaten, he gets more afraid. If a person's fear keeps growing bigger, all the treatments you can give 'im aren't going to make 'im better. You know, after you work around here a while you get a feeling for these guys. I believe there are people that lives within twenty miles of this hospital that don't realize the hospital even exists. Before I went to work at Gallipolis I used to drive past it but I had no idea what went on inside."

It was 9 P.M. He checked in with the operator again, then he and Shafer got up and stepped into the hall and Shafer yelled, "Let's go, boys." Only six were still watching television. One, a serious young man wearing glasses, snapped the television off and unplugged it and carefully wheeled it down the hall to a closet; he did that every night. The others walked down the cross hall to the porch, Shafer and McClaskey following, opening doors on the private rooms, looking in at the patients asleep, locking the doors, peering in at the dormitories. Nearly everybody was already in bed. On the porch all but one were undressing by the time the attendants arrived. Shafer told the laggard to hurry up and he did, muttering resentfully. The patients piled their clothes in little heaps around the porch, as the others had done, then walked barefoot in their underwear to the dormitories. One went past the dormitory; Shafer chased him and told him to go to bed. He was a wizened little old man; he said, "You shut your damn mouth and keep it shut," but he went into the dormitory.

Shafer and McClaskey and Rurode went into the dormitories, switching the lights on and making bed check on a clipboard. They found one patient in bed with his clothes on; Shafer hustled him to the porch, watched while he undressed, then brought him back. McClaskey found one in the wrong bed; he woke him up and moved him. They finished. In the dim half-light the beds were ranked in long neat white rows. One patient had made a tent of his sheet, fastening it to the head of the bed so he was completely hidden; he did that every night. It was quiet. Most patients were already asleep. The attendants checked the rooms in the hall and the seclusion rooms in the annex. The old Austrian was still puttering around the annex in half-darkness. They let him alone. They went back to the office to finish up their reports. Everybody was present except Jimmie Fisher, and he wasn't due till 9:30. Except for the scratch of McClaskey's pencil, the ward was quiet.

Leaving, one walked through Ward 4, where a couple of patients still were watching television, and Ward 2, where everybody was in bed and a mouse was scampering into the kitchen. Outdoors, the night was crisp, a fall haze in the air over the deserted hospital grounds, and on Broad Street, night traffic rolled quietly by; and after a day on the ward it was the outside world which suddenly seemed alien.

7

Lobotomy

■ The doctor who admitted Barbara
Little to Columbus State in 1949, and assigned her No. 01685, wrote:

This admittee, placed on Ward #5, is a 30-year old, white, unmarried
female who is tall, thin, undernourished, and ambulatory in a quite re-
stricted manner. She is co-operative, courteous, agreeable, spontaneously
loquacious and, in her inadequate way, attempts to aid the interviewer to the
best of her ability. She is oriented in all spheres, with moderate memory
defects for the recent and remote past events. Hypomobility, superficiality
of contact, emotional blunting, etc., are continuously present.

As to affect Miss Little states, "I am worried because I guess I am a
problem but I am just tired and worn out. I am afraid of nothing; only
that I may not be able to get this all straightened out. . . ."

She admits a preference for her own company, indicates that she has
engaged in social endeavor quite minimally during the past few years,
and declares, "I like to read and not be bothered."

The stream of talk is rather continuously irrelevant with goal idea
attainment frequently difficult.

Delusional perspectives, paranoid type, are expressed as the patient
relates, "People talk about me more than they do the average person. They
try to run down my reputation. They are after something I possess, a
most valuable bit of information which I have. I have often thought and
wish now that I could get in touch with the FBI. I can't give this information

to anyone but a lawyer or the FBI. I have been followed. I guess they were after the information, that's the only reason I can see. You know this is of great value. . . ."

Impression: This case appears to be a schizophrenic process with paranoid coloring and catatonic features.

Let us study Barbara Little's case and, through it, psychosurgery. For she has undergone not one but two brain operations.

2.

There are in every hospital patients on whom every treatment, including the most heroic, has failed. Such a person is Barbara Little. She was thirty years old when she came to the hospital, not really a pretty girl but one with an interesting face. It was a triangular face, the forehead high and broad, the chin narrow, the cheekbones high and prominent, the eyes wide-set, the lips heavily lipsticked. Her face seemed somewhat lopsided, twisted and pulled down on the side. Her hair was piled high and upswept in back. Her neck was a long and slender stem. Her collarbone showed clearly.

She was the youngest of several children; her parents were middle-aged at her birth. Her father, a minister, always had been a "soft-spoken, easy-to-get-along-with" man, interested in books; he was quite close to Barbara. Her mother was a college graduate. Nobody in either family ever had been mentally ill, so far as is known. Barbara graduated from high school, attended business college and went to work as a secretary. She was well liked at work and had an excellent rating.

Barbara suffers from schizophrenia but her prepsychotic personality was not the typical schizoid personality—not shy, shut-in, seclusive. Rather she was jovial, sociable, of an "even disposition." She made friends easily, went to many movies, "liked to be on the go." She was clean and neat. Clothes were her hobby. In her whole social history can be found but a single ominous note—she showed no interest in boys until she was eighteen or nineteen years old.

Dr. Kovitz, discussing Barbara's case, said, "In about a third of schizophrenics the prepsychotic personality shows no overt withdrawal or shyness. Often they are the most difficult of all for us to treat. They are people who always seemed to be the picture of health. But the health isn't genuine. The shyness, the withdrawnness, is there—but it is hidden beautifully. From the minute such a person began to deal with people, she learned to hide her inner feelings. And for a while it worked fine. But it won't work forever—sooner or later she runs into a situation where she can't hide her feelings. This doesn't have to be a major disaster, a huge problem. Sometimes it can be simply the challenge of growing up. Of developing a relationship with men."

What situation arose that Barbara Little couldn't handle we do not know. The records show only that, three years before she came to the hospital, she suddenly quit working because she "suffered from nervous exhaustion." For days on end she wept. Her parents took her to a doctor, a general practitioner, telling him that her depression was the result of a disappointment in love: Her boy friend had promised to marry her but had gone into the army instead. The doctor gave her a mild sedative and told her that probably everything would turn out for the best since she had known the boy friend but briefly.

She apparently got along all right for two years. In 1949 her parents asked a private psychiatrist to call on her, and he found her at home, confused, weeping, talking to herself, hearing voices and believing that others were talking about her and persecuting her. Prognosis guarded. He ordered her to a private hospital, gave her fourteen ESTs, and reported that she "made a very dramatic recovery."

But it didn't last. In a private sanatorium she was diagnosed schizophrenic and given six more ESTs. She showed little change. She was violent and had to be kept in restraint. Her parents had spent all their money on treatment. And she was too sick to be home. Yet they could not bring themselves to sign commitment papers that would send her to a state hospital. The psychiatrist signed them, and she was taken to Columbus State, where so many others wind up after all else has failed.

3.

She was given No. 01685 and taken to Ward 5. She was quiet, cooperative and oriented. To a psychiatrist she said, "Why am I here? Well, because I was rather confused, for one thing. General confusement, I'd say. Very seriously so, and also I was told by the gentleman that came to the sanatorium that I could make a sort of contact here— a phone call. I felt I needed some sort of legal advice. I was very unhappy there. I don't remember my exact words to the doctors there before I severed my connections when I made the suggestions." Only after much prompting did she reveal there was a conspiracy against her, the nature of which she refused to divulge, and she denied hearing voices or seeing visions. (Such patients often are as expert at concealing their psychotic symptoms as they were at concealing their true feelings before their psychotic break.) "I am not mentally ill. I am tired. I need rest." The staff diagnosed her as schizophrenia, mixed type, paranoid and catatonic. She was given insulin shock. She complained a good deal; attendants found her "demanding." She was moved to a chronic ward and her insulin continued. She seemed to improve, gained weight, was more co-operative, and was allowed to go home with her mother for a day. Returning she became nervous, confused, frightened, and paced the hall till 1:30 A.M., when the night attendant gave her a sleeping pill. Next day she was badly disturbed, very noisy. She became resistive and combative and refused to eat.

Abruptly her condition changed: The attendant reported she was "much improved, clean, very neat, good mixer, is good ward worker." She was moved to Ward 5 and started on EST. She became afraid, upset, paced the hall constantly. One morning when she was due for EST she collapsed limply. Next day her mother sent her flowers; they upset her. She cried throughout her mother's visit. She lost her false teeth. The attendant wrote, "Condition very poor, crying, falling around over beds in dormitory. No sedatives given. Checked by doctor."

Then abruptly she improved again, was "quiet and co-operative, appearance neat and clean, appetite good, sleeps well." So she was sent back to a chronic upstairs ward, 27. In a few weeks she relapsed again —became excited and sarcastic, wept, lit matches in bed, wouldn't dress, wouldn't eat, talked and cried all through breakfast, upbraided herself for talking; and the attendants called the doctor, who ordered her back to Ward 7, the disturbed ward, before she blew up completely. After a week or so she was moved to Ward 5 again for EST and the whole weary rounds started over—on 5 till she leveled off, up to 27 till she became disturbed, then back down to 7 yelling and laughing and dancing and fighting, spitting at other patients and hitting them, put into restraint and seclusion.

This went on for three years. By then she had had a total of more than two hundred ESTs. This is too many. Dr. Kirch ordered EST stopped. But she could not be left untreated—she staggered around the halls, threw herself to the floor, wrecked furniture, spat at other patients and hit the attendants. The doctors tried EST again. The results were as before. On June 23, 1952, she blew up in the main dining room, while hundreds of patients were eating, and it took three attendants to drag her to Ward 7. They put her in a seclusion room; she tore up the sheeting and tried to wreck the bed; they restrained her and gave her a hypodermic sedative. Next day she was staring into space, seemingly mindless.

Something had to be done. What? The staff doctors consulted among themselves and called in their consulting neurosurgeon. Everything else had failed; they decided to perform a brain operation. Dr. Kovitz called her father in, and he signed a release authorizing the operation. The same day attendants took her out of her seclusion room, bathed her, sent her denture to the dental clinic for safekeeping, and took her to Ward 1, then a medical ward. She was operated on next day in the hospital's only operating room, a small tiled interior room just off the ward, fitted with an antiquated operating table and lacking modern safety devices.

4.

Now brain surgery as a treatment for psychosis is only about twenty years old. It was introduced in Portugal in 1935 and quickly brought to the United States. The operation was originally suggested by animal experimentation and by several human accidents, such as the famous "crowbar" case of 1848. In that year a man in Vermont had accidentally had an iron crowbar driven through the frontal region of his skull but he had lived for twelve years afterward. Before the accident he had been an efficient workman but after it his personality deteriorated, he decayed intellectually and emotionally, he lost the finer feelings, became childish, and was unable to hold a job.

It is thought that the fibers connecting the brain's frontal lobes and the thalamus are concerned in some special way with the relationship between the intellectual and the emotional aspects of mental activity. It is thought that cutting these fibers prevents pathological ideas from generating emotion. The surgeon seeks to cut these fibers so that emotional ideas no longer dominate the patient but yet so that sufficient frontal lobe is left intact to permit the patient to live usefully.

The surgical technique probably most widely used is prefrontal lobotomy. In it, the surgeon bores two holes in the patient's skull, one at each temple, about the size of a quarter; he inserts a delicate blade and severs the white fibers connecting the frontal lobes and the thalamus. He must work "blind," by touch alone, aided only by his knowledge of the anatomical landmarks; he cannot see what he is cutting and sometimes cuts more and sometimes less than he intends. (Some doctors make a larger opening and work visually.)

In topectomy, another technique, the surgeon removes a section of scalp and skull above the forehead and cuts away a portion of the gray matter of the frontal cortex itself. He can see what he is doing. He removes more matter than in lobotomy; the difference is between severing the connections between brain centers, as in lobotomy, and in actually removing a portion of the brain center itself, as in topectomy. Both these operations are performed under a local anesthetic unless the patient is violently disturbed; they may take up to an hour.

In transorbital lobotomy, a third technique, the patient is given two electroshocks and while he is still in a coma after his convulsion, the surgeon pushes an instrument shaped like an icepick through the sac behind the eyeball and drives it through the skull into the frontal lobe of the brain, severing the fibers between frontal lobe and thalamus by moving the needle up and down and from side to side. After the surgeon finishes working through one eye socket the patient is immediately given a third and sometimes a fourth electroshock and the surgeon works through the other eye socket. Some doctors use a conventional anesthetic, not EST. This operation also is, obviously, blind; it is very speedy, taking only a few minutes, and easy to perform, requiring no special preoperative preparation and being done on the ward. Some doctors have warned that it is too easy to perform and hence tends to be overused.

Brain surgery, when it was first introduced, was widely hailed as the long-sought method of treating psychosis, as from time to time many other methods have been hailed. Its use increased rapidly. Approximately 25,000 people had been operated on in the United States by 1955. And the operation helped some patients. They lost their anxiety, became cheerful and friendly, took an interest in themselves, even were able to work. The fearful hold of emotional tension seemed broken. But as time passed, doctors began to have second thoughts. Patients' feelings were coarsened and made shallow. They lacked sympathy, were irresponsible, seemed tactless, lazy, childish, silly. And in many cases results were much more disappointing. Some patients no longer climbed the walls of the ward but neither did they in any wise resemble "normal" men—they were nothing but vegetables. Some were no longer hallucinated; they simply seemed mindless. Some were worse than before they were operated on. Others developed new symptoms, convulsive seizures, for example. Some died during the operation or shortly after it.

Over the years, as psychosurgery spread doctors debated, sometimes acrimoniously, its wisdom and even its morality. Its critics argued that it is irreversible—once done, it can never be undone—and that nothing so radical should be done when so little is known. To this the surgeons replied that nonetheless the fact remained that the operation did help some patients. The severest critics said that psychosurgery amounted to an inhuman punishment inflicted on patients who would not behave —that it was a last desperate attempt to enforce conformity upon a patient after all else had failed. To which the surgeons replied that hospitals had to be managed some way and, further, if they could not make new men out of psychotic ones with a knife, they could at least relieve the terrible emotional pain of the most disturbed patients. Dr. Walter Freeman, a leading exponent of psychosurgery, said that of all the patients operated, 75 per cent have improved in the sense that their distress is lessened and their disturbing behavior reduced; 20 per cent were unimproved; 3 per cent were worse and 2 per cent were dead. Many of the patients, though improved, were unable to live outside hospitals.

Most hospitals tended to reserve psychosurgery as a last resort. (And surgeons pointed out that this may explain why they had no more successes—they were dealing with the most hopeless patients.) A few hospitals, particularly those backward understaffed custodial institutions in isolated areas, did little for their patients from day to day, then once a year called in a surgeon from the outside world to lobotomize the most unmanageable. But hospitals were using psychosurgery less and less and in many it had virtually disappeared. The main reason was that the new tranquilizing drugs, such as Thorazine and reserpine, tended to make the difficult patients manageable—those impulsive ones with intense emotion who formerly were lobotomized because nothing else could be done. Surgery, however, still is used in certain types of cases which the new drugs don't help.

Over the years Columbus State had operated about one hundred patients in all. About half of these had left the hospital, improved in varying degrees; the rest were still here. About a third of the total showed excellent results; a third were improved; a third were the same or worse. By 1955 the hospital had abandoned surgery. Drugs had taken its place. Moreover, neurosurgeons already had refused to operate here because they considered the postoperative care inadequate. Nursing is of the utmost importance, not only immediately after the operation but for as long as a year afterward, for a patient often forgets everything he ever learned, including toilet training and how to use a spoon. Columbus State, like most state hospitals, simply could not provide good enough nursing care.

5.

In 1952, however, when Barbara Little was operated on, Columbus State was performing a good deal of surgery. Let us see what effect it had on her. The surgery, a topectomy, was performed on June 26. After it, she was given 500 cc. of whole blood and 1000 cc. of dextrose in water immediately and phenobarbital and penicillin daily for ten days. She was very restless most of the time. Three weeks after the operation a doctor wrote, "It became obvious within a relative short time following surgery that the patient was mentally worse than she had been previously. During this interval the patient also picked at the incision and developed two circular infected areas which were slow to heal." The nurses tied her hands so she could not pick at her head. Two months after the operation, she was returned to her own ward, the disturbed ward, 7.

For a few days, she was quiet and co-operative. "Wanders around ward aimlessly," an attendant noted, "but does not bother anyone." She was accordingly transferred to a quiet acute ward, 3. Immediately she became very disturbed, wandering into other patients' rooms, urinating on beds. On September 4 she was moved to Ward 5 and kept on the porch with incontinent and unclad patients; that same night she had her first convulsion. It lasted about ten minutes; she fell face down on the floor. A doctor was called. She had another seizure at 4 A.M. and was put in seclusion. Next morning she was confused and silent. Moved to Ward 7, she fought the attendants putting her in seclusion and restraint. They kept her that way for nearly three weeks, tied down in bed, locked up alone in a bare little room with barred window, receiving no medicine or treatment. Every time they untied her she banged her head on the floor. Once she seemed better for a few days and was let out; but soon she was yelling at an imaginary person, telling them, "Stop or you will be killed"; and on October 11 she had another seizure. She had them regularly for two weeks. She wasn't epileptic, never had had seizures before the operation. (One authority, in a textbook written about the time Barbara was operated on, said that topectomy already had been virtually abandoned because it was so frequently followed by convulsions.)

This went on until early December, when the doctors decided to operate again. Accompanied by two attendants Barbara walked out to Ward 1 at 3 P.M., noisy and combative all the way; next morning a nurse shaved her head, gave her atropine, and took her to surgery at 9:20 A.M. This time the surgeon performed a lobotomy. She was returned from surgery at 12:15 P.M. still anesthetized. The nurse gave her glucose, took her temperature and blood pressure every fifteen minutes, and noted that she was "very restless—moving head about." Changing the dressing at 1:15 P.M. she found bright red blood on it. A doctor examined her. The nurse checked her every fifteen minutes all afternoon and evening; doctors came in and out; she responded when spoken to at 5:30 P.M.; she was restless till 9 P.M. At 2 A.M. she had a "light seizure," and the nurse called a doctor, who gave her caffeine and sodium benzoate.

Next day a doctor found she moved all extremities and responded well. She ate well, spent a good second night, and rested quietly the next day. She seemed "much improved"—quieter and more co-operative. On the fifth day 150 cc. of bloody fluid was aspirated from her head, and she sat up in a chair briefly. She was getting phenobarbital, streptomycin, penicillin and Dilantin, an anticonvulsant. She seemed to be progressing well, though the nurse had to tie her hands because she scratched at her incision, making it bleed. She was feeding herself and sitting up most of the day in a chair, and nineteen days after the operation, she was sent back to the disturbed ward, 7.

6.

For two weeks there Barbara couldn't stay awake long enough to feed herself and had to be spoon-fed. Then she began to improve—she would go to the bathroom by herself and if she did wet her bed she would get up and change the sheets herself. She was moved to Ward 5. But in another week she began to get into arguments with other patients; if they talked to her she became extremely agitated, and she was sent back to 7 "due to yelling and profanity."

There she would get dressed and spend the day sitting quietly on the ward but toward evening would begin to scream. Soon she was back in seclusion, then out again. A new ward doctor, Dr. Maria Madi, wrote, "She is back now on Ward 7, taking care of her appearance, explosive at times, pouring a deluge of verbal abuse on one of the old disturbed patients, quieting down abruptly, retiring into her room. Patient's insight is fair, has consciousness fair to clear, emotionally unstable, at times blocked, eruptive, verbally abusive, then underproductive the rest of the time. She belongs to a chronic ward."

Barbara began to help with the ward work. She was co-operative and polite much of the time. But occasionally she became disturbed and strode up and down the hall screaming curses at other patients, especially Negroes, and starting fights. Dr. Madi, thinking it might be better to get her out of the hospital occasionally, gave her permission to go home on short visits with her mother. She got along all right. Once she failed to return for six months. Her mother brought her back. For a time she had been fairly well except for occasional "nervous spells"; but then she had become "much worse"—very talkative, wouldn't eat, paid no heed to her mother.

She lasted two weeks on Ward 3 then got into a fight with another patient and was sent to Ward 7. She got along well and was sent to Ward 9. But then she had two grand mal epileptic seizures, severe enough for the attendant to notify the supervisor; and after that she was kept on Ward 7 or Ward 15, both disturbed wards. She was off and on EST irregularly. Occasionally her mother took her home but only for weekends—"She doesn't belong at home," said Dr. John W. Roper. Most any day he passed through Ward 7 he would see her striding up and down, a tall thin figure wearing a bright handkerchief wound turban-like around her head. Sometimes she played cards with another patient, a sociopath and alcoholic. She moved fast. Sometimes she spoke nervously to the doctor as he passed by—"Can I see you a minute, Dr. Roper? My left eye's bothering me again," and he would listen gravely and send her to the eye clinic, knowing there was nothing wrong with her eye. Once in a while a patient new on the ward insulted her till she couldn't stand it and fought; then she had to go to seclusion. "I've tried to talk to her," Dr. Roper said, "to get her to ignore the others but Barbara just can't do it." She was getting no treatment except EST when she became disturbed. "There's not much more we can do for Barbara," Roper said. "Lobotomy is pretty much of an end point. When she goes home, she stays in the house mostly, and friends and relatives come in to visit. The best sign I've seen is that a while back when she was home she made a date with a man to go to a ball game but then didn't keep it—she didn't think she could stand the excitement. This is pretty good for Barbara."

8

Something Like a Miracle

■ One day Dr. Kovitz was talking about difficult cases. He said, "I can think of one patient—well, the nurse told me if we didn't do a lobotomy on her she was going to kill someone. We didn't operate, yet she's home today and doing fine." Her name was Lillian Hill, and she made an almost miraculous return from the land of the living dead.

2.

When she came to the hospital, a withdrawn catatonic schizophrenic, her prognosis was not good and she went steadily downhill. She was youngest of many children born to a "quiet and bullheaded" working-man and a woman described as obstinate and hard to get along with. Lillian left high school to work in a factory. She always had been odd. She was nervous, shy, seclusive. She always kept things to herself. She refused to go into restaurants or other public places, saying, "I don't like people." If someone took her for a ride, she would ask him to avoid driving through town. She read avidly, especially love stories. She had few dates. She would go uptown only with her mother. She was un-attractive—a fat girl with meaty features, curly hair, double chin, small eyes and mouth, big nose and big face.

When she was twenty-five she married a factory worker, James Hill. They lived alone in the downstairs of a big old farmhouse. The upstairs was empty.

Marriage apparently was for Lillian Hill the crisis she could not meet. Moreover, almost immediately after her marriage a struggle for her affection began between her husband and her mother—a fierce and dreadful struggle that continued even after she broke down and came to the hospital.

She had been married only a short time when she accused her husband of seeing other women, complained of various physical ailments, and went home to her mother, weeping. Hill thought her mother was trying to break up his marriage. Her mother said Lillian wanted her marriage annulled. She called their family doctor, who "doctored her for her nervous condition," then advised her to see a psychiatrist. Her mother telephoned Hill; he "went into a terrible rage." Lillian went back to him. Two days later her mother called "and she was alone in a cold house and had not seen a doctor," so the mother had her son and his wife take her to Lillian's house; they would rescue her. "Lillian flew around the house, and gathered up all her personal belongings, hurrying so, because she feared Jim would come home before we could get away. She told us we should have brought more help along. . . . She asked us to drive as fast as we could to get away in plenty of time."

Lillian seemed better at her mother's house, her mother said, but then became so depressed and restless that the family doctor said he could do no more, she would have to enter a hospital for EST. Her mother called Lillian's husband; another stormy scene ensued. Hill put Lillian in a sanitarium; she was there three weeks and had five treatments. Hill took her home because, he said, she was improved; because, her mother said, he ran out of money. Her mother said Hill ignored the sanitarium's suggestion that he put Lillian into a state hospital for insulin treatment but, instead, found "a quack" who treated her with a worthless patent medicine, a treatment ended, the mother said, only by a court order she obtained which "forced" Hill to put Lillian into a sanitarium in Columbus. Jim Hill said simply that Lillian relapsed, and he put her in the Columbus sanitarium.

The warfare over Lillian continued there: Hill ordered that he alone was to be permitted to see her; her mother quarreled with him and telephoned the sanitarium repeatedly. Lillian went home to visit her husband for a day. Her mother and father and brother went to see her —"It was a wonderful reunion," the mother has said, but when Lillian went back to the sanitarium next day she was worse. This sort of thing went on for six weeks. ("As soon as Lillian was better," her mother once said, "she wrote me very sweet letters, reminiscing of all the things she and I used to do, our good times together, and especially our shopping trips. Understand, we want to do everything in our power, and in the right way to help Lillian back to her own sweet way of life.")

The doctors at the sanitarium said later that while on EST Lillian talked freely, displaying paranoid ideas, hallucinations and delusions. They stopped her treatments after eighteen. She promptly headed back into her mute, catatonic, negative state. The doctors told Hill he must plan for prolonged hospitalization, and that the outcome was uncertain because of her poor prepsychotic personality. The doctors added that the family friction was an unfavorable factor—"It is our impression that all of them have been somewhat stubborn and unreasonable." So in 1948 she was transferred to Columbus State Hospital, which, like most state hospitals, is asked so often to solve problems after everyone else has failed and indeed has seemed bent upon making them unsolvable. Let us see how Columbus State dealt with this one.

3.

She arrived at the hospital mute, in a catatonic stupor. Her face was blank. She stared straight ahead. If the examining doctor ordered, "Sit down," or "Walk toward me," she would do so, but that was all. If he made a sudden loud noise, she did not indicate she heard. If he lifted her arm and bent it and released it, she left it where he put it; when finally she moved it, she seemed confused. Once in a great while she laughed for no reason. Once she said, "I'm all mixed up. I don't understand." Otherwise she was silent. All this is classic catatonic schizophrenia. She had been pulled in many directions no doubt from childhood, and had been terribly hurt by the pulling and hauling. The warfare had turned inward, and her interior personality had been pulled to pieces. The conflicts within her immobilized her—she no longer knew whether she should raise her hand or lower it, so did neither. She had lost, or jettisoned, the power to deal with her hurtful surroundings, the power, indeed, to speak or move. She had retired within herself.

She was put on Ward 5. She had to be dressed and fed. She talked to no one. She did nothing but sit on a chair and stare into space. She was started on EST, one shock every three days, and after only two treatments improved markedly, making beds on the ward. After two weeks she was transferred to another ward; this was too much for her, and that night she blew up, choked a patient who slept near her and was taken to Ward 7, the disturbed ward, by the night nurse.

She was started on insulin shock. For a time she was fairly quiet and co-operative but then she became disturbed, was seclusive and resistive, and when anyone came to the ward door she screamed and hid her face. The doctors put her back on EST. But one day she very nearly died under treatment. The doctors moved her to a chronic ward and gave her a month's rest. She worsened, merely sat. Electro-cardiograms and other tests being normal, Dr. Handcock ordered EST resumed.

Now, one might have hoped that the bitter contest between her husband and her mother would cease in State Hospital, that the hospital would truly be for her asylum. It was not so. Hill complained that she was worse after her parents' visits and asked the doctor not to let them in. The doctor agreed. But her parents protested. Lillian began complaining because she could not see her relatives. The doctors decided to let them visit. More rows ensued; Hill protested; so did the relatives. The harassed doctor let both visit. He let Lillian go out for a day at a time with her husband. She returned from one holiday so combative that she was taken to Ward 21 and fastened in bed with belt and ankle cuff.

After several months she got well enough to work in the general dining room. She was given full privileges and then sent home for a five-day visit with her aunt, who subsequently wrote a two-page single-spaced typewritten report on the visit. She detailed Lillian's every move. The first evening a couple of Lillian's sisters and brothers and their husbands and wives dropped in. Lillian spent the next morning looking through snapshot albums, ate lunch, walked uptown with another sister and went window shopping "after which they enjoyed root beers and Cokes," then visited with her sisters and aunt. She helped cook dinner then went dancing with two of her brothers and their wives.

Next morning Lillian "did not lounge around in her robe, but dressed before coming downstairs for breakfast." She helped with the housework, then went calling on friends and relatives. "Her conversation with them was clear and intelligent, needing very little prompting." Just as she was retiring that night another sister brought her family to see her and stayed too long; she went to bed overtired. Next day more brothers and sisters called.

Lillian smoked cigarettes while she was with us, but not excessively, nor did she appear to have any craving desire for them. Lillian has acquired a good many mysterious and rather confused ideas concerning the Bible, and goes overboard, so-as-to-speak, in regards to her respect for the colored race. Many of her remarks concerning these subjects do make sense. . . . At no time did any of the relatives approach the subject [of her husband] or attempt to influence or encourage her ill feelings toward him. . . . Lillian seems to have the idea that the hospital is her home and that it is where she belongs; that she is not supposed, due to some reasons of God's, to live as other people. . . . She also believes the shock treatments are only a form of punishment and have nothing to do with helping her get well.

On the fifth day one of her brothers took her to Columbus and got her back to the hospital at 2:30 p.m. He left. Almost immediately her husband, Jim Hill, arrived. She didn't want to see him.

She visited her aunt again for Christmas. The visit went badly. Her aunt's husband wrote:

Her mind seemed to be confused, and she would make remarks which just didn't make any sense at all. . . . To make a long story short, Lillian made very little sensible conversation during her entire stay. [One evening] I told the girls if they could make arrangements for a baby sitter and be dressed, that when I returned, we would go out and enjoy a few dances if they wished. . . . I returned at 9:30 and found somewhat of a different situation. It seems that as soon as I left the house, Lillian became perturbed because we were not going to take the children along with us, and after her aunt explained that we never kept the children out that late nor took them to such places, but that we always had a baby sitter for such occasions, she became worse. My wife tells me that Lillian became raving mad and really put on a scene, screaming, etc. for about two or three minutes. She did nothing to try to stop her, letting her get it out of her system. . . .

4.

Back at the hospital Lillian was so disturbed she had to be put back on EST. The doctor advised the family not to take her out again for a few weeks. Her husband, Hill, came to visit; she refused to see him. The doctor wrote, "She is now under the influence of her family." The family took her out again, evidently hoping to keep her out, but soon brought her back: She was too excitable. Toward the end of January she got interested in her husband again and wanted to go home with him every weekend, not with her relatives. In February and March she went out alternately with husband and relatives; between times she received EST and kept other patients awake nights. In February of 1951 a doctor interviewed her and wrote:

> This patient has to have two more ESTs every few weeks, usually after contact with her people. She is disturbed and confused. "I went to heaven on a piano key and come back." Mentions a high school boyfriend whom her people disapproved. "Now wait a minute, there's an old black hat and a white, and there swinging around, changing colors. Don't let that change the U—U—USA." Ideas of reference are indicated as by exclaiming irritably regarding a patient on the hall, "O, let them laugh."

She got worse—ran around the hall, threatened an attendant, wouldn't get out of bed, giggled, had crying spells. And EST did not help as much as formerly, not even temporarily. On October 1 Dr. Handcock asked her husband to give permission for psychosurgery, and he did.

Dr. Handcock hoped topectomy would control her impulsiveness permanently as EST controlled it temporarily. But the doctors hesitated to operate without her parents' consent. Her husband said her parents would oppose the operation if they thought he favored it. Matters drifted. She got worse. When an attendant told her to quit smoking in the hall she tore the attendant's uniform off and bit another attendant who came to help. She was given EST more and more often. She was idle most of the time. In October she blew up, attacked an attendant, broke her glasses and threw them away; two male attendants were called and she tore the clothing of one. Her tractable periods grew shorter and farther apart. She was always on a disturbed ward and frequently in seclusion. She had received more than 150 ESTs. Dr. Handcock's note of 1953 sounded resigned: "Has permission for brain operation from her husband but not from her own family who are closer to her at present than he is so it probably would not be done under these conditions." One night in 1954 the attendant found her in bed with a Negro patient; told to go to her own bed, Lillian came out fighting, and the attendant had to call for help to put her in a seclusion room. Next morning they gave her two ESTs. An attendant wrote, "This patient is very dangerous when disturbed. Which is more often than usual." The attendants made other similar notes that spring: "Has been in seclusion for few days, is too combative to be on hall. EST given does very little good."

Then suddenly on July 29, 1954, the attendant made this rather cryptic note: "Rx C—8 A.M. Very co-operative."

"Rx C"—prescription "C"—was the hospital's code for Thorazine, one of the new drugs the hospital was then experimenting with.

5.

Now, the so-called new miracle drugs are neither very new nor very miraculous but they are the most striking development in psychiatry in years. There are many new drugs but those most commonly used in 1955 were Thorazine—a trade name for chlorpromazine—and Serpasil—a trade name for reserpine. Thorazine was synthesized in the 1940's during a search for antihistamines. It was neglected till 1950, when French chemists discovered its unique sedative action, and it was introduced into American mental hospitals in 1953. Reserpine is a substance extracted from a plant which was used in ancient times in India for the treatment of mental illness. Used in modern times in the management of high blood pressure, it had a calming effect and was used on mental patients in 1953.

The new drugs seemed to quiet disturbed patients. They made some patients drowsy yet their effects were different from those of ordinary sedatives—the patients slept differently from sedated patients, they could be aroused to eat, and they did not lapse into drunken lethargy. Smith, Kline & French Laboratories, manufacturers of Thorazine, wrote in a brochure:

The discovery of "Thorazine" and its use in treating institutionalized psychiatric patients may well represent the start of a new era in the treatment of severe mental disorders. It appears to be a major breakthrough in the battle against mental disease resulting in an accelerated recovery rate, more rapid rehabilitation and earlier discharge of patients from our mental institutions. "Thorazine" modifies abnormal human behavior in a unique fashion, without producing narcosis or coma, and at the same time restores or increases the patient's capacity to respond to psychotherapy. . . . Equally encouraging is the result of "Thorazine" on the overall operation of mental institutions. The administration of "Thorazine" has effected a dramatic quieting throughout previously disturbed wards—the use of physical restraint largely abandoned, and the morale of both patients and staff improved.

Many doctors and superintendents were even more enthusiastic. Dr. Douglas Goldman, clinical director of Longview State Hospital in

Cincinnati, a leading exponent of the new drugs, wrote in his annual report:

> The nature of the entire Institution in the last year has undergone rather remarkable change as the result of the introduction and application of the new drugs. . . . The most important gain from the application of the new treatment has been in the "chronic," "disturbed" and deteriorated wards of the hospital, and in the wards which were formerly considered "violent." The patients are now quiet and cooperative. They are now capable of responding to recreational and occupational therapy efforts, and the physical condition of the wards has been modified so that flowers, flowerpots, pictures, television sets, and radios can be left safely open and exposed with no danger to the apparatus or the patients. . . . The use of restraint of any kind has diminished close to the vanishing point. . . . In the more chronic "deteriorated" wards . . . the proportion of denudativeness and incontinence has diminished appreciably. . . . A final personal note seems indicated. This year of 1954 to 1955 . . . has represented the dawn of a new day in this type of work.

When the drugs first came along, laymen received the impression that the drugs would empty the hospitals and "cure" the mentally ill. Some doctors' early enthusiasm soon evaporated. A leading investigator said that the drugs and their effects have not yet been studied thoroughly and until they were should not be used indiscriminately nor with too much hope. Another researcher said, "The new drugs don't make anybody less schizophrenic. They simply lessen the anxieties of some patients and let them deal better with their own problems. The drugs don't cure anything. They make patients more manageable." It was often claimed that the drugs made patients more accessible to psychotherapy. True, a patient who was climbing the walls wasn't "accessible," and if the drug made him stop, he was; but many psychoanalysts complained that this was quite different from becoming accessible in psychotherapeutic terms. Dr. Agosten at Columbus State said, "The patients will talk to you all right, they will talk and talk, they will talk your arm off, but they never say anything useful or helpful." Furthermore in state hospitals accessibility is largely meaningless, since individual psychotherapy is rarely available anyway. In addition, the new drugs produced undesirable side effects, such as jaundice, drowsiness, and tremors and other symptoms akin to Parkinsonism. To date none of the side effects has been shown to be serious or permanent. On the other hand one researcher has pointed out that there may be more serious long-term effects as yet unknown. Some years ago a new drug was discovered for obesity, and it was given wholesale for several years, until it was discovered that patients using it had developed cataracts on their eyes and gone blind. There is no reason to believe that the new drugs will have any such effects but until they have been used for some years no one can say whether they will. Talking to psychiatrists around the country one heard of deaths of patients on drugs. SKF recommended Thorazine in conjunction with EST but, as has been said, a patient on Thorazine died during EST at Columbus State; yet no one could say for sure that the combination killed her. A study reported to the American Psychiatric Association showed that although some thirty undesirable side effects were observed in patients on Thorazine, it "is a safe drug although there are some risks involved in its use."

6.

What was the experience of Columbus State with these drugs?

The hospital began experimental use of them July 29, 1954, about six months after the publication in medical journals of the first reports on the drugs. Lillian Hill was one of the first patients to get them. Dr. Kovitz picked three groups of fifty chronic patients, half men and half women. Most were schizophrenics ill many years who had failed to respond to EST or insulin. To one group he gave Thorazine, to another Serpasil, and to another a placebo of sugar. The three pills looked identical, they were called A, B and C, and not even the attendants or ward doctors knew which was which. "The pharmacist and I counted out the pills," Kovitz recalls. After six weeks he stopped the drugs, observed the results for a month, then switched drugs for another six weeks. Some doctors had suggested that a patient's mere knowledge he was getting "one of the new drugs" might improve him, and it was true that at Columbus State a few patients on sugar pills did improve briefly, but Kovitz felt sure the group getting drugs were better than those getting the placebo. "About half the patients were better—less excited, less noisy, more co-operative, more accessible, more interested in their surroundings, less impulsive and less excited. Sometimes they said they felt better—less tense and so on." Some patients did better on Serpasil, some did better on Thorazine. The usual side effects occurred.

By 1955 Columbus State, like most state hospitals, was relying increasingly on the new drugs. Of the patients who had received Thorazine, 37 per cent had left the hospital. Of those who had received Serpasil, 30 per cent had left. "So about two-thirds are still more or less unimproved," Dr. Kovitz said. "But that 30 or 40 per cent who did improve is important. Remember, some of them were sick a long time. And some of them are probably going to stay out. I've got one girl out on trial visit, I used to see her dragged down the hall hand and foot, screaming all the way, and you had to keep your eye on her every minute. Today she's out of the hospital, taking Thorazine. She's a little listless and guarded, she still is bothered by other human beings and feels she has to watch herself, but she's able to get along." Most patients were continuing to take the drugs on the outside. They returned regularly for checkups—a talk with the doctor about how they were getting along—and he might change their doses, doling out the precious little orange pills from a bottle in his desk. A few patients could quit taking the drugs. Kovitz said, "I had one thirteen-year-old boy with a terrific attack of panic. He was so anxious he clung to the nurses like a baby. You couldn't pull him into an office chair. Thorazine melted his anxiety. We tapered the dose down to nothing and released him and so far he's still all right. Of course he was young and in an acute stage. These drugs seem to work best on acute patients with intense hostility or anxiety, with a great deal of excitement or agitation."

Why the drugs worked no one knew. They were said to exert "a unique, selective depressant action on the central nervous system and both divisions of the autonomic nervous system" but just why this was so or precisely what it meant was unknown. Kovitz said, "Here's something chemical, a simple pill, easy to give, patients are not afraid of it and they do respond to it—well, you start getting excited. We try to be conservative here but there is no doubt that the drug is somehow affecting the sick person's physiology. Freud predicted that his treatments would be superseded by chemical treatment. It isn't a cure-all, any more than anything else is. Some patients don't respond to Thorazine and Serpasil. They're no good for depressions. No drug would help organic brain damage, of course. But some patients who have been fixed for years in a dreamlike inaccessible state do respond. A patient to respond has to be still under tension. When the delusional system is well fixed, they are hard to change. Thorazine doesn't help much with hallucinations, either. There's another new drug, Frenquel, that's said to be specific for hallucinations. If you can cut down hallucinations you may be able to prevent a delusional system from forming. The drugs don't cure psychosis. I'm not even convinced they cure symptoms, as some people claim. Patients on drugs don't lose their psychotic symptoms. They just learn to live with them. They're happier but they're still psychotic. We're going to have schizophrenics with us for a long time to come. We've had them in every culture. A certain amount of humility and caution is wise along with enthusiasm."

Dr. Robert Dane said, "Some years back a new drug was discovered that was helpful in tuberculosis and it was thought that it was going to get those people out of the sanitariums in a few hours. It didn't, though it helped. The new drugs are just another weapon."

There is no doubt that the drugs have made the disturbed wards quieter, have cut down seclusion and restraint, have reduced EST, and have made many violent patients manageable. All these are real gains, and nobody who has ever seen a violent ward in a mental hospital, or talked to a doctor confronted daily with the proof of his failure, or watched an attendant deal physically with a combative patient, would criticize doctors or attendants for being grateful and enthusiastic about the drugs. Dr. Paul Kirch said recently, "These drugs are not going to empty the hospital, this is not an antibiotic of the mind, but they sure do help us."

They help patients in the outside world too. Dr. Dane said, "Thorazine helps the patients take their relatives. And it reassures the family. This means a good deal. I've got one patient who went home on it and still didn't get along with her husband so I prescribed Thorazine for both of them and now they're getting along beautifully. Probably the first time in years they've gotten along. There's a joke around here that we should give Thorazine to the family and let the patient go home." Psychiatrists in private practice have reported that with Thorazine they can care for some patients in their offices whom they formerly would have had to hospitalize. But it is probably not true as has been suggested that the drugs will prevent nearly all patients from going to hospitals—schizophrenics won't seek help early.

At the time of our visit in 1955 only 213 patients in Columbus State were actually receiving the new drugs—79 men and 134 women. This was fewer patients than were receiving sedatives. The reason was money. The drugs were expensive—from $13 to $15 per month per patient—and the hospital budget was limited. For its experiment in 1954, two drug houses, SKF and Ciba, gave the hospital about $5,000 worth of drugs. After that the hospital had none. The downtown office bought $120,000 worth of drugs for all Ohio state hospitals and asked Columbus State how much it wanted. The hospital, thinking the downtown office merely had a few extra bottles lying around, asked for only "a couple of bottles." Every other Ohio state hospital got more. After that, realizing the state intended to buy large quantities, Columbus State estimated it would like to have a third of its 2,700 on drugs and that it could do this for $37,700 a year. But the hospital's budget for all medicines was only $40,000. The budget was increased in 1955 to $55,000 for all drugs. Dr. Kirch hoped that by holding down purchases of other medicines he could eke out $15,000 or even $20,000 for psychiatric drugs.

Patients were spending a lot more on drugs than the hospital— about $2,794 to $1,992 per month. Superintendent Wedemeyer felt uncomfortable asking relatives to buy drugs for patients but he could do nothing else. Few relatives seemed to resent paying for drugs. Some trying to exist on Social Security payments themselves were eager to spend $12 a month on drugs for a relative—and sometimes uselessly. "It's pathetic," one doctor said. "Relatives barge in here after reading an article in the paper on Thorazine, and you know the patient won't benefit. You hate to see them waste their money on drugs, but sometimes it's hard to talk them out of it." The relatives bought the drugs at "hospital prices," about a third lower than retail drugstore prices. They paid considerably more than the hospital itself paid, however. If they deposited $11.40, enough to buy a bottle of a hundred tablets of 100 mgm. each, a month's supply, the hospital would order the single bottle from a drug wholesale house. This way each tablet cost 11¢ each. But for itself the hospital bought in larger quantities, and each tablet cost only 7¢ each. The hospital might have saved the families a good deal of money by buying for them in larger quantities, but it didn't because the bookkeeping would have been too complicated.

The hospital reserved its own limited supply for new acute patients and violent chronic ones. This meant that the quiet chronic patients —the great mass of patients—got left out. Dr. Maria Madi was doing more for them than any other doctor. An intense Hungarian woman of restless intellect, she ceaselessly badgered Kovitz for more drugs and proposed new experiments. On her chronic wards she tried to spot patients who seemed to be "acting out" their problems, indicating they still were under tension, and who also showed an interest in work and had a home to go to. She believed that the hospital could discharge 40 per cent of its chronic patients and 70 per cent of its acute ones if it had enough drugs. Superintendent Wedemeyer said, "We undoubtedly would use more Thorazine and Serpasil if we had more funds. But I don't think anyone that the staff feels strongly needs drugs is going without them." Ward doctors, however, spent a good deal of time trying, and not always successfully, to figure out how to get the precious pills for patients.

7.

How did the new drugs act on Lillian Hill?

She was chosen for the experimental project, according to Dr. Kovitz, "because she was an impulsive, aggressive, unpredictable, very tense, severe chronic schizophrenic who hadn't improved with anything else and had a very poor prognosis." She had been here seven years; 228 ESTs and more than 50 insulin treatments had helped her not a bit.

She received Thorazine twice daily, at 8 A.M. and 8 P.M., and for two weeks, starting July 29, for the first time in years, the ward nurse wrote down nothing on her chart but "co-operative" or "very co-operative." On August 11 she hit another patient in the face, came out to the hall, hit another; and the nurse had to call male attendants to seclude and restrain her. For three days in seclusion she was given Thorazine by injection. She then came out onto the ward and took it docilely. The attendant wrote, "Seems more co-operative, quiet, works sometimes. Does not mix well with patients. Eats and sleeps well." So the entries went, through August and September and October, and she was moved to a quiet ward for the first time in years and there in late November an attendant wrote, "I have never seen her combative or resistive."

She blew up once more, a few days later—hit a patient, pulled out her hair and said she would kill her, then sulked alone at the end of the hall, refusing to let anyone come near. But soon she was transferred to a good ward, whence patients go home and where she had stayed briefly a long while before, and after two weeks there an attendant wrote, "This pt. gets along well." Soon her drugs were stopped. She did not relapse. She was moved to a quiet chronic ward of Dr. Madi, who wrote, "She was in good contact, appropriate, pleasant, having memory defects for the acute phase of her illness only." Dr. Kovitz, who had known her of old, thought she had done better on Serpasil than on Thorazine and ordered her back on Serpasil. The nurses were keeping detailed behavior charts on patients on the new drugs; day after day they checked Lillian's chart, and in the slanting lines running down the close-ruled chart one could see graphically the drug's effect: "Neat, follows routine, offers to help, polite response, joins of own accord, works regularly, privileged, reading, writing, speaks first." For a time they marked her "underactive, uninterested, unhappy," but not for long. They never marked her "demanding, distrustful, faultfinding, angry, vulgar, profane, refuses to help, resists routine, picks, scratches, destroys or damages, tries to harm self, tries to harm others, wets or soils, won't stay dressed, disoriented." She no longer was any of these things.

She started going to Occupational Therapy, and those in charge reported her interested in checkers, chess, ping-pong, baseball, bowling, tennis. She read the Bible and the *Saturday Evening Post.* She played the piano and sang. She liked to dance. She began to work in the hospital's little commissary, waiting on patients and guests. She did it well. In May her ward doctor told Social Service to begin planning weekend visits. Her parents seemed pleased she might come home. Her husband had divorced her in 1953; that war was ended.

She went home for a weekend and told the social worker she enjoyed it. She said she would like to live with her parents, perhaps she could get a job in a restaurant. She was looking forward to leaving the hospital. She had been here seven years. Wouldn't it be hard to leave? She said she'd miss the hospital but felt she could make out. She would come back once a month for a checkup. She felt that Serpasil "had done wonders for her" and she intended to keep on taking it. Dr. Kirch had so little doubt about her readiness for trial visit that he approved it without referring it to staff. At a final examination she showed no psychotic symptoms. The social worker called her parents and they came for her. They worried because she smoked; the doctor reassured them. He gave them a prescription for Serpasil, and she went home. In a month she came back for a checkup. The doctor wrote, "The patient was neat, well dressed, more outgoing than during her hospitalization. She seemed slightly tense and said that she was nervous about coming back to the hospital. There were no indications of abnormal speech or actions throughout the interview."

She came back another time, further improved. So far as the hospital knows she still is getting along fine, doing the work she learned in the hospital: waiting on tables. Dr. Kovitz says, "Serpasil doesn't do the same thing for everybody but it did it for her and that's something."

9

The Dancing Man

■ One always hears of the lobotomies and the miracle cures on new drugs, or the murders and escapes at any state hospital. One never hears of the great mass of patients, those human hulks whom the textbooks call "old asylum material." And there is good reason for this—there seems little to say about them except that they sit on the ward and wait for death. They have been here for years and seem unlikely ever to leave alive, and it is hard to think of them in any other way. Yet once these half-dead were people, not much unlike all of us.

In 1955, on Ward 18, a quiet chronic third-floor ward of Columbus State, there sat a tall thin man with a face that once had been sensitive and intelligent but now was coarsened and stupid-looking. Most of the time he just sat. When asked to do chores he arose and shambled about the dim-lit ward. Sometimes he stood in one position and made peculiar rhythmic movements with his hands and feet. He had been a drum major in the college band. But that had been long ago. He had been here since 1933.

2.

His name is Donald Stone, and he was only twenty-three years old when he came here. His father was a professional man, his mother a college graduate. Several of his relatives had been in state hospitals; one had committed suicide. Stone once said, "There is a taint through

228

the family of becoming worried and pacing the floor, most of the family are retiring and not sociably inclined."

As a young man he had a rather sullen expression. He had a long nose, long soft wavy hair, lips that curled up a little in what looked like an attempt at a worldly sneer. His face was thin and pimply. He had a washed-out, pale-eyed appearance. He looked big-headed and puny-bodied. He did not quite look sensitive and artistic; rather he looked like a young man trying very hard to look sensitive and artistic. His eyes were close-set. His face was rather lopsided, the left side pulled up a bit as though by wires.

All through school Stone was considered a "brilliant, impractical boy." Stories of the occult appealed to him strongly. He wanted to be a magician. He insisted on going to business college to take a secretarial course so he could become secretary to a world-famous magician. He traveled with the magician for a year. But the work disappointed him: He could not have a show of his own. He became depressed. He quit.

He took a trip west and returned sick. His parents put him in Harding's Sanitarium. He improved, left, and demanded that his parents send him to college. They could ill afford it but did their best. He went a year to a university in the East. His money ran out, he came home, he went a year to a small Midwest college. To save money he went without meals. "He worked until late night," his case record reads. "He became a socialist. Did not drink, smoke, nor use drugs. He was a very high minded boy. He went with girls very, very little. He was very dominating about the house and was always thinking the family should do greater things. He would not use the same towel as others. He would not use the same razor. For the past six weeks he has been quite aloof. He stayed in his room most of the time. He was void of sympathy. He did not appreciate what his folks did for him and always belittled their ability." He threatened his father if he didn't send him to an Eastern university next term—"I have warned you for the last time." He told his mother, "I'll murder my father in cold blood." They found a revolver in his suitcase. His father had him taken from class and committed to Columbus State.

3.

The admitting doctor wrote, "A brilliant, impractical boy, always lacking in affect, who has ruined his family financially by his demands for higher education. Their resources at an end, he is baffled by the necessity of facing facts regarding his own inadequacy and is showing evidence of a schizophrenic shift, paranoid homicidal type." Stone said another doctor had advised him that science was not sufficiently advanced to understand him. "My ideas are not strange to . . . intellectual people, they are to laborers and the like." He talked rapidly and coherently. He said it was absurd to think he had threatened to kill anyone. He used high-sounding intellectual phrases. He lacked common sense. "He says he is not a socialist or a communist but he is against capital and suggests that people be taken from the cradle up and develop them under ideal conditions so they will not be economically low and intellectually high. He says in his case there is an extreme unbalance between his economic condition and intellect and that is his trouble now. He says if he had plenty of money he would be perfectly normal."

Staff diagnosed him as schizophrenic, paranoid type, and sent him to a maximum security ward to prevent escape. In those days the hospital put more emphasis on security than today. And it had fewer treatments—little except hydrotherapy.

After Stone had been there a few months he wrote a three-thousand-word document which he called "An Introspective Case History." He wrote of himself in the third person.

It was evident he had a considerably nervous behavior pattern from birth. He also was born with a somewhat frail body which led to an inferiority complex from the beginning of his life and did not permit his aggressive personal defense, a trait which he has carried down to the present time. . . . When about seven or eight years of age, together with his physiological inferiority complex he developed a social inferiority complex (not distinctly abnormal but sufficient to have himself called timid) and due apparently to no particular reason, but to just his general behavior pattern, and why he should be addressed and approached in such a manner seemed to be a result of no more than his radiance reflection or personality, not sufficiently normal to be truly sociable and yet not abnormal to a degree to be called odd.

Stone wrote that he had changed high schools "due to a fanatical and life long ambition to be very successful." He mourned his failure to pursue a musical career. He "was very successful as a magician and entertainer but owing to his poor executive ability his individual effort was a financial failure." He blamed his failure to organize his own magic show on "the general displacement of vaudeville."

He wrote:

He abandoned magic and a stage profession to follow and demented went to Arizona with the idea to be no more than a laborer on a ranch the remainder of his life and although not interested in obtaining wages at all and even offering his services for nothing, he was unable to locate any ranch which could use him even on these terms due to his size and experience in that work. It had been suggested by [the magician] that he become associated with rough men and do difficult manual work to build up his health and rid him of complexes which he had observed in him. Broken-hearted he returned to Ohio and had a dreadful nervous break-down.

In college, he said, he received "very good grades" and he "was very successful as Drum Major." He planned to study architecture. Architects told him of "the bitter struggle of the profession." The depression was on and the distress of the unemployed upset him. He determined to study law and business administration to prepare "to enter into the political ring in later years with a party somewhat socialistic in policy which would help eradicate the ghastly contemporary political, economic and social conditions as they appeared to him." Since capitalism's difficulty seemed to him rooted in Wall Street, he studied finance. Soon he realized that "the prevailing social arrangement was not to change overnight" and he would need a job after college; he pressed his financial studies, intending to become a stock broker himself. He read all the books on brokerage in the New York Public Library and the university business library. He became "considerably expert in trading stocks for profit." But, overburdened, he went home "to rest." A little later he broke.

Stone did not think the real root of his troubles lay in his overwork at school but, rather, "he would lay the chief fault himself due to his natural behavior pattern and recently to growth." He wrote:

In Donald's candid opinion, upon arriving at the hospital he was neither insane in his vision of objects, behavior or speech and only slightly over energetic in his thinking. However, he did need a rest badly and was overworked mentally with perhaps ⅜ inch of the fore part of his brain clogged. Here he remained, his spirits drifting lower for no reason which he could explain. He had little interest in being conventional with anyone. In the latter part of August he seemed to adopt a new mental condition which relieved the depressive pressure but this proved to be treacherous and a day or so later he experienced strange mental disturbances and mental spells and a somewhat collapsing effect in the fore part of the brain in the former ⅜ inch which had been clogged. These spells came in a daily series of fading and returning effect from an abnormal condition mentally to a somewhat normal mental condition on their return. Combined with these were various types of queer phenomenal mental disturbances in the forepart of the brain, some affecting the regularity of his heart beat to an extent which frightened him considerably as well as spells occurring when he thought he was near death by the peculiar feeling he experienced. . . .

From the observations he has made since arriving at the hospital he has noted one termed insane is not usually a shouting and writhing individual as seems to be the common opinion but a person with a slight mental irregularity causing a sufficient abnormal behavior in a few of his actions or habits to be termed insane although perhaps the majority of his behavior is correct. This has caused his belief that perhaps a larger percent of society are mental cases than is the common belief. . . .

He is especially concerned with the possibility of any "Growing" of his neurological system and mental makeup from a normal and correct arrangement into any condition causing abnormality as to behavior, feeling or appearance. He believes the behavior of the individual depends largely upon his brain construction and neurological arrangement as well as common moral choice in actions. . . .

The trend of his thoughts since birth have been in the very frontal part of his brain and his wit and some of his thinking in its peculiarity has brought to him to some extent rebuke and unhappiness due apparently just to his personality. He would suggest that perhaps the passing of normal people's thoughts possibly through other sections of the brain, more to the rear, might influence their personality to cause it to appear more natural in general.

It has been considerably alarming to Donald that with growth in the last six months since coming to the hospital and more so at present times, that he suspicions his nervous system flowing into wrong channels to cause him to feel as he presently does, the majority of this having taken place since his mental difficulties in August, and would like consultation regarding the validity of this and its curtailment. This factor could be best noted in the curling of his toes during certain mental spells and the occurrence of cold chills followed by perspiration and at other times his sudden warm feeling for no apparent cause. In this matter he believes physician's assistance or at least their consolation in interpreting it to Donald and assurance of its removal with recovery, healing and growth would be of benefit. The only remedy being applied at the moment is regular rest, meals and sleep in the hospital.

For whatever bearing it may have on the case, Donald has always felt himself sexually abnormal, especially as to his sexual potentiality which has caused him to practice masturbation to some extent and probably more so due to the accidental friendships he occasioned during his younger life but he does not believe this factor is sufficient to be looked upon as a major cause of this mental trouble. He never knew it was morally wrong until the age of twenty and did not know of its connection with mental conditions until after being at the hospital. In intercourse, he has participated but upon one occasion but believes possibly his refraining from regular intercourse, considering his abnormal sexual condition, has done him as much injury as some of the previously mentioned difficulties and believes normal sexual relations would have been an aid to his health. . . .

Since the age of about fourteen Donald has been afflicted dreadfully with blackheads and pimples and in younger years was very susceptible to eczema, acne and ivy poison. He has had Ultra-Violet Ray treatment, and facial baths, diet treatments from meats and pastries and medical treatments and yet is unable to escape these. . . .

As to his life-long behavior difficulties, he would suggest the reasons in his opinion as follows:

Morally wrong decision behavior	10%
Nervous system and mental mechanism	50%
Glands	20%
Perhaps unknown to Psychiatrical and medical science as yet	20%

. . . If a diet of chiefly brain foods would aid in restoring the present damaged tissue, he would be interested in having a list suggested. . . .

As Mussolini has set forth recently, he believes the standardization of the human mind psychiatrically and educationally could be adopted as a beneficial social policy. He believes possibly that individuals with good neurological systems and brain construction to be better arranged for good behavior and moral character than those of lesser health and with less effort. . . .

At the moment, during the effort to change, Donald is experiencing phenomenal effects in his heart actions, from various pains to odd changes in the pulse rate. This seems to be his major temporary ailment of immediate importance and would be grateful to be advised regarding this as well as to his case in general.

4.

His case, however, received little attention, then or later. On admission he was bathed and put to bed and given calomel. He was described as "nervous and excited, very talkative." That was June 21, 1933, and the next note on his chart was made two years later: "He has improved nicely and we believe he will adjust himself very well." He was evidently released to his father but how long he was out or what happened does not appear on the records. On November 17, 1937, an attendant noted, "Returned restless, talks to himself, cooperates and doesn't want to stay here." He was given the privilege of the grounds but soon he went downtown to see a lawyer without permission. His doctor revoked his privilege and moved him to Awl cottage to work on the farm. He "was not of much use as a worker." He was bounced around among several chronic wards.

In 1939 something new came along: Stone was sent to Ward 6, for "we feel that they might wish to try the shock treatment on him." EST was new then, the shining hope that drugs are now. But there is no record Stone ever got it; the only notes made on him in succeeding months say that he was working in the main building, "still anti-social," "tries to sneak off alone," "inclined to be a little slovenly," and soon he was back in Awl cottage, assigned to the green house. His doctor thought him able to leave the hospital but his father didn't want him. In January of 1940 the doctor reported that Stone "had been warned" about a new rule forbidding privileged patients to go beyond the hospital fence onto Broad Street but "in spite of this he was seen on Broad Street yesterday morning by one of the attendants." Accordingly his privilege was revoked.

So it went through the weary years. Columbus State was giving Stone nothing but custody. There is, indeed, no record that he ever received any treatment whatsoever in all his twenty-two years there. He worked on the "house cleaning gang," he went again without permission to see an attorney about getting out, he got a blister on his hand, and the attendant dressed and soaked it. His doctor wrote in 1940, "He [does] not seem to be getting any better, has a tendency to stand around in corners with his hands in his pockets, incapable of doing much work and does not seem able to comply with the rules of the hospital." Rules seemed more important than treatment.

On down the years every month or so the attendants made their useless semiliterate notes on him: "Very peculiar has delusions about drum major jumps sidway [*sic*] and then back wards"; "There is no change"; "Is very nervis"; "Very peculiar when on ward tryes to get in room out of your sight"; "There is no change teeth inspected by Dentes"; "Took shots for flew"; "Weight 130"; "Very nervis at times but work for Mr. Canady."

Usually they wrote "There is no change," but in 1942 more ominous notes, indicating regression and deterioration, began to appear: "Very much disturbed at times" and "Very nervis or untidy." For a time he improved, and an attendant wrote, "Likes to listen to the Operas on the Radio on Sat. Afternoons. A very nice patient. Very nice manners." And, early in 1943, "Works every day. Wants to go home. Gets mail regularly. A nice boy." The doctor thought Stone was hearing voices but was concealing it. He frequently wrote to attorneys, asking them to help him get out. His parents visited him every week, brought clothing and asked the attendants to try to keep him looking nice. After a few years he told them to take the clothing home. He did not want to look nice. An attendant wrote, "Does not like to change clothes. An argument always on bath day before he will give up his soiled clothes. Says the laundry has ruined all of his clothing. Wants to wash them himself." A doctor wrote, "He has many mannerisms as he walks about the grounds, he will be coming along with 3 or 4 steps. Step to one side, take two or 3 steps, skip along like a small child. Stop suddenly, whirl about and repeat the same process."

During the seven years between 1942 and 1949 no doctor wrote a note on his records. Then one wrote, "The patient is fair in general appearance. His physical condition is highly nervous. He is cheerful, co-operates well, intelligence is above the average. He assists with ward work and has privileges. Has visitors occasionally; no treatment." It was two years more before another doctor wrote another "progress note":

This patient is a chronic schizophrenic. He is circumlocutory and manneristic; everything he says he says at least 4 times, and squirms around when he says it. During the past 14 months he has not been overtly psychotic, and if he hallucinates or delusionizes, he keeps it well hidden. He is a very good worker; his daily assignment is cleaning the stairs from the fourth floor to the basement. The rest of the day he has to himself. He takes care of my car, and does an excellent job. He has full privilege. His main recreation is listening to the radio and he knows more about operas than the rest of the institution combined. His health is good, and he eats and sleeps well. His weight is 131 pounds. He writes regularly, receives regular mail, and occasionally has company.

And that was all—in 1955 no doctor had given Donald his attention since 1951. Few people around the hospital knew anything about him. He was simply one of the gray almost faceless forms that populate the dim interior landscapes of American mental hospitals. Dr. Kovitz, when Stone was called to his attention, said, "He'd be a good prospect for Thorazine if we had unlimited supplies. But the type that gets first call for drugs are the very aggressive impulsive patients, the serious management problems. They're the ones the doctors get concerned about and say, 'Let's do *something*.' This fellow doesn't cause trouble and he's privileged and he washes cars. He's odd rather than crazy. It's the fighters that get the attention."

10

A Boy Amid Psychotics

■ The number of psychotic children seems to be increasing. Psychiatrists working in institutions for wayward children report that an increasing number of them are schizophrenic. Psychiatrists in private hospitals report the same thing. Dr. Roy Grinker, Director of the Institution for Psychiatric and Psychosomatic Research and Training at Michael Reese Hospital in Chicago, said recently, "We're getting an increasing population of adolescents. The kids are getting sicker and sicker."

Why this should be no one knows. Perhaps it is merely that doctors today more than ever before are on the lookout for psychoses in children. But the fact remains that not only are institutions encountering more and more seriously ill children but also that psychiatrists in private practice who treat children are probably more overworked than doctors in any other subspecialty.

Occasionally sick children turn up at state hospitals. Rockland State in New York has about 650 youngsters among its 8,000 patients. Columbus State since its very beginning has always had a few on hand. One who came to it was Peter Bell.

Peter Bell was in 1955 a boy of thirteen, a good-sized lad for his age, with big hands and thick lips, a close crew-cut and clear beautiful skin, a high forehead and muscular neck and a nice smile. His face was heart-shaped. His appearance was marred only by a tendency to allow his mouth to gape open. He seemed relaxed, almost too relaxed, sprawling in a chair with legs stretched wide while carrying on an important conversation. He frequently said he was "tired" or "bored"; he yawned and covered his yawn with an elaborate gesture; he made much of always being hungry; he sighed deeply; one felt he tried very hard to create an impression upon his elders. At least, this is the way he looked when he was committed to Columbus State by the probate court upon complaint of his mother and father as mentally ill and epileptic. Columbus State is not intended for children, and its superintendent thinks it ought not have children—they must be mingled with the run-of-the-mill psychotic patients, including senile persons in their seventies and violent patients; this isn't good for the kids and, moreover, they are high-spirited and delight in teasing the older patients or playing tricks on the attendants, which isn't good for the hospital. But Columbus State must accept what the courts send, and since Ohio has no institution especially intended for the prolonged care of psychotic children, at any given time Columbus State is likely to contain a half dozen kids under sixteen and sometimes it has twice that many. It tries to get rid of them. If they are feeble-minded it tries to send them across the street to the State School but the latter has a three-year waiting list. Longview State Hospital at Cincinnati and Dayton State have small units for children but they are so crowded that Columbus rarely can get a child in. So the doctors try to send the kids back home or into a foster home or a private institution. But if the child is truly psychotic he must stay; Columbus State has a sprinkling of patients now in their thirties who came here as children.

2.

It was hard to know what to do with Peter Bell. Almost he was one of those children for whom there seems to be no place in the world. Yet here he was, alive and a problem. He was born at Columbus and given for adoption to an orphanage. It is said that his birth was accomplished by instruments and that he had "some" French or Spanish ancestry; nothing more is known of his origins. Mr. and Mrs. Bell took him home when he was four months old and the adoption became final about a year later. Mr. Bell, the foster father, was then in his forties, an office manager. His wife was several years younger, and was a "good housekeeper" and "fond of children," a social worker once reported—"Her interest centers around her church and home." But she too worked. A couple of years after they adopted Peter they adopted another little boy. He was also a "retarded child," the social worker wrote. Peter remembered bumping his little brother's head against the playpen.

Peter was "an adorable little child, had very appealing ways," the social worker wrote. But when he was eight or nine his parents sought help from the probate court because he lied, didn't get along with other children, and was "quite aggressive and belligerent" both at home and at school. The court's social worker wrote, "His language is most disturbing to the father and his attitude has been so disturbing and pronounced the father has suffered from nervous chills. The child is completely irresponsible and unreliable." One cold night Peter ran away from home without a coat; his father, searching for him in the streets, caught sight of him, but he ran on and was found only after hours of exposure, cold but defiant. His behavior worsened. "In order to prevent the child leaving the house on Saturday and getting into difficulty," the social worker wrote, "the parents have frequently locked his day clothes in the basement to keep him in the house."

Peter knew he was adopted. The social worker reported that his parents threatened to "take him back where they got him" if he didn't behave.

He may have some fears they will do this and of course his ideas of the place may be most frightening to him. He is sometimes very verbal in questioning of discipline of himself and his brother. He feels he gets a great deal of punishment and his brother little. . . . Home is located on one of best residential streets in the city . . . modern, in good condition, large lawn and well kept. Parents are financially able to provide well for children. I have had casual acquaintance with family for years, and consider them to be solid people living the simple wholesome life.

When Peter was nine or ten he began having seizures. They lasted from three to five minutes. "He loses consciousness and body becomes rigid," the social worker wrote. "The parents believe and the doctor so states, he is more apt to have seizure when looking out of a window screen into the light." A doctor diagnosed the seizures as epileptic and prescribed Dilantin and Mebarol.

When Peter was eleven he became involved in petty thievery of an unspecified nature; "upset," his parents sought help from the probate court. The judge sent Peter to a children's diagnostic clinic.

3.

At the clinic Peter did not get along well. He liked to play baseball but quarreled with the other kids. He organized a skit for the kids to perform, but they thought him "too bossy." He announced himself the leader of the "Six Aces" but each morning one of the six would drop away until there were none. He tried to buy the kids' friendship with candy. Rebuffed, he curried favor of the officials, which made the children dislike him more. He ran away. He spent half his time at the clinic in isolation, sometimes as punishment, sometimes as self-sought protection from the other children. Peter had an IQ of 107, high average, but his emotional problems interfered with his performance and his intelligence potential probably was higher. His mother wrote, advising him, "Don't eat meat on Friday; if you do, be sure to confess. Write to us. Make your father something for Father's Day." Once she announced she and her husband wouldn't be able to visit him for a while because they were going on vacation.

Peter stayed at the clinic a little more than two months while psychiatrists and a psychologist, doctor, educational consultant and social worker studied him. Their report to the probate judge differed materially from that of the first social worker. They said, "The history of these first years in the Bell home points up rigidity in handling on the part of the parents, special effort not to spoil the child by either interrupting his fixed schedule, picking him up when he cried, or caressing him too much." They noted that his parents had been married for many years when they adopted him. "They were unable to say what children mean to them or the reasons for wishing to adopt. ... It would appear that the adoption of this boy did not go smoothly for either the child or the parents. This would appear to be a maladjustment of long standing."

The doctors were not certain whether Peter's seizures were "true epilepsy." An electroencephalogram was abnormal, showing deviations often associated with epilepsy. But a seizure he had while at the clinic did not appear to be a typical grand mal epileptic seizure. Moreover, the psychiatrists believed that Peter used his seizures as a means of gaining the attention of his parents and others. Peter himself once said he used them to escape unpleasant situations. The doctors said that whatever brain abnormality there might be did not account fully for Peter's serious emotional disturbance.

The clinic concluded he was "a very tense and insecure child whose present level of personality organization is quite precarious. He is not at this time psychotic. . . . [Peter] has been dominated, pushed, punished and rejected by his parents much more than he has been loved by them. He has a great need for love and affection, but his distrust of people, and his failure to develop adequate social skills prevent him from satisfying this need. . . . [Peter] is in great need of help of an intensive variety . . . if further disorganization of personality is to be prevented." But where was he to get it? The clinic recommended placement "in an institution for residential psychiatric treatment where a dynamic program of individual and group psychological help would be available." But where? "The Children's Aid Society of Cleveland can be thought of as suitable"—but that was in Cleveland. The usual type of institution for children wouldn't do—he couldn't get along with other kids. Maybe some Catholic institution could be found. Moreover, the parents needed "some kind of professional help" in understanding themselves and their child; perhaps they could get it from a community mental health center. The clinic urged the probate judge to give the parents and the child all the help he could and as quickly as possible because of "the certain harm to [Peter] if treatment . . . is postponed very long."

He went home. One day in April of 1955 he took a little girl into his garage and "took her britches down." He did not harm her. She ran home and told her mother. She told the Bells and the probate judge. She was the daughter of a social worker who had handled his case before.

4.

Apparently at the judge's suggestion Peter's parents took him as a voluntary patient to Columbus Receiving Hospital, a state institution for mentally ill persons in need of brief intensive treatment. He was there about a month. The hospital reported he was suffering from idiopathic epilepsy and "personality trait disturbance," it thought the prognosis "quite guarded," and it made about the same recommendation as the clinic: "Residence in a controlled environment for an extended period of time, preferably where he could have psychiatric treatment. . . . In other words, an institutional placement."

Again Peter went home. He spent a good part of the summer swimming while his parents tried to find some place to put him. They found a private school in the East. But they didn't send him there, whether because the school would not accept him or for other reasons, such as cost, is not clear. They told Peter he would have to have some treatments or tests—he wasn't sure which—before he could get into the school. And in September they signed a complaint in probate court, and the judge ordered a doctor to examine Peter, and the doctor found him mentally ill and epileptic and gave as the reason for recommending his commitment to a state hospital "inability to have him placed elsewhere," and two days later Peter's parents brought him to the ancient ornate doors of Columbus State Hospital.

5.

A doctor interviewed him in the hall by the Coke machine, then his father and the attendant supervisor took him to Ward 2, the gloomy first-floor ward cluttered up with newly admitted psychotics of all descriptions and old psychotics with fractured hips or other physical ailments. There he was interviewed next day by Dr. Dane, the young resident. Dane had noticed Peter in the X-ray line the day before and had been curious about him. Now, as the admitting doctor, he went to see Peter for an official interview. On the way Dane stopped in the hall to talk to another doctor who had seen Peter briefly. The staff worries a good deal about the kids that find their way here. Dr. Dane found Peter standing in the doorway to a small private room on the ward, his legs spread wide; he said he was on guard, helping the nurse who was caring for a patient inside. Dr. Dane said, "Do you want to come with me for a while?"

Peter said, "Okay," and executed a neat dance step, whirled and followed Dane quietly down the hall to a small examining room. Dane locked the door. Peter looked around the room, climbed up on the examining table and lay down, stretching elaborately, yawning, saying, "Let's make it comfortable."

Congenially Dane said "Sure" and asked him his name, his age, the date of his birth, his interests. He answered readily. He talked at length about sports but was not convincing and Dane thought this was merely to impress Dane, who looks like a man interested in sports. Dane asked why he'd been brought here. "Well, what happened was—well, I don't really know, myself. Mom was trying to get me to go to a boys' school—a judge and the school got together and said I should come here and have some tests and get some what you call it treatments and then go over there."

"How do you feel about being here?"

"Well—" he hesitated then looked up and said, "To tell you the truth right now I'm scared. Those guys with TB over here—" patients with tuberculosis when admitted are kept in isolation on Ward 2 till they can be diagnosed and moved to the tuberculosis cottage—"those guys with TB here, it gets me just a little bit worried. I don't think it's catching, is it?" Dane reassured him. He went on, "That's the only thing I'm scared of. Yesterday one of 'em got out and started to run around. Then today Father was hearing my confession and we didn't know it but there was a man under the bed on which we were sitting. The doctor and the nurse came in and told us a man was missing and they were checking all the rooms and one of them tripped over his legs, they were sticking out from under the bed." (This actually had happened.) "You asked me why I happened to be here, why I got here. Well, what happened was, I got a little interested in girls, and there was a little girl lived down the street and I stripped her and she went to her mother and so I was brought to the judge and they decided to send me to a school. So they found out about the school in the East." He said he wouldn't mind going there—his mother wanted him to, though "I know Dad would rather have me here." He explained he'd been at the clinic and at Receiving Hospital. He didn't seem to resent any of it.

He said he didn't like school very well but got along all right. How did he feel about his parents? "I think they're very nice to me. If it hadn't been for them I might have been right where I started out —in the orphanage. You see, I'm adopted, me and my brother." What did his parents do? "Well, they hardly get to do anything. Usually they're around home. They stay around home. They stay around home a lot. Dad, all he does is working. By the time he gets to the paper in the evening he's dead tired. Mom, she's dead tired from work too." What about weekends? "I have to stay home. We usually stay at our house. Sit around and watch television." Why? "I don't have any clothes to wear—Mom washes on Friday and they're out on the wash-line drying." How did his parents feel about letting him out nights? "I don't go out nights at all."

Dane asked several other questions about his parents but he said nothing derogatory. Dane asked, "If you had a chance to change your situation, what would you change it to?"

"What do you mean?"

"If your life was a blackboard and you could erase it and start over, what would you do?"

Peter's voice was charged with emotion for the first time: "I'd start all over. Right from the third grade on. That's when I started getting ornery. That's when if somebody came up to me and said anything I'd probably blow my top and go after 'em."

"So?"

"So I'd get the devil."

"From whom?"

"Mom. I don't mean to say she'd whip me," he said hastily. "I'd go after 'em and they'd tell their mother and she'd tell my mother and Mom would give me the devil. Once I got hit in the head with a ruler, the kid was three years younger than I, and I took out after him and landed him three hundred feet from our yard. The judge took care of the rest."

Dane asked about his molesting the little girl. Peter said he didn't hurt her. He was simply curious. "I just took her pants down, looked at her and let her go." How did this make him feel? "A little sick to my stomach. A little scared. I told her not to tell anyone what happened." How did he feel after his parents found out about it? "Scared; and I hid out back of the garage for a while. A half-hour, and Mom called me to come into the house and I got up nerve enough to go." His mother had told him "not to do it again," he said, but he couldn't remember what else she'd said. Did he think the incident important enough to get excited about? "Yes. It could have amounted to something, started something." He said his father had told him repeatedly he'd better not do it again? "Why not?" Dane asked. "He said if I ever got caught by another adult they might call the police and I might be sent down to BIS—" the state Boys Industrial School, a correctional institution—"instead of to the school in the East."

"Did he give you any other reason for not doing it?"

"No," then, glancing out the screened and barred window, "Boy, it's hot out."

Dr. Dane asked him about his "spells." He said, "Oh, yeh. Every once in a while if I look out of a screen for a minute or two, like this," and he sat up and looked through the screen, "it's about like that screen, and my eyes'd go blind and tch," he made a spitting noise, "out it'd go and I'd find myself on a bed or davenport." How did he feel at such times? "Well, I'm doing my best to keep away from screens and all that. I haven't had any in eight months." Did the spells frighten him? "No. But it could be dangerous. I could hit my head on something sharp and it might kill me." Did this worry him? "No. I hardly ever worry about anything."

Dane asked him to describe the spells more closely. He said, "I'd look out at the screen, start starin', something that would get lights reflected or something, it'd get vague and a little bit vaguer and finally it'd black out and there I'd go." Did he breathe hard before the spell? No. Did his heart pound? No. Did he feel weak? Sometimes a little dizzy. Did he ever see anything just before he blacked out? No. Just after he awoke? No, except "maybe a few white spots." Ever lose control of his bowels or bladder? No. Ever hurt himself when he fell? No. Ever bite his tongue? No. What time of day did this happen? Almost any time. Ever at night? No. Had anyone ever seen him in a seizure? His mother, once; and at Receiving Hospital the doctors had asked him to induce one, and he had, and they had caught him.

Did he remember the first spell he ever had? "Yeh, I'd just come back from playing a game of baseball. I stopped in the door and turned around and looked out through the screen and I just started to stare and let my mind wander and tch, I was out." His team had won the ball game and he had been happy at the time. He hadn't known what to think about the spell. "I asked Mom what happened. She said she found me on the floor. She saw me pounding the floor and called the doctor." Dane asked if he ever had bad dreams. Once, he said, and it wakened him. Did he ever have the same dream again and again? "I had one come back once." What was it? "Let me see. It was about when I was a baby. I was about a year old. No," he exclaimed forcefully, "I can't say that. My brother was about one year old, he was in his playpen, and I tripped and hit the pen and knocked against his head." This seemed to be a description of how he had pushed his baby brother in his playpen, and Dane inquired closely into it, but he insisted it was a dream.

Dane asked him a few more questions, mostly about how he was getting along in the hospital—he said he had eaten three trays of food for lunch—then told him he'd see him again and left him. Back in his own office, Dane looked puzzled. He said, "He seems fairly tense and agitated today—did you notice how he was wriggling around and wringing his hands? He's had an abnormal tracing—" an abnormal electroencephalogram—"and some sort of spells but whether it's epilepsy I don't know. Often kids can produce a spell at will. I think I'll order an electroencephalogram of our own. There's something inconsistent about his picking on a four- or five-year-old girl just to see what she looks like. If it was natural curiosity he'd pick a girl his own age."

He thought a while, fiddling with a pencil. "This isn't a typical organic brain picture. In fact, there's not much organic about it." Today was Friday. Peter probably would come before the staff for diagnosis on Monday. Dr. Dane was due to start his vacation today but he wanted to write up Peter's case before leaving. He wasn't satisfied with what he now knew, however, and so decided to talk to Peter again tomorrow, though it would be Saturday—"I haven't any other life anyway so I might as well be here."

6.

Dr. Dane was only twenty-nine but he seemed older, perhaps because he seemed quiet, calm and confident. He had three small children of his own. He liked dogs and kids and old men and beer and jazz. He had bought a small house in an outlying section and was fixing it up himself. Evenings when he came home, his kids climbed all over him, and he liked it. His house was somewhat noisy and cluttered, with a television and a playpen in the living room, but this didn't bother him. Not much seemed to bother Dr. Dane. The Danes did not live at the hospital because they felt the outlying schools were better than those near the hospital and they thought it better for the kids to be raised away from the hospital—"There are psychiatric brats as well as army brats." Dane had been at the hospital more than a year, longer than any but one of the 1955 crop of residents.

Originally he came from Cedar Rapids, Iowa, and so did his wife; they had known each other since they were fourteen or fifteen. Dane's great-great-grandfather had homesteaded an Iowa farm. Dane's father, a farmer, had died when Dane was only ten, so Dane had worked his way through college. He had graduated from the University of Iowa Medical School in 1953 and come to a private hospital in Columbus to intern because he had friends here. He had gotten interested in psychiatry as a medical specialty at Iowa—his faculty adviser had been a psychiatrist, and he had worked at a children's behavior clinic. While an intern he had met a doctor who was a friend of the superintendent at Columbus State and who "gave me a taste of what they were doing here," and when he finished internship he had applied for residency here and got it.

"Besides all of which," he said, "I was always considerably interested in Dr. Freud." Dane considered himself more of a Freudian than most of the other staff members at Columbus State. "Last year the staff was younger and more analytically oriented. This year I guess there are only three of us who are disciples and we're not very strong ones. I'll probably go on and get my analysis but I don't expect to become an analyst, it's such a limited field, it's principally of value in treating the neuroses—psychotics are much too sick."

Dane always had thought he would take his two-year residency training here, then hurry on to another hospital accredited for third-year training and from there go immediately into private practice. But recently the state of Ohio had raised salaries, so Dane was tempted to stay. "Most of us can pay off our debts on the new salaries," debts incurred in getting through medical school. "The only reason to go into private practice at all is money. I like hospital practice. There's a good deal of freedom here. There's plenty of material, Lord knows—" that is, plenty of patients of all descriptions—"and I could study to my heart's content as long as I take care of my ward and go to staff meetings and don't goof up anywhere. Of course, some doctors leave a place like this because it's so crowded and their work load is hopeless. Some want to see results—they figure the surgeon cuts out the tumor and he's rid of it, why can't psychiatry be that way? I don't think it can be, I know a lot of patients we discharge are going to come back, and I'm optimist enough so it doesn't bother me a great deal. Besides, it's heartening to see people come here after being treated in private sanitariums outside without making progress and then after a couple of months we can send them home. There's nothing in the world more satisfying than seeing someone get well and leave this place."

7.

Dane was probably more interested in Peter Bell than in most patients for several reasons. Dane was a Catholic, so was Peter. Dane had children of his own. Dane felt strongly that Columbus State was not the place for disturbed children. Peter's case presented a challenge. How was it to be diagnosed? And what was to be done with him?

On Friday afternoon Dane kept mulling the case over. He consulted other doctors. A doctor who had talked to Peter's parents told him that the mother had described Peter's transgressions "with some relish." She had called his looking through a screen "defying God." The father, the doctor said, was conscientious, very restrained, fond of Peter, grieved by his misbehavior and eager to do the right thing. Peter, the other doctors told Dane, seemed to be making out well on the ward. He ate "like a horse." He was "busy as a beaver," emptying trash, helping the the nurses. He wanted to go to occupational therapy or recreational therapy. He didn't seem to mind being here. Dane also talked to the Catholic chaplain, Father John Grady. The Catholic and Protestant chaplains at the hospital regularly make rounds on the wards, give religious counsel to patients, conduct services on Sundays, bury their indigent who die and talk to patients' relatives. Better than anyone else, they can prepare some fearful patients for EST, staff or a major operation. Father Grady had been talking at length to Peter Bell. Dane asked about getting Peter into a church institution. Father Grady said he would inquire.

On Saturday morning Dane took Peter to his own office, a little room like all the other doctors' offices. Today it was dead quiet. They talked for more than an hour. Peter talked more freely than he had the day before. Dane said, "We were talking about your folks, you said they were nice people."

Peter said, "If it wasn't for them I'd probably still be over in the orphanage."

"What did they tell you about that?"

"If they hadn't come along and picked me out of a couple of hundreds of kids I would still be over there, a little orphan, no place to go, and when I got to a certain age I'd have to leave and get work. Maybe I couldn't be able to get a room or any place and have to sleep outside," and he went on, picturing the horrid life of an orphan.

Dane asked if this was what usually happened to orphans. No, but "it could, it's one of the many things."

"But—" Dane suggested, and Peter took it up: "But I was lucky enough to be picked out of hundreds of kids, Mom had to pay expenses of course, I would need good clothes and everything. They went home and thought it over, whether it was worth it, then they came back and got me."

Dane said, "Then what?"

"Then I turned out to be a bum. What they say, no good. I'm off on the wrong track. This is where I ended up," and he yawned widely and explained he had been sleeping when called to this interview.

"Ended up?" Dane said.

"Lots of the things I've done of course, I deserve this. Of course if it hadn't been what I'd done to that little girl I wouldn't be here."

"Have you done things before?"

"Well, yes. I swiped things, but I always paid either the money or gave the merchandise back."

Dane asked for examples of his thievery. After considerable thought he described how he once had stolen some BBs from a store and once had used another boy's bicycle without his permission. All this had been about five years earlier; his father had "tanned my tail." He said that more recently his parents, instead of spanking him, had hidden his clothes to keep him indoors or had forbidden him to ride his kid brother's bicycle (he had none of his own, he said).

Dr. Dane asked when he had learned he was adopted. When he was about five, he said. "I'd met a boy who told me he was adopted and I happened to ask my Mother what adopted meant and she told me." What had she said? "She was telling me how they go to the hospital, they look around for the child they want, if they find the right child they'll take him. They'll pay for the bill of course. She told me about how she had to sign certain papers to release me from the hospital to her," and he smacked his lips and made an odd sound with his mouth, a sound he often made. Had she ever threatened to take him back to the orphanage? No. Had his father? "No—oh, if he'd get mad enough not to know what he was saying he might say, 'I wish you were dead,' or something like that. Course I knew he didn't mean it." His mother hadn't talked to him that way. "If she got mad she'd go to her room and sit and pout and make us wait for her for dinner. She has little ways of getting even with us."

He liked snakes and sometimes scared his mother with them. Once his father killed his pet snake with a ball bat "and I tell you I really flipped." Saturday, he said, always was a long day—he wasn't allowed out of his yard. "I'd tippy-toe up the little tree and eat all the pears," he said, his voice curiously infantile. He rarely went anywhere except to church. Mostly he watched mystery dramas on television. Once in a while he would sneak out to a show after being locked into his room. "I'd tippy-toe out onto the roof and slide down the television pole. But there was a spider on the pole and I was afraid of it." He denied that he was treated unfairly—"The next-door neighbor's kids stick around home a lot, everybody has to stay in his yard," but he wouldn't look at Dr. Dane while he said this. He wanted to be liked, he tried to be friendly.

After he had molested the little girl, her mother had come to Peter's house. Peter's father had sent Peter upstairs while they talked but Peter had tried to eavesdrop through an air duct; his father had caught him at this too. He thought they were right to send him here. "They didn't hit me—they took their time and found out the right thing to do." He seemed to resent nothing, nor did he repent. This had happened; the result might have been expected; all was in order. And at bottom it probably was this odd attitude toward his situation more than anything which disturbed Dr. Dane and would lead another doctor, when the staff met on Monday, to suggest that Peter was "a sociopath in the making."

After he left Dr. Dane looked over his notes, leaning back in his chair, then suddenly tossed his notes onto his desk and said, "I'm still not satisfied. There's something wrong with this whole picture. It ain't enough. He's here because he stole some BBs or peeked under a little girl's dress—and it just ain't enough." Carefully, he read through all Peter's medical records. He noted that Peter was said to have been hospitalized in 1952 and found to have a low blood sugar level. He looked up in a medical paper the relationship between hypoglycemia and electroencephalographic abnormality. (It has been theorized that a rapid fall in the blood sugar level is associated with sociopathic outbursts and also that sociopaths show abnormal electroencephalograms. A sociopath, or psychopathic personality, among other things lacks a conscience and has something wrong with his emotions that makes it impossible for him to live in society, though he is not psychotic.) Once in a while, Dane said, you saw certain electroencephalographic irregularities in children with behavior disorders, "but he doesn't seem to fit that particular pattern very well either." Dane wanted to get a new electroencephalogram. The former one, made two years ago at the clinic, was too abnormal to ignore. Dane gathered up his notes and headed for home, saying, "I'll write him up tonight at home. I may get clobbered for it at staff but I'm going to say I don't think he's psychotic."

8.

On Monday morning the staff met at ten o'clock, six doctors seated around a long oak table in a bare sunny room. They spent an hour on four other cases. Dr. Dane was absent, on vacation. At eleven o'clock Dr. Shortridge, new to the staff, presented Peter Bell's case, reading from notes of his own, case records and Dane's summary. He concluded, "My original impression was CBS [chronic brain syndrome] associated with convulsive disorder with psychotic reaction, but after finding out a little more about him I'm not entirely convinced in my own mind that the boy is psychotic."

Others had drifted in—four or five social workers, another doctor finishing his rounds, the Catholic chaplain. Interest in Peter was high. At 11:16 Shortridge went to get him. Peter had been waiting since before ten o'clock, sitting on a bench in the hall, wearing the white nightshirt and loose white overalls of a newly admitted patient. Today was one of the most important in his life. What the staff decided this morning might well determine the whole course his life would take, and perhaps he sensed this, for he was quieter, more subdued, less given to yawning and posturing than previously.

He sat at the head of the long table, and, while all the others gazed at him, he answered Dr. Shortridge's quiet questions. How did he feel? When did he come here? Why? He told the story of the social worker's daughter in a straightforward way. Shortridge inquired about his parents, his schoolwork, his relations with his brother, and all his answers were courteous, correct, friendly and brief. Shortridge paused. It was dead quiet in the room. Peter looked scared.

Shortridge looked around the table at the other doctors, and two or three of them asked questions. Why had he changed schools? Were his grades good? How did the teachers treat him? Was he afraid of male teachers? (He had none.) Did the teachers punish him? ("They give you a good talking to or paddle you.") Now about his seizures, did he ever get one while watching television? No. Get them at school? Never. At home? Yes. After school? Once before school. But always at home? Yes. The doctors, interested in this, looked at each other. At what hour? Oh, different hours, sometimes 2 P.M. But wouldn't he be in school at 2? "Yes, but take on Saturday—this usually happens on Saturday and Sunday." No seizures during the week? No.

The staff had finished. Dr. Kovitz, who had been sitting next to Peter, his head tipped forward, looking up at Peter but saying nothing, closed the interview. He asked how much anticonvulsant medicine Peter had been taking and whether it had helped. It had. Dr. Kovitz asked how he felt about being here.

"Well, outside I was a little nervous waiting."

Dr. Kovitz asked if there were further questions.

A social worker asked, "If you had three wishes what would they be?"

"All the money in the world," he said. "Then, to be the best sports player. Then, to get to read the comics every day. I miss the comics here."

It was his first attempt at bravado at staff. Dr. Kovitz said he'd see if they couldn't get the comics for him, and said, "Thank you for talking to us, you can wait out in the hall now." Grinning, Peter got up and left. It was 11:33; he had been here fifteen minutes.

The doctors discussed his case. Psychiatrists share one instinct with policemen: When a citizen complains he has been robbed policemen first investigate the citizen himself before commencing a search for robbers; and when parents bring a problem child to psychiatrists, they study not the child but the parents. This instinct serves both policemen and psychiatrists well. The doctors around the table now devoted their first and fullest attention to Peter's parents, mentioning that they had threatened to return him to the orphanage, that they seemed motivated by money, that his brother also was "retarded," that the brother had a bicycle and Peter didn't, that "the parents have a very strong sense of responsibility for him and give the impression of trying very hard to make the best of what they feel is a bad bargain."

It was getting late, 11:41 A.M. Staff would end at noon. Dr. Kovitz said, "Let's get the lineup of our opinions. I think, Dr. Shortridge, you originally said chronic brain syndrome with psychosis."

Shortridge said, "I think I may have been wrong."

"What do you suggest now—chronic brain syndrome with convulsive disorder without psychotic reaction?"

"I think his behavior pattern is eccentric."

"Behavioral reaction then?"

"Behavioral reaction superimposed on chronic brain syndrome with convulsive disorder."

Dr. Kovitz called next on Dr. John Roper, another young man, who said, "Rather than call it chronic brain syndrome, I'd prefer to call it personality trait disturbance, a transient situational disturbance of childhood."

Kovitz said skeptically, "You call it personality trait disturbance in an epileptic? All right. Dr. Lande?"

Dr. Lande, a tall handsome gray-haired Hungarian woman, said,

"Whether the epileptic seizures are the direct cause of the difficulty I doubt. This is a behavioral reaction not really caused by the brain disorder. I can't see psychotic, I see behavior disorder. I would not like to see him here," and she turned to face the chaplain, "I would like to see him in a Catholic school, Father Grady."

Father Grady, sitting in a corner, said, "I don't know of one around here offhand. His home is in another diocese, anyway. I doubt if I can find a place for him."

Dr. Kovitz called on Dr. Saul Bookspan, a little mustached man with several years in state hospital work, who said, "I don't think it really is CBS with convulsive disorder. He doesn't have his seizures at school or at play, when he's really in an excited state. He has them when he's home on weekends. When he has nothing to do but look out the window. Or when his parents are present. As to the behavior disorder, I'd like to know what behavior it is that the teachers complain of. I'd like to know what he does. Does he break things?"

Dr. Shortridge looked at the records. "There is a complaint of frequent lying. Unreliable. Has been destructive. His mother mentioned that he broke the lock on a hundred-year-old chest because he thought she had hidden his knife inside. He brought his brother's bicycle home with one tire shot full of holes. He threw rocks."

Dr. Bookspan shook his head. "Each of these things doesn't seem the result of a brain syndrome. It seems to be a personality trait disorder. I'd rather split the diagnosis—one, personality trait disorder; two, epilepsy. Or," he added, smiling, "just put down adolescence."

Dr. Kovitz said, "There's some question whether this is full-fledged epilepsy. At the clinic or at Receiving they observed one seizure and said it was not a typical grand mal seizure. That doesn't prove it isn't epilepsy, of course. Everybody agrees these seizures of his fulfill a psychic function but that also doesn't rule out epilepsy. Certainly the emotional component is very great."

Dr. Mary Lou Hippert, who, as the ward doctor on the acute male wards, now would have Peter as one of her patients, said, "I'd like another electroencephalogram. I feel the seizures are entirely unrelated to his behavior. All these episodes of terrible behavior have been pretty well responsive to feelings of rejection. And I can't get too alarmed about the little girl."

Dr. Kovitz turned to Dr. Maria Madi, and she said, "I think what we are seeing is a sociopath in the making. But I don't know whether you can call a child of thirteen a sociopath."

Dr. Kovitz nodded. "I'd rather not," then he hitched his chair around again and said, "I agree with Dr. Roper that we're not justified in calling it CBS. I don't see any evidence. The psychological tests don't support it. I can offer two diagnoses. First, let's assume that there is a fair probability of a diagnosis of epilepsy. [Subsequently a new electroencephalogram did show abnormalities commonly associated with epilepsy.] Epilepsy can influence behavior, we know that. But we speak of chronic brain syndrome when there are signs of impaired intelligence or loss of emotional control due to brain damage. Second, there's this personality disorder which has a lot of interpersonal roots in the family life. A lot of his behavior could be accounted for by feelings of rebellion and rejection. It's been going on too long to call it transient. At this age I'd rather call it an adjustment reaction of childhood and adolescence. But no matter what we call it, we've got a serious problem here. This boy has obviously developed poorly. He's never had proper treatment. He's had examinations but that's only the beginning. At the clinic what was done for him? I don't know that anything was done. Diagnosis is useful but it misses the point—what are we going to do with him? Sending him back to his family doesn't seem to be the answer. Probably taking him out of his family and putting him in a good residential treatment center would be the answer—if it could be done," he added, smiling—he knew the state had no such public institution and the parents probably couldn't afford a private one. "This has already been recommended by the clinic in so many words, two years ago. The clinic also said the parents need help. I think we ought to try to help work out this arrangement—get him into a family treatment center somewhere and perhaps get the family also into treatment. This seems to me to be primarily a problem for Social Service."

One of the social workers said, "There are no facilities in their community. And they're pretty rejecting of any suggestions that they need help themselves. I doubt if they'd do it."

Kovitz nodded. "Well, have them come in and try to talk to them. If we meet a stone wall we'll have to concentrate on the boy—getting him placed somewhere. He doesn't belong here."

Dr. Shortridge said, "You want a new EEG?"

"Yes."

"Do you want to repeat psychological testing?"

"If it hasn't been done since 1953 at the clinic."

"It hasn't. You want it for mental deficiency?"

"No, for personality problems. Try the TAT"—the Thematic Apperception Test.

As the doctors arose to go to lunch, Dr. Lande said, "And somebody give him the funnies every day."

9.

Subsequently, the doctors diagnosed Peter officially as not psychotic— "adjustment reaction of childhood and adolescence, with epilepsy." About a month later, Peter's parents, with the help of the hospital's Social Service Department, Father Grady, and their own parish priest, found a Catholic boarding school for "problem children" which would accept Peter, and they sent him to it.

11

The Back Wards

■ "The Back Wards"—a phrase that has shamed and disheartened psychiatrists for years. Every prolonged-care state hospital has them. True, each hospital has its own Ward 8, where the heroic struggle against acute psychosis goes on; it has its own Ward 9, whence women who are getting well go home; but behind and beyond those busy wards stretch the desolate spaces of the back wards—the place where patients go who do not respond to treatment, the place where patients go when the doctors give up on them, the place for the hospital's failures.

In a big hospital, if the acute cases are numbered in the hundreds, the chronics who inhabit the back wards are numbered in the thousands. Year after year they accumulate, and as they overflow their accommodations the state builds more and more and bigger and bigger buildings. (Or so it has been till now; lately a new trend seems to be setting in.) A back ward starts, as did one at Elgin State Hospital in Illinois, with a row of beds on each side of the ward; as patients pile up the doctors put a row of beds down the center aisle; then they move the beds closer together, until the ward is a solid mass of beds shoved almost together and finally the ward's dining room is filled with beds, which the patients, elderly women, have to fold up and remove each morning so meals can be served. In one ward at Elgin 250 women, many of them naked, all of them regressed schizophrenics, stand facing the locked screen door, staring mindlessly at it, and one says to a doctor passing by,

"It's a shame, what are you going to do with us, there are a lot of doctors and nurses in the world, aren't there, I'd be better off in a pigpen." In one back ward at Chicago State Hospital a few years ago the attendant kept thirty or forty untidy patients in the toilet day in, day out, year in, year out; there they stood, or sat on the tile floor, naked or nearly so, urinating and defecating, regressed to infancy, and the attendant, guarding the door, kept them there so they would not soil the floor in the rest of the ward; he was proud of its cleanliness. A doctor passing through remarked, "It isn't the disease that has done this to them—it's the hospital. This is the disgrace of this institution. And this is what we call a hospital."

2.

At Columbus State Hospital in 1955, Dr. John Roper was taking care of three chronic women's wards. He was a young man and came to Columbus State in 1955 only a few months out of internship and Indiana University Medical School. A tall dark-haired serious man with a somewhat expressionless face, he lived at the hospital with his wife and new baby. He liked it here. He thought he might stay on in state hospital practice after finishing his residency. His large patient load did not discourage him. Moreover, as he said, "I see the worst end of it too—I've got the chronics. On the acute wards, you know a lot of them will go home." But it didn't seem to bother him; he was outgoing, unruffled, interested in his work and, probably fortunately for both him and his patients, the full horror of what he daily saw did not seem to have struck home to him, and perhaps it never would. He went along day to day on an even keel, doing what he could for the twenty-odd patients (out of his two-hundred-odd) that he thought he could help.

The female side of the huge main building is always noticeably noisier than the men's side—more screaming, more senseless yelling, more wild weeping and laughter. Doctors are inclined to be a bit leery of female patients. One recalls that the only patient that ever hit him was a woman. Oddly, although about half the patients in Columbus in 1955 were men and half women, the women got a great deal more treatment than the men—ninety-six women on Thorazine but only forty men. Kovitz said, "More women seem to get disturbed than men, and women who become disturbed are really disturbed. Women give a more picturesque picture in psychosis, there is an amazing richness about their hallucinations and delusions, and this may be what interests doctors in doing individual psychotherapy with them. But why they get more disturbed or why their hallucinations are more picturesque I don't know. Maybe it's because they undergo more suppression all their lives than men."

Ward 7, Dr. Roper's chronic disturbed ward, was located at the rear of the first floor, behind the female admitting ward and a female medical ward. "They have a tendency to put anyone who becomes combative on Ward 7," Dr. Roper said one day, entering the ward and relocking the door. "It is a pretty good idea on this ward to keep your hands in your pockets and not to bring a pocket knife with you." Barbara Little was on this ward. The ward was long and narrow and dark. The television set was on but no one was watching. About twenty-five women were sitting in chairs against the walls or walking around the ward.

Walking slowly down the ward past the patients, he said, "I think I know everybody on this ward, at least by name." A little dark-complexioned woman lay huddled on a bench, a gray blanket wrapped around her like a shroud. She looked up quizzically. Roper said, "Are you cold? You're in a blanket."

She said, "I catch cold," and smiled. Her skin was an odd color. She looked Hindu.

Roper said, aside, "That little woman weighs eighty-seven pounds and has one leg off but she's the most feared woman patient in the hospital. She's a terrible fighter. When they get her arms pinned she uses the stump of her leg to beat them in the abdomen." He turned to look at her, and she arose and, drawing the blanket about her thin body, hopped off down the long gray ward.

Roper went on and stopped beside an enormous bloated old harridan with white stringy hair sitting cross-legged on the floor. He fingered a healing scar on her scalp and said, "It's coming along fine, Nancy."

Looking up resentfully, she said, "Who are you?"

"Do you know who I am, Nancy?"

"No, I don't know. And I don't care."

"Who are you?"

"I'm Nancy Billings, and that's all there is to it."

"What do you do for a living, Nancy?"

"What do I do for a living? I've got the government and the President's protection," and warningly, "That's all there is, that's all there needs to be." He walked on, and she began to call loudly, "Anna Hahn, Anna Hahn, Anna Hahn."

Roper said, "Do you know who Anna Hahn is? I didn't either, till I happened to run across it in the paper. She was the first woman electrocuted in the state of Ohio. In 1938. Sometimes Nancy says, 'I saved Anna Marie Hahn that day.' Nancy is a general paretic. Her life expectancy is not long. Penicillin can cure syphilis but not paresis. Paresis is irreversible. Sometimes we can stop it in its tracks but that's all—we can never reverse it, once the central nervous system is involved. She thinks both her ankles are broken so she sits on the floor all day and if she wants to move she scoots along like a small child. You can't make her stand up. She's been that way for years." (She actually had broken a bone in one ankle fourteen years ago.)

Roper walked on back to the annex, a rectangular room built recently, with tiled walls. It was darker here. Around the walls were the seclusion rooms. Five of them were in use. The door of one was open, and a middle-aged Negro woman was standing inside, talking loudly to herself, and when Roper asked, "How are you?" she replied loudly, "I'm fine. What's Roosevelt got to do with it," and laughed loudly, and began to dance and clap her hands rhythmically, then to sing but there was no sense to her singing, just disjointed unintelligible syllables. She was a noisy patient and preferred to be alone.

Roper left her and unlocked the next room. A large soft-faced middle-aged white woman lay on the bed, a deteriorated psychotic epileptic. Roper examined her puffy skinned-up knuckles; she'd been fighting. He told her to make a fist, but she didn't understand; he demonstrated, and pushed her fingers; finally she said, "Oh, like that." The noisy woman came dancing in, and Roper laughed at her and told her to go away, but she wouldn't, and the epileptic reached out one hand from under the bedclothes and took her hand, and a look of compassion crossed the epileptic's heavy features, she felt sorry for the dancing woman. Only as she moved the bedclothes did one notice that her ankle was tied to the bed with a strip of heavy cloth: she was in restraint.

Roper left, urging the dancing woman ahead of him. In the next room was an enormous white-haired woman dressed all in black, curled up under a blanket on the bed; she was in seclusion because it was near dinnertime, and she was on a diet, and if let out onto the ward would have seized the food of other patients and devoured it.

When Roper had started visiting the seclusion rooms a woman in a gingham dress had been sitting on a window ledge with her back to the iron bars and the window pulled down onto her knees, squeezed into the narrow space between window and bars; silently she had watched him go from room to room. Now as he prepared to leave she raised the window. Roper said, "What are you doing—getting a sunbath?" She grinned, pleased, but said nothing. In a corner in the shadows sat a tall rangy Negro woman alone in an attitude of prayer. Roper said, "How are you?" and she instantly got up, strode to him and, in a loud oracular tone, said, "I'm saving them all. I'm helping the President and the Lord to save them all." She was tall, erect, vigorous, her manner apparently friendly but determined and missionary-like. Roper said, "That's fine," and she went on with her harangue. Leaving, Roper said, "It isn't good psychiatry to agree with their delusions—I wouldn't do it with a patient there was some hope for but I don't think it does any harm in this case."

The porch was full of flies. One of the screens was rusted out. Though the windows were open the odor was overpowering. A patient was mopping, endlessly mopping. Here on the porch, sitting on benches or lying on the floor or squatting on the window ledge, were twenty-five women who either wouldn't keep their clothes on or were incontinent. Roper walked slowly around the porch. A thin old Negro woman pressed against the wall was grimacing horribly; the grimace started with her mouth and progressed till her whole face was involved, and, watching, Roper said, "That means something. But what it is we'll never know. Notice that the hair just above her forehead is all rubbed away? She does it with her hand, rubbing her head over and over."

Indicating a powerful rawboned woman opposite Roper said, "You often hear it said that the American Indian is never psychotic but there's a full-blooded one who is." A woman was perched on a chair stork-like on one leg. Roper paused in front of a little woman all curled up on a chair, bony knees drawn up under her chin; he said to his visitor, "How are your nerves?" then to the little woman, "Hello—how are you?" Instantly she bared her teeth, drawing back her lips, and hissed and snarled, spit flying catlike; she kept doing it so long as Roper was near. Crossing the porch, he said, "She's always like that, always the same."

He went up to an old Negress who was sewing on a patchwork quilt. Standing beside her, Roper said, "She helps us, she takes care of her girls, don't you?" and she looked up smiling. Two others had gotten up to pace the floor rapidly; she called sharply to them, and they sat. She wanted to show Roper her sewing. She said, "I get my thread this way," and showed how she ripped threads from a piece of sheeting. "I had a bigger needle but she stole it," indicating a woman opposite, "and now all I've got is this and it's too little without glasses."

Roper said, "I haven't heard any music all day—play us a tune, will you," and, urged, she put her sewing down and stepped to an old upright piano and standing before it—there was no stool—she banged out a song. The rhythm was fine but there was no tune. Immediately a large blond shapeless woman got up and paced to and fro in great agitation. "She always does that," Roper said. The rest sat. Soon the music died away; the pianist sat again to sew, oblivious now of Roper. He crossed to a big woman in a corner but she said to him, "You better go along now, you've been here long enough," and there was menace in her voice, Roper drifted on out. He paused in the kitchen to tell an attendant to take the needle away from the old Negress—she might jab someone with it. He waited to make sure the attendant could get the needle without help, then went back out to the hall.

A tense woman who must have been attractive once stopped him. "Can I have a word with you, sir?" She had a kerchief bound tightly about her head; she had been pacing up and down the ward rapidly, with long-legged taut strides. She asked, "Do I have to have EST tomorrow?"

Roper said, "You know better than that."

"The nurse said I did."

"Well, you don't. I'll see to it." Though nurses sometimes do threaten to punish patients with EST, it was not at all certain any nurse had threatened this one, for she was as unreliable as a human being can be: she was a sociopath, or psychopathic personality. Sociopaths have no judgment. Once this one asked Dr. Roper to slip her a few matches, which were forbidden. She told Roper now, "I guess the nurse just didn't know. She's new. I'm going to help her."

Roper said, "I know she'll appreciate your help." Moving on, Roper said, "Her daughter had her brought here six years ago. She was sleeping all around and drinking—the typical case history. She's escaped innumerable times. She'll tell the doctor, 'I realize I done wrong, give me one more chance,' and you'll give her a privilege, and next day the police will pick her up downtown, drunk, and bring her back and say,

'Here's your girl friend again.' She tries to manipulate me—she knows one of my jobs is to censor patients' mail so her letters are full of compliments to me."

Before leaving the ward, Roper paused by the door in front of a frail, pale young girl. "How are you?" he asked. She did not answer; she was sitting rigid in a chair, holding her hands in her lap and looking down as though reading a book; but there was no book. Roper said, "I had a letter from your mother." No answer, no movement. Roper took one of her hands in his and raised it to shoulder height, in the position of one taking an oath; he removed his hand; hers remained where he put it. "Cerea flexibilis," doctors call this, or waxy flexibility —the patient will allow his body to remain in any position in which it is put, so determined is he not to resist the world but to withdraw from it and let it work its will upon him. It is a leading symptom of catatonic schizophrenia. The girl had been only sixteen when she came here in 1952.

An only child, she had become seriously disturbed at ten when her mother had borne another child. Her parents had taken her to a private psychiatrist for psychotherapy, had put her in a private sanitarium for EST and insulin shock. She had failed to improve, and her parents couldn't afford more treatment. They evidently had made one last desperate effort to avoid putting her in a state hospital—had taken her to a "professor" who had treated her "by hypnosis." It had made her worse, and at last her parents had taken her to Columbus State, having followed the sad course so many follow.

There, asked whether anyone was trying to influence her, she had replied, "Uh-huh." In what way? "For example she put her urine in the food and wet the spoon with it and made me eat it." Had she been influenced in any other way? In a loud and hostile tone she had said, "No, just eating belts and peeking down urine when they are menstruating and peeking in guts to see if you love them and peeking in blood and bone." She had not known who she was or what the year was. She had known she was in a hospital; asked what kind of hospital, she had said, "It is kind of a psychiatric office of a fiend." What would be her future plans? "Be good." What had that meant? "That I don't want to be bothered by anybody of any sort," which is precisely the way catatonics feel.

She had steadily deteriorated, become mute. Everything had been tried on her. Forty-nine ESTs had only confused her. Moved to a chronic ward, she had become incontinent and had begun having epileptoid seizures. Anticonvulsant drugs had not helped. She had had six seizures in a half-hour and been sent to the medical ward on a stretcher as an emergency. She had become destructive, throwing flowerpots and trays of food about and one afternoon demolishing the parlor furniture on Ward 15. Dr. Kovitz had decided to have her lobotomized, though she was only eighteen, and had obtained her mother's consent. But, given a pneumoencephalogram as a preliminary to the operation, she had developed an irritation of the cerebrospinal system, and by the time she recovered the hospital had quit performing psychosurgery.

Roper, leaving her now, said, "What's she doing now? Just sitting. A while back I talked to her parents about putting her on Thorazine but they can't afford it. I can't get a lobotomy. So now we keep her on Ward 7, and every two or three days she throws a wing-ding—gets up, stands up, looks around for someone and piles into the nearest person. She sweats when she does it, and she's small and wiry and hard to hold—the attendants lay her down on the floor and lie across her and hold her down for maybe ten minutes till she calms down. Then they let her up and she'll get up and go sit on a chair and be all right again. This is catatonia—deep catatonia. When an excited catatonic comes in you have to treat them fast—give EST two or three times a day, or otherwise they'll exhaust themselves and die." Hadn't he tried to get Thorazine for her from the hospital supply? "I haven't because I couldn't get it, I know without trying. She's not acute enough right now."

3.

Upstairs on the chronic wards on the male side of the hospital dwelt 683 patients. Some were on anticonvulsant drugs, a few were on the new psychiatric drugs, and occasionally when one became disturbed he was given shock. But for the most part the patients merely lived here. It was a pleasant hospital fiction to call these "chronic convalescent wards." Convalescence implies recovery; few of these patients were recovering, they were staying the same or deteriorating.

Dr. Saul Bookspan, unlocking the door of Ward 18, said, "This is my good ward." Dr. Bookspan took care of all four upstairs wards on the third floor—18, 20, 22 and 24. About 285 patients in all. Bookspan had worked his way through medical school in Chicago, interned in Toledo and worked at Toledo State Hospital. During the Korean War, the army, short of psychiatrists, had assigned Bookspan to duty as a psychiatrist; after it he had gone back to Toledo State Hospital. But Toledo had not been approved for psychiatric residency training, so Bookspan had come to Columbus July 1, 1955. He intended to stay on here. "I don't intend to go into private psychiatry," he said. "Ohio realizes it has to train psychiatrists. And it has a right to call on them to work for it. A man interested in psychiatry now has a place to get training and a place where he can use it. I see myself as an Ohioan and as working for the state of Ohio. They'll get their money's worth, the people of Ohio will. The average citizen is paying my salary now. I'll give it back."

Dr. Bookspan's "good ward," 18, was clean, fresh-painted, soft-lit, its wooden floor well waxed, curtains hanging at the windows, wooden tables and chairs standing about. A patient was perched in a high ancient barber chair, and another was cutting his hair. As Bookspan arrived patients arose and clustered around him. One gave him a letter to mail; Bookspan examined it; it was all in numbers. Bookspan asked, "What's this—I can't understand it."

The patient said, "They will understand the code. They want me to write in code so the other forces won't know."

Bookspan asked, "What kind of work do you do?"

"I'm an investigator for the hospital," and then, passing a hand over his brow, "I wonder if anything happened last night."

Bookspan put the letter in his pocket and patted him on the shoulder, saying, "Don't work too hard at your investigating work—get some sleep too." Others spoke to him, importuning him about a visit home, a wicked attendant, a sore nose; and Bookspan, moving down the ward in their midst, they moving with him, said, "If you want to talk to a patient for long you have to sit down with him somewhere else—on the ward they try to tear you from all sides. Their problems are important to them, even though they're deluded." He went into the nurse's office.

Much of Bookspan's time was taken up with looking at a hernia, dressing a lip split in a fight, writing a prescription for the X-ray of a swollen hand, making out a report on accidents, doling out Thorazine, resolving problems. The hospital kitchen wanted the man with the swollen hand to come back to work, he was needed there, no other patient could brew coffee so well, but Bookspan said the hand had to be treated first. The patient was worried; and now the dining room called again to insist that he return, until finally Bookspan told the attendant, "Tell her that's her worry, the coffee—tell her to call the supervisor and get somebody else for a while." Bookspan left the office, remarking, "You can spend as much time as you want on a chronic ward. It's surprising how much good you can do. At least you can keep the patients quiet and well. They're human and have needs—though psychotic ones. If I don't make rounds one day, the next day the ward is more upset."

Carrying a thick notebook, he moved quickly through his first three wards, 18, 20, and 22. They were much alike, though toward the rear of the building the patients seemed progressively worse. An old man standing in the hall was making an odd motion with his hands; he clasped them together and raised them over his head, then brought them smartly down and across his body, somewhat as though driving a posthole digger into the ground, twisted them, stooped slightly to thrust them closer to the floor, then straightened abruptly; he did it over and over, vigorously, with single-minded concentration; and other patients strolled near him without paying the slightest heed.

A man was sitting sideways on a bench with his legs hanging over the end of it. He was sitting on his hands. He was all curled up but had he stood up straight he would have been seen to be very tall. Bookspan stopped beside him and said, "How are you feeling?" No answer. Bookspan put a hand on his shoulder and said it again. Slowly the man looked up, his face without expression, his eyes glazed over. But he spoke. "All right," he said, then quickly looked down again. The attendant, moving away with Bookspan, said, "That's the first word I've heard him speak in three years." All his life the patient had been shy and seclusive. He had made his psychotic break at twenty-nine— had seemed dazed, quit work, sat speechless for hours and days, whipped the children if left alone with them, said he wanted to "jump off the end of the earth," taking them with him. His wife, fearful, had had him committed. He had told the doctors that "they"—the mysterious "They" of schizophrenia—had plotted and persuaded his wife to have him sent here. That had been in 1948. Since then he had gone home on trial visit, threatened his wife and been brought back forcibly by the sheriff; doctors had all but ignored him till one day in 1954 Dr. Madi had examined him and had found him repeating in a stereotype way, "They will work it out." But "they" wouldn't, and neither would he: He had given up the struggle; it was all over with him.

Beyond Bookspan's three better chronic wards lay Ward 24. It was the chronic disturbed men's ward and it was used for "security" cases. "The only really dangerous men in the hospital are on 24," said a doctor. The floor here was terrazzo. The ward was very bare—few chairs, no curtains, no television set, no little tables, no flowerpots. (You can tell by the number of flowerpots what kind of patients are on a ward. Flowerpots are dangerous weapons in the hands of a disturbed patient.) The odor noticeable on any ward was stronger here—a heavy pungent odor compounded of disinfectant, perspiration, urine and feces—and it was overpowering in one of the bare seclusion rooms, and, inspecting this room, Bookspan told the attendant somewhat sharply it should be cleaned. The attendant replied that he mopped it every day and scrubbed down the walls and ceiling once a week. (On some wards seclusion rooms were so filthy one would think they were never cleaned.)

Nearly all the ninety patients were out on the porch, and there they sat all day, a husky attendant watching over them. Today the porch was flooded, somebody had thrown something down the toilet, and in the cross corridor leading to it Dr. Bookspan met a large muscular red-faced patient with a lobotomy scar on his head carrying a plumber's pump. It was a heavy instrument, and the patient, a manic, said he was taking care of it for the plumber; Bookspan took it away from him and told an attendant to lock it up, then went onto the porch, remarking, "He probably didn't intend to hit anybody with it but you never can tell. He has a disturbed period about once a year. He's been showing signs lately of going into one and we've got him on Serpasil to see if we can't carry him through it."

On the porch Bookspan walked slowly along in front of the patients. They were sitting on chairs and benches against the walls. Most ignored him. They were packed tight together. Most of them had been sick at least ten years. Bookspan halted in front of a tall Negro with bulging eyes and a hostile expression; he continued to stare straight ahead. Bookspan asked how he felt. No answer. Nor did he reply to other questions, or give any sign he had heard. The police had picked him up on the street three years earlier and brought him to the hospital, struggling, cursing his wife, cursing the president of a Southern college who had contacted the police by "electrostatic waves." He had had no wife, had planned to marry that summer. He had been a college dean. But in the hospital he steadfastly maintained he was illiterate.

He was combative; he made advances toward female attendants. He had been given electroshock and insulin shock and much sedation; nothing helped; he had been in seclusion or restraint most of the time.

Bookspan stopped in front of a wizened little man sitting with his hands on his knees and his head bowed down and asked, "Hello, Joe, everything going all right?" He looked up. His eyes were slits, his neck muscles tense, his expression a lowering scowl. It was the mask of a man once dangerous but now burned out. In his record some years ago a doctor had made this notation: "Without a doubt he is the most dangerous patient in the hospital." He first had come here in 1933. He had improved, gone home, worked a year, begun to hear the voices again, gone west, been picked up in California and sent back to Ohio. He had said, "I don't believe in science, blood relatives or kindness. I never stick right. I want to kill people because they have no ideas. I am a socialist. I don't know what that is. I have no money and no politics. I was not supposed to have money. I am supposed to keep believing in darker things and keeping in the dark." In the hospital he had fought patients and attendants alike for two years. He had said he wanted to go to Lima State Hospital for the Criminally Insane and that he would go there if he had to kill someone to do it. He had been kept locked alone in a seclusion room for months on end, and finally in 1940 had been sent to Lima, disoriented, mute, and with his ears plugged with paper, evidently to keep out the voices. At Lima he had sat. And had kept paper stuffed in his ears, answered questions in monosyllables and lived in a world apart. After a few years a doctor had written, "This patient is so deteriorated he is practically a mental blank." In 1949, having done nothing violent for several years, he had been sent back to Columbus and put first on Ward 8, the acute ward, and then on 24. For months on end he had sat on the same spot on the same bench, looking, a doctor had written, like a threadbare and bedraggled scarecrow staring at the floor. The doctor had given the attendants permission to restrain him or seclude him whenever necessary, and they had done so most of the time. Thus unable to attack attendants any longer, he offended them by being dirty, untidy and destructive. One noted: "Same old filthy patient." Occasionally he was given EST to quiet him down. And recently he had been put on large doses of Thorazine; he no longer had to be secluded or restrained but could safely sit on the porch with the other patients.

Bookspan walked on around the porch. A very tall, very powerful white man approached, moving slowly, picking his way over the legs of sprawling patients. He had a shiny lobotomy scar across the top of his bald head. He said, "When can I go home, Doctor?"

Bookspan said, "We'll see—whenever you're well enough," and moved slowly on, remarking, "When he gets upset he can chase eight attendants out of here. He's on Serpasil now, and it's holding him so far. He walks around all the time, won't sit down. He is very delusional. There are snakes in his bed and he has to crush them. He has nihilistic delusions—his stomach is split wide open. Now that he's on Serpasil he can talk about his delusions and they don't excite him. The drugs don't destroy the delusions but the patient doesn't act on them. Every paranoid schizophrenic is dangerous when he is projecting—projecting his hatred to the outside world. When the voices threaten him, he may strike out. But on drugs they don't seem to. That patient used to try to kill. Now he can wander around the ward safely.

"In fact," Bookspan added, "I think there's only one man still in restraint now on the whole ward—out of a hundred violent patients. So the new drugs do help. At least they help from a management viewpoint. We might only have six men on this ward out of the hundred who are disturbed at any one time but they would keep the rest in a turmoil. So if we can keep those six quiet with drugs, the whole ward is quiet."

He moved a few steps away and halted in front of a huge Negro—the only man on the ward still in restraint. A heavy leather strap was looped around both his wrists and fastened to another heavy strap about his waist, so that his arms were bound fast to his abdomen. They were powerful arms; his shirt sleeves were cut off at the shoulder, and his muscles rippled powerfully. He was a very black Negro, tall, with a small head. Dr. Bookspan said softly, "Sometimes Roland hurts people. I don't know why. We don't think he means to but sometimes he does anyway." Roland stared straight ahead. "Roland is getting Thorazine now and it is helping him," Bookspan went on, looking at Roland but speaking to a visitor. "Until he began getting Thorazine he had been either in seclusion or restraint or both most of the time all his life."

Roland Smith came here in 1919. He was then nineteen years old. He was one of those anonymous homeless drifters cast up on the beach to public notice by chance—he was picked up on the street by the police for vagrancy—and seemingly without a past (though obviously he had one, and a hideous one it must have been). He did not know how he happened to be in the city of Columbus, or where he had come from or when he had fallen ill. He once said he was born in the South, never went to school, had had five or six brothers and sisters who had died. He had worked for a circus for a while and had hurt his head. No more is known.

Brought to the hospital from jail he was mute. But after he had been here a while he became very voluble. He told a doctor, "I am God myself. I have God's face. My face has never come. My right name is King, God, Jesus Christ. I have solid fire in my body. My hands aggravate me. They jump around. [His fingers, extended, did tremble markedly.] I have got the tree of life in my body. I talk to Jesus Christ and men who have left this earth. I hear voices all the time. I see all kinds of things. I never saw Jesus. I seen an angel with a robe on. I have only got two years to go. I came out of the blue stone. God is on this side," and he pointed to the right side of his body. The doctor wrote:

Says he has two heart beats, one wanted to do good and the other wanted to do evil. He says that the power pulls him from one side to the other and sometimes he becomes plumb crazy; that one voice in him will be cursing and one praying and one preaching. Says he can cause lightning storms to come up. Says he can cross one knee on his hand and put his other leg over his hand and in less than two hours he can have lightning flashing around. Says he can put his left hand on his right shoulder and he will have tornadoes, wind and lightning. "This body was born by I don't know what. I was taken to the jail house." Said something came and talked to him a long time and told him there would be no white people; would be all black people in the next world to come; then Jesus Christ came and told him there would be no world at all, nothing but the heavens and hell.

Smith had some insight into his condition—he said once, "I'm crazy as a baby." He was diagnosed schizophrenia, catatonic type. But whatever clinical interest the hospital felt in him evaporated quickly, for he became a serious management problem almost at once. It was his habit to sit mute and frozen against the wall and then without provocation or warning to spring upon anybody that passed near. Whenever an attendant was alone on the ward it was necessary to restrain Smith. By 1921 his doctor wrote, "He is exceedingly vicious at times, biting and striking attendants, and is very difficult to control on account of his delusions. Our facilities for caring for this class of patients, in our overcrowded condition, are not good." So he was sent to Lima.

He arrived there in a catatonic stupor, mute, stubborn, opposed to being handled. Soon, while being taken out for exercise, he grabbed an attendant around the neck and bit a piece out of his ear. He stabbed an attendant with a spoon; he threw dishes in the dining room. Thereafter he was locked up in a room alone. And with few exceptions he was kept locked up in a room alone for more than twenty years. Every day several attendants had to take him out of his room, bathe him forcibly, change his clothing and put him in another room while they cleaned the room he had fouled. One morning when an attendant alone opened his door Smith knocked him down, jumped on him and tried to bite him in the neck; three patients came to the rescue. Occasionally the attendants tried to give him some freedom. He always fought. Once somebody, apparently another patient, gashed his head deeply with a heavy metal doorstop. By 1926 a doctor wrote, "Mentally, his case seems hopeless." Another wrote in 1931, "This patient is a dangerous man and acts more like an enraged beast than a human being."

But apparently years of solitary confinement—for that is what his hospitalization amounted to—or perhaps the mere passage of the years wrought a change, for by 1944 Smith's doctor wrote, "He is a blank mentally and is very untidy, but withal is not difficult to handle." And two years later he was working on the ward. Lima sent him back to Columbus.

He was put on Ward 8, the acute disturbed ward, mute, standing rigid or lying in bed in a fetal position. He was put in a cottage with older men, but though his arms were bound to his abdomen he shoved the old patients down. So at last he came to Ward 24, and he has been here ever since. He sits on the same spot on the same bench on the porch, day in, day out. Sometimes he plays with a Teddy bear. He rarely speaks. It is doubtful that he understands questions. Now and then he arises and tries to fight. He is secluded at night. In 1951 an attendant noticed his face was swollen; he had a fractured skull. It healed. In 1952 he started smoking cigarettes. There is nothing more to say about him.

4.

Behind the main hospital building, near its powerhouse and shops and garage and laundry, stands a cluster of six cottages. Five are substantial two-story brick structures built around the turn of the century; the sixth is a new low modern building. Four are for women, two for men. In them live some 900 patients. They are the old people. Some came to the hospital young but the doctors never were able to get them well enough to leave. Seeing them now, ancient and mindless, one had difficulty realizing that some of them once had been attractive tense young women, precisely like Sally Bennett. Others were old when they arrived—seniles brought in by their shamefaced children unable to care for them. Most will die here. Every state hospital in America is full of them today. And getting fuller—the American life span is lengthening, for medicine is continually prolonging life. (But not mitigating its terminal miseries; just prolonging life.) Time was when old people went to old folks' county homes, or when if Grandpa became a little odd the children put him in the spare room. But the county homes have closed, or are jammed; and today the children live in apartments in the city, there is no spare room; the old folks come here, and to virtually every state hospital in America.

One patient out of every three in American mental hospitals is over sixty and one of every four is sixty-five or over, according to the Council of State Governments. Thus while people sixty-five and over constitute 8.2 per cent of the total population, they make up 25 per cent of the mental hospital population. One authority has estimated that in ten years 50 per cent of the hospital population will consist of senile and arteriosclerotic patients.

The reasons lie in the nation's population shifts. In 1900 there were only three million people sixty-five and over. Today there are more than fourteen million. In ten years we can expect twenty million. More-over, the rate of increase of older people has been twice that of the population as a whole. In 1900 only one in twenty-five living persons was over sixty-five; by 1950 this ratio had changed to one in thirteen. The life expectancy of United States men rose from 46.3 in 1900 to 66.7 in 1955; that of women rose from 48.3 to 73.6 years, according to Institute of Life Insurance Reports. The "fragile male" has been variously but never fully explained. The trend to increased longevity is now subsiding; further increases can be expected only from a general breakthrough in the treatment of diseases of later life.

Psychiatrists classify the old folks who come to mental hospitals into two main categories: Those suffering from chronic brain syndrome associated with cerebral arteriosclerosis, and those suffering from chronic brain syndrome associated with senile brain disease. It is some times difficult or even impossible to distinguish between the two.

As to cerebral arteriosclerosis, the term is, strictly speaking, a misnomer, according to Dr. Arthur P. Noyes' standard text.* Arteriosclerosis means hardening of the arteries, a process occurring in the aged; but it is not the hardening as such which makes trouble but a slightly different process, atherosclerosis, that is, the narrowing or even complete closing of the arteries. When this happens to the blood vessels supplying the brain, the flow of blood to the brain is choked off and gradually the brain cells, starved, deteriorate. Hemorrhage or thrombosis with infarction may occur—a "stroke."

As to senile psychoses, these are psychotic reactions to the problems, organic and nonorganic, of growing old. As a man grows old, anatomical changes occur in his brain due to deficiencies in cerebral blood flow and metabolism. Personality changes begin. His energy and initiative wanes, he fails to respond, his interests narrow, he becomes self-centered and childish. All this makes him anxious. At the same time he becomes lonely because his friends are gone and his children ignore him. To overcome his anxiety and loneliness he utilizes various protective devices, such as turning to the past, paranoid projection, self-assertiveness and so on. "From these mild, senescent mental changes," Dr. Noyes writes, "there is a sliding scale to the extreme impoverishment of mental resources that characterize senile dementia. The dividing line may be a matter of individual opinion." Patients suffering from senile psychoses present symptoms ranging from mild confusion to hallucinations to complete deterioration. Noyes writes, "Although of great importance, organic disease of the brain is often not the only factor in the development of senile psychoses. It is increasingly accepted that frequently the senile psychoses result from the interaction of organic and psychological factors. . . . It would appear, therefore, that not all the factors producing senile dementia are known."

As to the prognosis in cerebral arteriosclerosis, Noyes says it is "naturally unfavorable" but not always uninterruptedly progressive, since some patients enter a hospital confused or excited and apparently demented but under the simple hospital regime recover from their acute symptoms; they may live on for years, although in constant danger of an apoplectic stroke or another confused episode. As to senile psychosis, Noyes writes, "The prognosis of advanced organic senile dementia is manifestly hopeless."

* Arthur P. Noyes, *Modern Clinical Psychiatry*. Fourth edition, Philadelphia: W. B. Saunders Company, 1955.

The death rate from "strokes" due to cerebral arteriosclerosis has remained remarkably constant over the years. Cerebral arteriosclerosis is, after schizophrenia, the leading cause of first admissions to state mental hospitals. Probably half of the patients with cerebral arteriosclerosis die during their first year in the state hospital.

It is by no means certain that all these deaths are inevitable. In recent years new anticoagulant drugs have come into use to prevent the blood from clotting and thus causing a cerebral accident. President Eisenhower and Sir Winston Churchill have been kept on anticoagulants since their first strokes. Anticoagulants have been found most effective in cases where embolism has occurred. If a blood clot forms in the heart, it may break off and go through the bloodstream to an artery in the brain which has become partially closed by atherosclerosis, thus knocking out a portion of the brain. A person who has had one such embolism is likely to have more, until one is fatal. If he is given anticoagulants, he may not have more. Little use has been made of such drugs in state hospitals.

In most state hospitals the old people receive little treatment of any kind. They are considered largely a problem of care and custody—keeping them warm and clean and fed, preventing them from getting hurt, caring for their medical needs. Many of them are bed-ridden, so that the geriatric ward of a state hospital, unlike other wards, resembles a ward in a general, not a mental, hospital—long rows of beds with patients lying in them day and night. Some hospitals, such as Norristown State Hospital in Pennsylvania, have constructed cheerful new buildings for their aged patients. Others cram them into ancient dark firetraps. But in any case they dwell in the back wards.

Some hospital administrators say that most of the old people do not need mental hospital care, only nursing care, and they rail at relatives for dumping their problems into the state's lap. In 1955 at Columbus there were about 650 old folks. Perhaps so many as three hundred of these did not really need mental hospital care. But, as Dr. Raymond T. Beitzel, who as head of the medical service spent most of his time dealing with the physical ailments of the aged, said, "Where else are you going to put them if not here?" They could not take care of themselves. They were confused, would get lost or hurt if put on the street. They were out of contact, destructive. Many were incontinent. One authority estimated that not more than 10 per cent of the old people in most state hospitals could be cared for at home or in nursing homes.

The rest required institutionalization of some kind, and this meant state hospitals. (And building new institutions for the aged would gain nothing but peace of mind for their relatives.)

At the hospital they were a problem. They filled the cottages, which might have been used for convalescent care; they cluttered up the acute wards and medical wards in the main building. Thus Ward 4 in the main building was supposed to be for acute patients newly admitted but actually it had filled up with the chronic aged—old men brought to Ward 2 for medical care but who had been moved to Ward 4 because Ward 2 was overcrowded and because from Ward 4 they could go to the main dining room without climbing stairs. (All sorts of such practical considerations, and not alone psychiatric ones, govern patients' classification.) The old people got little or no psychiatric treatment. Dr. Beitzel said, "We have some on Thorazine to quiet them down when they get disturbed. That's about all. They are senile and demented but the main problem is that they are so physically handicapped that they need nursing care and their families can't provide it. Some families put them in a nursing home until they run out of money or until the nursing home can't handle them. If I ran a nursing home I'd rather take care of a tidy patient than an untidy one, wouldn't you? At least the linen bill would be less. So the families reach the point where there's nothing else to do. It's a big problem, and everybody's aware of it— the American population is aging and what are we going to do about it?"

Some of the patients were content and happy here. Some, usually aged paranoid schizophrenics, complained bitterly that they were being held illegally. Some probably had been odd all their lives; aging, they had become suspicious, had threatened people and sued people, their judgment had worsened and they had ended up here. Some, sitting and rocking day in, day out in a dim hallway, looked like anybody's grandmother. Some, demented, naked, sprawled on the floor in a puddle of urine, looked like animals. "They are waiting to die," one doctor said. "There are many worse things than death."

Not all were hopelessly deteriorated. (Deteriorated is sometimes used synonymously with regressed but strictly this is wrong. A regressed patient is not willing to participate in the life around him but a deteriorated patient is not capable of doing so.) Many of the men in Awl cottage and the women in Harris cottage worked—cleaning up the grounds, tilling the farm, working in the greenhouse or laundry or kitchen. In all, the hospital had 181 patients on the payroll, receiving from a dollar a month up, and another 521 worked without pay, mostly ward work. This was called "industrial therapy." Working did the patients no harm. Indeed, it prevented them from sitting idle. No patient well enough to leave the hospital was kept here to perform a job. At the same time, this was one way of getting cheap labor. And since patients were kept on the same job for years on end, and since little effort was made to give new patients an opportunity to work, it seemed clear that hospital jobs were used more as a means of keeping the place running than as therapy.

Awl cottage, named for the first superintendent of the hospital, William Awl, was a quiet rather pleasant old place, a square brick building with white columns on the porch. It could have been left unlocked but for a few patients who might have wandered away. Beside it was Greer cottage, for fairly well-behaved middle-aged women, chronic custodial cases. Most of them could get around and keep themselves reasonably clean. When one of them broke an arm the others would gather round to admire her cast. Occasionally the doctor saw one here who he thought might benefit by treatment and he gave her EST or drugs, and it did happen that a woman would go home from Greer, but not often. Richardson cottage was full of aged men, many incontinent, seniles, arteriosclerotics, schizophrenics. "It is a miserable place," young Dr. Dane said. "It smells horrible and looks horrible. One night a while back when I was on night duty a patient died there of a stroke and I had to go over. Most of the rest weren't in contact enough to know anybody had died. When we turned the lights on they opened their eyes and stared up at the ceiling; when we got through and turned the lights off they snored. They had about as much life as a vegetable garden."

Gundry cottage was a two-story brick building full of chronic ambulatory women—"They aren't going anywhere though, psychiatrically speaking," said Dr. Kirch. "It is custodial care and medical care and that's about all." Those able to climb stairs lived on the second floor. The difficult nursing problems lived on the first floor. On one ordinary day about sixty of them were sitting on the porch in chairs packed tight together. In an upstairs hall a woman with a silly smile was wandering about, carrying a tiny naked doll under her arm; she was smiling happily, and obviously she thought the doll a baby yet she carried it under her arm like a book—the fantastic inappropriateness of the psychotic. After her came a youngish woman sucking at the nipple of her own breast, and an old white-haired woman was lying in a big roomful of beds alone, weeping. The dormitory was jammed with beds; they were four inches apart. In a dayroom a little woman was sprawled in a corner on the floor. Dr. Kirch, passing through, said, "No matter how much you get them up on the chairs, they'll get down on the floor and under the beds."

In these wards in some state hospitals, as has been said, the old people lie in beds, row after row, and in Longview State Hospital at Cincinnati before 1955 some of the aged incontinent patients had been kept in sawdust beds, sawdust being easier to change than sheets and (it was claimed) less likely to cause bed sores; but at Columbus every effort was made to get the patients on their feet and keep them there. The psychiatrists said that once a regressed psychotic was allowed to lie down he was not likely to get up, being encouraged to regress further; the medical doctors said the patients got pneumonia lying in bed. And so for both reasons every morning the attendants got them up and dressed them and lifted them into chairs and tried to keep them there, even the feeblest ones. This of course was done at some sacrifice; Dr. Beitzel said, "Some hospitals are busier with their patients, you see attendants and occupational therapists concentrating on the hopeful ones. Maybe we could do more of that too if we didn't insist that everybody get up."

"B" Building, a new one-story structure, was the end of the line. It was full of aged incontinent women. It was the building that had shocked the legislators who had visited the hospital during the reform movement of 1955. "B" Building stank, the typical cloying sweet pungent ward odor, overpowering here. The dayroom was large and absolutely bare, terrazzo floor and tan tile walls and steel-sashed windows. In it were about a hundred women. A motion picture was being shown but only a few were watching. The light was dim and gray, not enough to be cheerful but enough to wash out the picture. A few patients were wandering to and fro obliviously in front of the screen; the rest were sitting on chairs or sitting or lying on the floor against the wall. About a dozen were restrained, strapped to their chairs to keep them from falling down or being knocked down. One was picking with thin fingers at the straps. A Negro woman, surprisingly young-looking, sat in a corner, her face like a grinning Halloween mask—wide white eyes, red gums, big white teeth bared, cheeks very black and swollen, hair frizzy. A little Negro woman was curled up on the floor in a fetal position. Some of the patients were naked, or nearly so. At many state hospitals no effort is made to keep clothes on patients like these, and in many a room are a hundred patients, all naked. Here, attendants were told to keep the patients clothed, no matter how often they undressed themselves. An attendant was fussing with a shroudlike hospital gown, trying to cover a little old woman's nakedness. A patient tied into a wheelchair was trying to move the chair but could not. They were on the whole quiet, they seemed placid. But there was an unreal quality about the place and, looking at them, one was struck by the thought: Are these really human beings? (The word "alienist," once used for psychiatrist, had a meaning: He treats patients who are alienated from the rest of us by their disease, and these patients did seem alien. Yet once they had been like us.) Always the attendants and sometimes the patients were mopping, endlessly mopping. There is a great deal more of mopping than of psychotherapy at any state hospital. There were 132 patients in this place, and only one was "tidy." There were five attendants. One said, "This is a terrible place to try to keep them tidy. You can't, that's all. You clean them up and it won't be five minutes till you have to do it all over again. I wish we were allowed to restrain more of them so they won't hurt theirselves. We have four combative patients that kick the others down. It's terrible." Dr. Kirch, sighing with relief as he left the place and breathed the fresh air outside, said, "You look at these pathetic people day after day —" He broke off, then said, "The surgeon can bury his failures, his incurable cases, but the psychiatrist has to look at his day after day."

12

America's No. 1 Health Problem

■ The size of the problem of mental illness in America is enormous. On any given day about three out of every thousand persons in the United States are in a public mental hospital. It is said that nine million Americans suffer from serious mental disorders. Probably another seven million have less serious forms of mental illness. During the last year it is estimated that not less than 2½ million Americans were treated for some form of mental illness, in hospitals, clinics and psychiatrists' private offices. Today there are more people hospitalized for mental illness than for polio, cancer, heart disease, tuberculosis and all other diseases combined. Some 850,000 people are on the books of mental hospitals on any one day. That is, one American family out of every sixty has one of its members in a mental hospital on any given day. Half the space in all American hospitals is taken up with mental patients. It has been estimated that one out of every twelve American children born today will spend part of his life in a mental hospital. That is, as things stand now, a member of every third American family will spend a part of his life in a mental hospital. About 300,000 patients will enter U.S. hospitals this year. The cost of caring for the mentally ill, including pensioned veterans, is over a billion dollars a year. It is increasing at the rate of a hundred million dollars a year. The states alone spend nearly three-quarters of a billion dollars. New York State spent in 1957 $195,000,000, about a third of its total operating budget. There are not half as many doctors in state

278

hospitals as are needed, less than a fifth as many graduate nurses and slightly more than a third as many social workers.

Indeed, mental illness has become a problem with serious implications for national policy. America, though considered the home of the good life, has numerous serious social problems, among them crime, delinquency, suicide, alcoholism, narcotics addiction and divorce; and mental illness plays a large part in them. During the 1942-45 war the armed forces rejected about 1,246,000 men for neuropsychiatric disorders—one out of every eight men called for induction. It has been estimated that mental illness eliminated more troops than the army sent to the Pacific theater. More draftees were rejected and more military men discharged for psychiatric reasons than for any other. When this became clear in 1943 it caused consternation in the General Staff, and later a general remarked, "Nearly as many men were being discharged from the Army as were entering through induction stations. The number of these discharges was enough to alarm even the most complacent." The country is still paying the cost and will be for a long time in veterans' mental hospitals.

Dr. Francis J. Braceland, past president of the American Psychiatric Association, and chief psychiatrist of the Institute of Living at Hartford, Connecticut, in a report prepared for the Hoover Commission, termed mental illness "the greatest single problem in the Nation's health picture today," and after outlining the magnitude of the problem wrote, "Were these statements true of any other illness, the situation would be regarded as a national emergency but in the case of mental illness the problem seemingly in large part is regarded with sympathetic apathy."

The mental hospital population has been rising faster than the general population. In 1903 there were but 186 persons out of every 100,000 in mental hospitals. Today there are over twice as many— 388. Are we getting increasingly psychotic? It is an old question, one asked a hundred years ago. Authorities agree that the answer is probably no. As the stigma of insanity is dispelled, more people are willing to go voluntarily to hospital. Sometimes community clinics, instead of cutting hospital populations as hoped, raise them, at least temporarily—they discover seriously ill persons formerly neglected. Probably most important of all, the number of old people is increasing.

The incidence of hospitalization for mental disease varies widely

from state to state. Six persons out of every thousand in New York
State are in public mental hospitals—but only 1.2 out of every thousand
in New Mexico. The six states having the highest rates are all on
the Eastern seaboard—New York, New Hampshire, Massachusetts,
Delaware, New Jersey, Rhode Island. Next in rank are Illinois and
Wisconsin, followed in order by Connecticut, Pennsylvania, Colorado,
Minnesota, Oklahoma, Vermont, Maryland, Nebraska, Maine, Georgia,
Ohio, Montana, Virginia, Michigan, North Dakota and Oregon, all
with rates above 2.85, the national median. (California, Louisiana
and Missouri have rates of 2.8.*) A variance in the geographical incidence of mental disease has been noted many times in many countries,
and numerous theories have been offered to explain it, including one
theory that urban life is more likely to cause mental disease than rural
life. The agency responsible for the figures just given points out,
however, that they deal only with the number of mental patients
hospitalized, not the number sick, and that many factors influence a
state's policy on hospitalization.

There were in 1956 1,144 mental institutions of all kinds in the
United States. They had on their books a total of 1,403,621 patients.
Of the 1,144 institutions, 526 were purely mental hospitals, and they
had 1,029,444 patients. Of these the 277 public hospitals—state, county
and psychopathic— had 838,657 patients, the more than 40 federal
(mostly Veterans Administration) hospitals had 102,474 patients, and
the 209 private mental hospitals had 88,313 patients. The 393 psychiatric services in general hospitals had 190,486 patients. And the 225
institutions for mental defectives and epileptics had 183,691 patients,
all but 9,669 of whom were in public institutions.

Primary responsibility for the care of the mentally ill and mentally
defective has traditionally rested with the states, as we have seen.
Until a few years ago the states discharged their responsibility poorly.
It is not long since almost any state hospital presented a picture of
falling plaster, leaky plumbing, hopelessly overworked doctors and
utter neglect of the patients. But a few years ago major reform began
in the states. Its impetus came from the federal government.

---

* These figures and others on comparison by states in this chapter are reported in *Thirteen Indices,* a pamphlet published in 1957 by the Joint Information Service of the American Psychiatric Association and the National Association
for Mental Health.

2.

Since Dorothea Dix's time the federal government had given psychiatric care to its wards in St. Elizabeths Hospital in Washington, D. C., and since 1930 there had been a small Mental Hygiene Division within the U. S. Public Health Service. But this was all. World War II changed things. The rejection and discharge of soldiers for psychiatric reasons made the nation realize its stake in mental health. In 1946 Congress passed the National Mental Health Act, the first direct large-scale federal entry into national mental health improvement. This act established the National Institute of Mental Health at Bethesda, Maryland. The Institute of Mental Health is one of seven National Institutes of Health concerned with various diseases, including cancer, heart disease and arthritis. The Institute conducts research of its own at Bethesda. It grants money to individual researchers in research centers around the country. It makes grants to medical schools to aid them in training more psychiatrists. And it makes grants-in-aid to states to help them develop community mental health services.

Just how far the federal government should go in the field of mental health is a question as yet unsettled by a national policy decision. From 1950 to 1955 federal appropriations for mental health increased, though slowly—from $11,000,000 in 1950 to $18,000,000 in 1956. By 1958 it had jumped to $39,000,000 and Congress was appropriating more money than President Eisenhower was requesting. Traditionally the pressure has been heavy to "keep the Federal government out of medicine." But in recent years pressure has risen on the federal government to provide for the public welfare. At present, no national policy decision as to the role of the federal government seems likely: debate over spending for national security on the military budget and foreign aid may shove aside moves to enlarge domestic welfare programs other than "emergency" economic measures. It seems probable, however, that in the future as now the tendency will be to put the federal government chiefly into research, training and prevention of mental illness—not, for example, into any program to underwrite the cost of care, as was proposed a few years ago.

3.

After the passage of the National Mental Health Act of 1946 the states bestirred themselves. At the Governors' Conference of 1949,

Governor Luther W. Youngdahl of Minnesota led a move to sponsor a study of state mental hospital systems. The result, a fat report compiled by the Council of State Governments, was a landmark and a shocker, showing that more than half the American state hospitals were over fifty years old, that nearly all were hideously understaffed, that three-fourths were overcrowded, that nearly all used restraint and seclusion and thirteen used the lock chair and that they were trying to "care for" mental patients for $1.74 per patient per day ($0.88 in Tennessee).

The states started building programs. They hired more doctors, nurses and attendants and raised their salaries. They matched federal grants. They reorganized their mental health departments. Preventive programs spread—community clinics, child guidance clinics, outpatient clinics. By 1953 the states were spending three times what they had spent on their state hospitals nine years before—half a billion dollars a year. Some states had multiplied their expenditures fantastically during that same period—Kansas by 610 per cent, Delaware by 527 per cent, North Carolina by 445 per cent. The national average cost per patient per day had risen from $1.06 to $2.70—150 per cent—while the cost of living index had gone up only 50 per cent. In Delaware it had risen from $0.97 to $3.09, in Kansas from $0.70 to $3.87. Capital outlays became enormous—New York spent $350,000,000 building hospitals. New research and training centers were set up. Salaries were increased until in some states mental health officials were earning more than governors. State spending far outran federal. The 1955 reforms we have observed in Ohio were really a part of a nation-wide movement.

Governors discovered that mental health had become the third biggest item in their budgets, following only after schools and highways. The first governors' conference in history to deal exclusively with the problem of mental health met in Detroit in 1954. It drew up a declaration of principles, advocating increased appropriations for mental health personnel, special appropriations for training and research, and improvements in teaching to attract good men to state hospitals. It set up an interstate information clearing house. Subsequently several states held regional conferences.

The mentally ill cannot be termed neglected any longer. People at large are more interested than ever before, at least than ever in recent times. And they are willing to help the mentally ill, as they proved in the Ohio bond issue vote. One authority said in 1955, "You can get any appropriation bill through a legislature you want if it's got mental health in the title." Why all the sudden interest? Citizens' groups, such as the National Association for Mental Health and the National Committee Against Mental Illness helped arouse it. So did journalists. As the stigma of insanity has been dispelled, it became possible to discuss insanity publicly. More and more people were going to mental hospitals. The hospitals were getting more and more crowded. They cost more. They swung enormous weight on state budgets. They forced themselves on the governors' attention. And about the same time the new psychiatric drugs came along, encouraging citizens to believe that psychotics can be cured—that pouring money into state hospitals isn't pouring money down a rathole. Finally, during the postwar years of national prosperity and material well-being, the country could afford to attend to the sick.

Not only is public interest higher; public understanding is more sophisticated. Not many years ago public interest could be stirred only by exposés of firetrap buildings or brutal beatings in state hospitals. Today people tend to take it for granted that buildings are satisfactory and care humane; they want to know what is being done for the patients, for they have come to realize that if nothing is done for patients they are not much more likely to get well in a gleaming new building than in a rotting old one—that brains are needed as well as bricks. When the recent reform movement in state hospitals began, most public discussion revolved around overcrowding. Faced with an overcrowded hospital, the obvious thing to do was to enlarge the hospital or build a new one. This is what had almost invariably been done in the past. But by now nearly everybody has come to realize that the process of building ever larger and ever more numerous and ever more costly hospitals in order to lock up an ever-increasing army of mentally ill is both endless and ruinous—ruinous both to the state and to the patients. As the director of the Kansas department, George W. Jackson, said, "No state can afford to put people in hospitals and leave them." So two alternative ways of dealing with an overcrowded hospital present themselves: Get more of the patients out, or prevent new ones from going in.

Getting more out means curing more. This means giving them better care. This means primarily more doctors, nurses and attendants. So the states have turned to spending money on training these people.

It also means finding new treatments, for if a pill should be found that was a specific for schizophrenia—a possibility so remote that most psychiatrists consider it an idle dream—the hospitals could be half-emptied overnight. So the states have turned to spending money on research.

Preventing patients from entering the hospital means better community out-patient clinics, which would catch and treat mentally ill persons early, before they need hospitalization, and it means keeping patients who don't need mental hospital care out of them, such as some aged persons. Increasingly the state hospital is being viewed not as an isolated institution but as a link in a chain that includes school, clinic, court, after-care home and rehabilitation services.

In 1955 the governors of half the states addressed their legislatures on the care of the mentally ill. Governor Robert B. Meyner of New Jersey, in recommending appropriations for more research, doctors and early treatment, said, "A costly new mental hospital has just been opened at Ancora and in a matter of months it will be filled to capacity. At the current rate of increase of mental illness—requiring five hundred new beds a year—New Jersey will soon need a fifth mental hospital, and then a sixth and then a seventh, ad infinitum. In 1949 and in 1952 the people of New Jersey approved bond issues of $50,000,000 for the Department of Institutions and Agencies. Must we go before the voters in the next few years with the proposal of another large sum merely to house the wards of the state, or should we attack the Frankenstein monster before it devours us?"

Some governors have discovered that improving the care of the mentally ill is politically popular. Senator Frank Carlson of Kansas made his reputation when as governor he inaugurated the Kansas plan.

Some governors speak movingly of the hospitals' plight but put nothing in their budgets for them. Some governors upon taking office have with great fanfare overturned the hospital system for political effect, driving good doctors away in disgust. And so a few states which showed much promise a few years ago are already beginning to slip back into the swamp of sheer custody.

At present state spending on hospitals has reached a high plateau. It is not likely to go higher soon. Some governors feel that the mental health program has been running away with the state budget and the time has come to stabilize—to pause and see what has been accomplished and what should be done next. The era of big capital expenditure is probably ended. The states are beginning to turn their concern toward community clinics and toward institutions and programs for other "problem" groups in society, such as wayward children, alcoholics, narcotics addicts, the aged and the criminal. If it turns out later on that some states have built more mental hospitals than they need, they may utilize the excess buildings for those other groups.

4.

What, in general, is the state of the care of the mentally ill in American state hospitals today? "Deplorable," exploded the clinical director of one state hospital who was asked that question. "We've got twenty-five doctors but only nine of these are doing psychiatric work, stretching the definition of psychiatrist as far as you possibly can. And we've got over five thousand patients. Oh, we feed them all, and they all have beds. But that's all they get. This is one of the biggest, wealthiest states in the nation. For a state like this to have a place like this is a disgrace. Go to England and you will see a hospital that is a hospital. There the nurses and doctors are trained for their jobs, and they are used to treating patients as human beings. English hospitals have on an average only twelve hundred patients—and there will be twelve psychiatrists in each hospital. Here we have two open wards in the entire hospital. The rest are locked. In England you have the reverse. Shackling the insane was called undesirable in Europe 150 years ago at the time of the French Revolution. This news has not yet crossed the Atlantic. In some states patients are put in jail until the sheriff can find time to take them to the hospital—under armed guard."

It would be hard to dispute his view if one visited only his hospital, or such places as State Hospital No. 3, at Nevada, Missouri, with over two thousand patients and seven doctors, none certified; or Weston State Hospital in West Virginia, which for years was obliged to use a building so decrepit that a radiator fell through the floor; or a Southern hospital which has one of the highest discharge rates in the country only because it's so crowded that when a new patient comes in the front door another must go out the back, or the brutal backward hospitals in remote rural areas, which were located there for political reasons and have become little but prisons for patients and rest homes for alcoholic doctors. And indeed no one would be cheered by viewing the hopeless patients in the back wards of any hospital.

And yet, taking an over-all view of state hospitals in America today, one would have to say that they are in better shape, probably, than ever before. (When we say this we must not forget that as yet not a single state hospital meets American Psychiatric Association standards, nor does any approach the ideal as it is conceived by experts.) Just how good the hospitals are is difficult to say. To determine how effective a hospital is, one needs to know what happens to patients after they leave the hospital—how many relapse and return. Such data are not available at any hospital.

Lacking such data on patients, experts rely on other yardsticks to measure the quality of hospitals; and by these standards hospitals have assuredly improved in recent years. One such standard is the ratio of patients to hospital employees. In 1939 state hospitals had 5.7 patients for each full-time hospital employee. By 1955 this ratio had decreased to 3.8 patients per employee, and Kansas had a ratio of 2.1 (and Tennessee had a ratio of 6.9). Nevertheless, to meet APA standards, the hospitals still needed 6,399 more physicians, 1,826 more psychologists, 31,992 more graduate nurses, 97,555 more attendants and other nurses and 3,574 more social workers. Another such yardstick is the amount of money the hospitals spend, and as we have seen this has risen greatly in recent years. Nevertheless, despite increased expenditures, psychiatric hospitals still needed more money, for with half of all sick people in the U. S. to care for, they spent only a fourth as much as nonpsychiatric hospitals. By 1955 state hospitals were spending an average of $2.97 per patient per day. But Veterans' Administration psychiatric hospitals spent $8.99 per patient per day, psychopathic hospitals spent $13.57 and short-term general and special hospitals spent $23.12. If each person in the United States contributed equally to the support of the state mental hospitals, he would spend less than one cent in every five dollars he received as personal income.

Various yardsticks have been devised to rate state hospitals. Using them, the joint information service of the APA and the NMHA has ranked the hospital programs of the states in 1956. Excerpts from its report follow, showing the U. S. average and median and five top-ranking and five lowest-ranking states, and Ohio, according to various criteria:

ADEQUACY OF PHYSICIAN STAFFS AS MEASURED BY APA STANDARDS:

	U.S. Average	45.0%
	U.S. Median	40.05%
1.	Kansas	150.9%
2.	Delaware	85.7%
3.	Colorado	79.4%
4.	Iowa	79.0%
5.	Connecticut	65.4%
27.	Ohio	38.8%
44.	Florida	26.8%
45.	Idaho	26.7%
46.	Wisconsin	18.9%
47.	Alabama	17.0%
48.	Wyoming	12.5%

NUMBER OF PROFESSIONAL PERSONNEL PER 100 PATIENTS:

	U.S. Average	2.8
	U.S. Median	2.5
1.	Kansas	5.7
2.	Delaware	5.7
3.	Connecticut	4.9
4.	Nebraska	4.5
5.	Massachusetts	4.0
14.	Ohio	3.0
44.	South Carolina	1.4
45.	Missouri	1.3
46.	Florida	1.2
47.	Georgia	1.2
48.	Alabama	1.1

AVERAGE DAILY MAINTENANCE EXPENDITURE PER PATIENT:

	U.S. Average	$3.18
	U.S. Median	$3.11
1.	Connecticut	$4.73
2.	Kansas	$4.59
3.	New Mexico	$4.34
4.	Michigan	$4.33
5.	Delaware	$4.08
22.	Ohio	$3.22
44.	Kentucky	$2.07

45. Texas	$2.07
46. Mississippi	$2.04
47. West Virginia	$1.90
48. Tennessee	$1.84

Many factors other than inclination influence the matter of how well a state provides for its mentally ill. Obviously a poor state cannot provide so well as a rich state. Psychiatrists are unequally distributed. And so on. Some of these factors are indicated in the following tables:

STATES RANKED ACCORDING TO NUMBER OF PSYCHIATRISTS PER
100,000 TOTAL POPULATION

U.S. Average	5.2
U.S. Median	3.2
1. New York	13.2
2. Connecticut	11.3
3. Massachusetts	10.5
4. Maryland	10.3
5. California	7.9
18. Ohio	3.8
44. South Carolina	1.5
45. West Virginia	1.5
46. Alabama	1.5
47. Mississippi	1.5
48. North Dakota	1.4

STATES RANKED ACCORDING TO MENTAL HOSPITAL MAINTENANCE
EXPENDITURES AS A PER CENT OF TOTAL GENERAL STATE EXPENDITURES:

U.S. Average	3.31%
U.S. Median	2.445%
1. New York	7.80%
2. Connecticut	7.59%
3. New Hampshire	5.95%
4. Nebraska	5.35%
5. Massachusetts	5.28%
11. Ohio	3.60%
44. Nevada	1.31%
45. Wyoming	1.28%
46. Wisconsin	1.23%
47. Louisiana	1.07%
48. New Mexico	.98%

Traveling around the country, visiting institutions, talking to psychiatrists and government officials, one gets the impressions that the state hospital programs of Kansas and Massachusetts are among the nation's best, and that the worst state hospital systems are to be found in the South.

Kansas and Massachusetts owe their superiority in no small part to the fact that their state hospital programs have been integrated with the programs of the Menninger Clinic in Kansas and with the programs of Harvard University and other colleges in Massachusetts. The same thing has been done in several other states. But it is to the shame of other states—and of the universities and private clinics within them—that all too often state hospitals have remained isolated backward snake pits scorned and shunned by psychiatrists in the ivory towers of universities and private clinics.

5.

At the end of 1956 statisticians came up with startling news: For the first time ever, except for a slight decline in 1943, the number of patients in American state hospitals declined. Since 1945 the number of patients had been increasing by about ten thousand a year. But by the end of 1956, thirty-four states had discharged as many or more patients as they took in that year and the U. S. total declined by seven thousand under 1955. And this happened in a year when first admissions rose to their highest point in history.

In 1957 the state hospital population dropped 3,227.

Why?

Some thought the decline might be a temporary phenomenon. But most agreed with Governor G. Mennen Williams of Michigan who said, "We have reason to believe that we have come to the top of the hill and that we can look forward to continuing decreases."

What had happened?

Nobody was sure. But a number of factors seemed to be involved.

The new psychiatric drugs were controlling patients and enabling many to leave the hospital who could not have left without them. The drugs and the new interest in hospitals created an atmosphere of hope among patients, doctors, attendants and relatives; and this very hopefulness helped some patients recover. The number of hospital employees—doctors, nurses, attendants, others—had increased about 100 per cent in ten years, and superintendents thought this inevitably meant better care and hence more recoveries and discharges. The increased use of nursing homes, "halfway houses," after-care clinics, vocational rehabilitation and other devices helped bridge the gap between the isolated hospital and the community, enabling many patients to leave the hospital who otherwise could not.

Doctors in private practice, by treating patients with the new drugs, prevented them from going to state hospitals. The increase in psychiatric wings in general hospitals was having the same effect. Early diagnosis in community clinics sometimes prevented hospitalization. But since first admissions to state hospitals continued to rise, these factors apparently had not yet stemmed the tide. Nor had the new state programs to train their own psychiatrists been felt much yet in state hospitals, for most were five-year plans and had begun five or fewer years ago. Therefore as all these factors came into play, further reductions in state hospital populations could be expected.

Now, statistics and predictions in this field must be viewed with much caution. Criteria for discharge vary widely from place to place and from time to time; a patient considered well enough to go home in one hospital might be kept in another hospital, and one considered well enough to discharge from one hospital today might, five years ago, have been kept in the same hospital. Moreover, readmissions rose at the same time the hospital population was declining, suggesting the possibility that more patients were being discharged only to relapse and return. Improved social service work arranges homes and jobs for patients, thereby getting them out of the hospital but not necessarily in any better mental health than before. Sometimes hospital officials make arbitrary bookkeeping transfers that distort the statistical picture. Finally, the states have spent so much money that their officials feel obliged to show results, and this means reducing the hospital population, so all sorts of means are devised to get patients out of the hospital—several states, for example, have begun moving aged patients out of the hospital into nursing homes, which does have the effect of cutting the hospital's resident population but may or may not be good for the patients: cleaning up one snake pit by creating a hundred new smaller ones doesn't help. Moreover, the states have yet another incentive to get a patient out of the hospital: So long as he is in he cannot get an old-age pension from the federal government but if he is put into a nursing home he can, and thus the state can shift the financial burden of his support to the federal government, though it may also have worsened his lot and evaded its own responsibility. All this is to say that the public outcry, "Get them out of the hospitals," and official response to it, may result in abuses and mislead the public.

Nevertheless, no matter with how much skepticism one views the decline in hospital population, one cannot but feel that the care of the mentally ill in America has improved considerably in the last ten years and that, barring always a serious economic collapse or other national emergency, the prospects for further improvements have never been better.

6.

What do we need for further improvement?

First, more psychiatrists. Only about 2 per cent of American doctors are certified psychiatrists—but half the country's hospitalized sick are mental patients. There are in the United States only eleven thousand psychiatrists (approximately half of whom are fully trained and certified by the American Board of Neurology and Psychiatry). Only about thirty-five hundred doctors are in mental hospitals, and not all of them are psychiatrists. It has been estimated that the country needs between ten and twenty thousand more psychiatrists. But all the training institutions in the country are turning out not more than five hundred new ones a year. Among these are only forty child psychiatrists.

To produce more psychiatrists, Dr. Daniel Blain, Medical Director of the American Psychiatric Association, has suggested that it may prove necessary to help medical education more. As the states expand their training programs, as Ohio is doing, they will probably offer enough residencies to begin to break the bottleneck. Yet they may well encounter a new obstacle: They may not be able to fill the residency positions they offer. Indeed, today nearly a third of the residencies in the country are unfilled. For young doctors do not seem to want to become psychiatrists. Only 7 per cent of medical school graduates go into psychiatry.

Dr. Bernard H. Hall of the Menninger Foundation, who studied the subject, found that many young doctors arrived for their psychiatric residency ignorant of psychiatry's fundamentals. He wrote, "The training in psychiatry in many medical schools is inferior to the training in all other specialties." A leading expert on medical education, Alan Gregg, said, "Perhaps the most desperately and thoroughly proven of all lessons from the war was that our medical schools had been giving grossly inadequate training in psychiatry. Their graduates, as a rule, misunderstood, ignored, and underevaluated psychiatry." Before the war most medical schools taught only thirty to sixty hours of psychiatry —a few lectures and a visit to a nearby state hospital. Today some of them teach as much as five hundred hours of psychiatry.

The teaching of psychiatry to undergraduate medical students has been handicapped in the past by the gap between the universities and the state hospitals. As we have seen, in the past the universities considered the state hospitals miasmal swamps where patients were herded for custody alone, the state hospitals considered the universities pristine ivory towers shirking their social duty, and it was not uncommon for state hospitals situated near great medical centers to have little or no relation to them. In some states—Nebraska, for example—this barrier is being broken down. In Massachusetts for years the state Department of Mental Health, in co-operation with three medical schools in Boston, has offered its residents training in university, private and state hospitals. Such a program gives young doctors broader, better training than they could get in any single institution. It also encourages them to remain in public health work. Of fifty-two doctors who completed basic training there, nineteen went into private practice, eighteen continued in advanced training and fifteen entered state service.

Former Governor Lausche of Ohio once said, "We spend money training doctors, then they graduate and go into private practice. The medical profession ought to make an introspection of themselves." Another governor who tried unsuccessfully for a year to hire a psychiatrist to run his mental health program for $30,000 a year complained bitterly that the doctors were shirking their social responsibility. One wonders if medical education has become overtechnical—if more training in the humanities might not awaken doctors to social responsibility.

Of course, not money alone lures doctors into private practice. Some doctors shun state hospitals because they are stagnant and backward. Governor Meyner, urging the legislature to lure young doctors by convincing them New Jersey had a progressive program, remarked that Notre Dame has no difficulty in attracting good high school football players. Many doctors fear state service means political interference, and all too often it does. Yet some doctors have an unreasonable suspicion of politicians, perhaps because of the narrowness of their own education. The states find themselves competing with each other for psychiatrists: If one state raises doctors' salaries and lures good doctors from a neighboring state, that state raises its salaries and lures them back. California mails brochures to psychiatrists in state hospitals elsewhere, offering high salaries and pointing out the beauties of California's climate. As one expert said recently, "You will never solve this problem until Park Avenue gets crowded—until psychiatrists get to be a drug on the market."

The states began to attack this log jam in the early 1950s when they set up programs to train their own psychiatrists. Many, including Ohio, adopted the five-year plan—required residents to intersperse two years of practice in state hospitals among their three years of residency training. The states paid residents handsome stipends—up to $7,000 for a first-year resident just out of medical school and internship, up to $10,500 for a third-year resident. It is probable that in no other medical specialty is residency pay so high.

In addition to training home-grown residents—native American general practitioners and medical school graduates—the state programs are training many displaced persons from Europe and many foreign students who have come to America to study on exchange programs, for today it is America, not France or Vienna, which is Mecca to people all over the world who want to study psychiatry. State hospitals are flooded with such residents today. As might be expected, their quality varies enormously, some giving excellent service in the state hospitals, some being almost worthless because of inadequate medical schools abroad, native inability or language handicap. Some will leave as soon as they get licenses to practice in America outside the hospital; some must go back to their native countries when their residency is completed. It is doubtful that the state hospital system will hold many of them—that the state will benefit greatly and permanently from them. Whether it benefits enough during their residency to justify their high salaries is hard to say.

But the basic difficulty with all state training programs is a shortage of people qualified to train residents. Many good senior hospital psychiatrists make poor teachers. Again, most state hospitals are badly understaffed with senior psychiatrists, and those available must spend all the time possible with patients, leaving little time for training. Some experts fear that the states, in their rush to train psychiatrists, may be establishing a lot of second-rate training centers around the country. They will turn out many "psychiatrists," but will they be any good?

7.

More doctors, however, is not all we need to improve the care of the mentally ill. For even if all the doctors in the United States were put to work in a single hospital, they would not cure everybody there because they simply don't know enough, any more than all the cancer specialists in the country could save the lives of the patients in a single cancer ward. The causes of the major psychoses remain to this day unknown, and so does the cure. The great need is for research. Yet the amount spent on research has been pitifully small. We shall inquire into this later on.

13

Where People Take Their Troubles

■ There are in America today four types of institutions which treat the mentally ill—state hospitals, psychopathic hospitals, private sanitariums and psychiatric wings in general hospitals. At big old Columbus State, we have studied the state hospital in detail. For contrast, let us glance briefly at the other three types of institutions. For only they, not the state hospitals, come close to resembling the ideal hospital that experts have visualized.

2.

The private sanitariums are likely to be lovely spots, a cluster of little buildings situated on landscaped grounds in quiet countryside, the whole looking more like a princely estate than a hospital. They usually take both psychotic and neurotic patients. Their purpose is primarily to treat patients for a fee, though they perform some research and train a few residents. Their fees are high—up to sixteen hundred dollars a month or even more. One agreed to accept a patient from a state hospital, a young intractable catatonic schizophrenic about to be lobotomized at the state hospital, but only on condition that her parents agree to leave her in the private sanitarium for three years at a fee of sixteen hundred a month, a total cost of nearly sixty thousand dollars; and it would guarantee nothing.

The good private sanitariums are heavily staffed—Chestnut Lodge in Maryland,* for example, has only ninety beds, but it has twenty full-time and four part-time doctors, including four analysts, and the Institute of Living at Hartford, Connecticut, has four hundred beds and thirty full-time psychiatrists. They rely heavily on individual psychotherapy—the Institute of Living reports that "every patient who can benefit is under some form of psychotherapy."

Private sanitariums take care of few patients—only $6\frac{1}{2}$ per cent of the U. S. total. And there is another side to the private sanitarium coin. Not all are good. Indeed, some are snake pits, whose patients would be far better off in state hospitals.

3.

The psychopathic hospital is usually connected with both a university and a state hospital system. It is small and heavily staffed with doctors. It is intended for the early and brief and intensive treatment of acute psychotic patients, not for prolonged care. It is also intended for research and training, and indeed is likely to put more emphasis upon them than upon the treatment of patients. Frequently it selects its patients for teaching purposes, and if it already has on hand one catatonic schizophrenic it is not going to take another, though twenty knock on the door; it will send them to the nearest prolonged-care state hospital. Ohio's "receiving hospitals" are really, to a large extent, psychopathic hospitals.

Probably the most famous—and justly so—psychopathic hospital in America is Boston Psychopathic. (Its name has been changed officially to the Massachusetts Mental Health Center, but it is known the world over as Boston Psycho.) It is administered jointly by the Massachusetts State Mental Health Department and the Harvard Medical School's Department of Psychiatry. It is a collection of old and new brick structures grafted onto one another and set down as part of an ordinary city block amid other buildings in Boston. It is built right out to the sidewalk, is surrounded by no parklike grounds. It seems a living part of the city.

The superintendent's office resembles a comfortable New England living room—slightly worn upholstered chairs and sofas, old prints on

---

* Readers interested in learning more about Chestnut Lodge should consult *The Mental Hospital*, by Alfred H. Stanton and Morris S. Schwartz. New York: Basic Books, 1954. Those interested in the Menninger Clinic, another excellent private institution, will find much material in the Clinic's own publications.

the wall, dark woodwork, a fireplace, many books. The atmosphere of the entire hospital is relaxed, comfortable, warm. The hospital seems old and wise, gentle and sure; it exudes a feeling that its doctors know about these things, that it belongs to an old civilization, as does Boston itself. Even on first visit, people conceive an affection for it.

Dr. Harry Solomon, superintendent of Boston Psychopathic and in 1957-58 president of the American Psychiatric Association, is a graying man of sixty-eight with a warm gentle smile and eyes. A while back, lounging in an easy chair in his office, he said, "The legislature gave our hospital three legs—care and treatment of the mentally ill, research into mental illness and teaching." The hospital accepts psychotics and severe psychoneurotics. It does not take patients with chronic organic diseases. Ninety per cent of its patients go home in seventy days, Dr. Solomon says, and some in a week. The median stay is forty-five days. If a patient is not ready for discharge after a year, he is shipped out to one of Massachusetts' prolonged-care hospitals. This happens to about fifteen per cent of the schizophrenics. Dr. Solomon says the hospital does not select patients for teaching purposes.

Patients who are able pay eighteen dollars a day; many pay nothing. The hospital spends about a million and a quarter dollars a year and recovers forty thousand dollars from patients. Patients, organized into a system of self-government, meet weekly to discuss their problems and the hospital's, forwarding their requests to the assistant superintendent —for a credit union, new mops, a toaster, pajamas, food on the ward. They arrange dances, bingo parties, picnics, trips to the museum. They elect their own officers.

Every effort is made to knit the hospital to the community. Nearly a third of the patients go home week ends. The hospital runs a day-hospital department, to which twenty or thirty patients come each day for treatment, but go home at night. It runs an out-patient clinic which sees some twelve hundred different patients a year and makes some fourteen thousand visits—trying to keep people out of the hospital. It runs a children's out-patient and in-patient department. It co-operates with the Rutland Corner House, which once gave service to women in distress, to provide a home for patients who have no other home to go to after leaving the hospital. It has a rehabilitation service, teaching patients trades and skills to help them find jobs when they leave. It has an active citizens' auxiliary. Across the street in an old house is a club where former patients listen to lectures and discuss their common problems, not the least of which is the stigma attaching to mental hospitalization.

How does Boston Psychopathic achieve what appears to be an almost miraculous record of recovery and discharge? For one thing, it does not accept organics; for another, it ships its intractable cases to prolonged-care hospitals; for another, Dr. Solomon probably discharges some patients whom other doctors would not consider well enough. Even so, its record is excellent. It uses no magic, only the usual therapies: insulin shock, EST, drugs, lobotomy, group and individual psychotherapy and "milieu therapy"—large numbers of attendants and nurses and occupational and recreational therapists to create a pleasant busy hopeful milieu which promotes recovery. It tends to emphasize psychotherapy more than drugs. A treatment survey in 1958 showed that half the patients were receiving psychotherapy and 35 per cent somatic therapies—drugs, EST and insulin. Boston Psychopathic never uses physical restraint. Today, thanks to the drugs, it rarely uses EST as restraint. The hospital is loaded with doctors, nurses and attendants. For its 140 patients it has 170 attendants, 15 nurses and about 75 doctors, including 33 residents and some half-time doctors. "You have to have a lot of people to treat patients," Dr. Solomon says. "You can't compare this place fairly with the ordinary state hospital." Doctors, instructors and consultants come and go constantly, moving between here and Boston's three medical schools. The place is always churning with professional people and graduate students working on special projects. There is a ferment about it.

Have the new drugs contributed largely to the rapid discharge rate? Dr. Solomon says, "Before the drugs we had reached a plateau where we had no more patients at the end of a year than at the start, and in fact the population trend had started down. This has been accelerated a little by the drugs."

Walking through the hospital one day a while back, Dr. Solomon stopped to talk a moment to a young woman with a bewildered expression on her face who was wandering about the halls murmuring, "Am I killing someone, Doctor?" She was a catatonic schizophrenic, and in most hospitals would have been locked up; here she was free. "Half our wards are open, unlocked," Dr. Solomon said. He paused to watch two women knitting; they were dressed almost alike, in sweaters and skirts, but one was an attendant and the other a patient: In this hospital attendants and nurses need not wear uniforms. Patients were sitting quietly in a dayroom, reading; they were making sandwiches for each other in a snack bar off the dayroom; they were playing ping-pong or watching television. This was a disturbed ward. The seclusion rooms had been converted into bedrooms with green bedspreads and curtains.

On an acute ward half a dozen patients were lying in their beds, some sleeping, some reading. "Beds are to be used," Solomon said. "As nearly as possible, everyone here is on his own." The rigid control, the prisonlike routine, of most state hospitals was missing. A patient was putting a coin in a Coke machine and getting a Coke just as he would in the outside world: Every effort is made to make the hospital resemble the outside. "We do a lot with OT here," Solomon said, "and even more with work assignments—typing, the chemistry laboratory, the coffee shop, the storeroom, clerical work on research projects."

Turning a corner in a recreation room he came upon a doctor sitting on a sofa beside a patient, talking quietly. In the day hospital male and female patients mingled freely. "We don't segregate the sexes," Solomon said. "The theory is that very few of our patients will be going into monasteries or convents, and we try to make life here as much like life in the community as possible. It minimizes the old hospital problem of getting men to shave and women to use lipstick. If they want to hold hands, fine. They don't do enough of it. By the way, if you are inspecting hospitals, you can judge a hospital by how many people in it are smiling." Everything in this hospital seemed relaxed and open, cheerful and light and sunny. The patients seemed free—free to do what they wanted, to talk, to lounge around, to walk about. Nurses and attendants worked with them. Doctors saw them often. They seemed to live here, not to be incarcerated here.

When patients are admitted they are interviewed privately by a social worker who serves tea and tells the family what to expect. A nurse takes the patient to his ward and introduces him to another patient "to make him feel he is among friends." Solomon said, "It's these details that make a difference. We try to get away from the old idea of stripping the patient on admission, bathing him, and taking everything away from him, even his wedding ring. You can imagine what that does. That's why you have combat and hollering on the ward."

Solomon seemed to feel a moral certitude that patients have a right to be treated like human beings. "Attitude," he said, "is more important than knowledge. We don't need to know everything to help patients get well. From 35 to 50 per cent of the patients get well in the first year in the worst hospitals. You just improve on that figure. The main thing is to make the patient feel like a person once more. And then the recuperative potential will flower." More, perhaps, than any other public hospital in America today, Boston Psychopathic uses the "moral treatment" of the nineteenth century, to which it has added the insights of Freud and such somatic therapies as EST and the new drugs. Some hospitals today seem to be so busy with modern treatment methods, and so overburdened with huge numbers of patients, that they have lost sight of the individuals in their care. In them the humanism of the nineteenth century is lost in impersonal science and the assembly-line administration of shock and pills. At Boston Psychopathic, and at a few other places, the warmth and gentle humanity of Dr. Awl, who ran Columbus State in the 1840s, seems to have been recovered, and it is a pleasant sight.

4.

On the South Side of Chicago not far from the lake front a patch of slums has been torn down and new buildings erected around burgeoning Michael Reese Hospital, a general hospital center; and one of these shining buildings is the Institute for Psychosomatic and Psychiatric Research and Training, a T-shaped low brick building on a rise of land opened in 1951. Its interior décor contrasts sharply with old Boston Psychopathic's—here are glass brick partitions and angular walls, metal desks and asphalt tile floors, electric typewriters and recessed fluorescent lights and pastel walls. This is one of the nation's best psychiatric sections in a general hospital.

In his large paneled, soft-lit book-lined office, Dr. Roy R. Grinker, director of the Institute, a large soft-spoken man with a firm manner, wearing a gray suit and gold-rimmed glasses, said a while back, "In 1939 we got permission from the medical staff to set up a psychiatric unit within a private pavilion. We proved we could operate without interefering with the decorum and quiet of the general hospital." Earlier psychiatric services in general hospitals in Chicago were an eleven-bed unit at Billings Memorial at the University of Chicago, also set up by Dr. Grinker, and a larger unit at a private hospital, St. Luke's, established by Dr. Francis J. Gerty. After Dr. Grinker started Michael Reese's unit, other hospitals did likewise, and today there are thirteen such units in the Chicago area with about five hundred beds. Michael Reese is the largest.

All over the country general hospitals are opening psychiatric wings. More than a hundred hospitals are using Ford Foundation grants for this purpose. But in the past, general hospitals opposed such establishments. When Dr. Grinker put a psychiatric unit into Billings Memorial, a professor of surgery begged him not to put up a sign identifying it. Superintendents of general hospitals feared that the outcries of psychotics would disturb the decorum of their hospitals. "And we had the antagonism of the general medical staffs to psychiatry," Dr. Grinker said. "The hostility of general medicine to psychiatry is still very strong, though lessening." A while back Dr. Grinker was surprised to learn that some psychiatric units in general hospitals around the country have no difficulty with the general medical staffs. "Then I discovered that the average stay of their patients was only seven to ten days. That meant electroshock only, and that was the explanation. If you do shock or use drugs exclusively, you are employing methods familiar to general medicine, treating symptoms, so you can get acceptance—you can carry a little black bag and prescribe pills and talk about physical complications. We do it differently here. With recognition of the fact that somatic therapies are valuable in certain cases, the staff of this hospital is greatly concerned with the pathology, with the psychopathology, of mental illness, and attempts to understand and to treat mental illness on a rational basis."

Dr. Grinker's unit at Michael Reese has space for eighty patients. It usually has a long waiting list. A few patients stay in the hospital for as long as a year or two. But most go home in forty-five or fifty days. Some, mostly paranoid schizophrenics, are shipped out to state hospitals. "They are the ones we can't do anything for," Grinker says. "They are so violent the nurses are frightened of them, and if you're afraid of a patient you can't help him. It would be better if we could get more male attendants but we can't—too many of them are psychopaths or alcoholics or homosexuals. It's a problem in all mental hospitals." Michael Reese is entirely a private hospital, and at least 80 per cent of the patients in its psychiatric wing pay twenty-seven dollars per day. The rest are charity cases paying from nothing to twenty-six dollars per day depending on ability.

The patients' wards at Michael Reese are upstairs. All but one are locked. Everything is kept clean and shiny, from the gleaming stainless steel kitchen to the handsome modern furniture in the dayrooms. Even on the disturbed ward men and women patients mingle. The doctors' offices are on the wards; they conduct psychotherapy there. The hospital uses no restraint and uses seclusion rarely. To one accustomed to visiting state hospitals, this place seems almost deserted—only a dozen patients on a large ward.

Michael Reese started out with a handful of psychiatrists. Today, to care for its eighty patients and to staff its out-patient clinic, it has seventy-five or eighty doctors, most of whom are also in private practice and have had psychoanalytic training. It has trained many of these doctors itself, for it has developed a training and research program in addition to its hospital function. It usually has seventeen or eighteen residents in its training program. It turns out five or six psychiatrists a year. Nearly all go into private practice in Chicago and join the staff here. None has gone into full-time state hospital work, but many work part-time for the state. During their training period, however, some of the residents spend several months at Chicago State Hospital —the kind of cross-fertilization between state and private psychiatric hospitals that is all too rare and that can benefit state hospitals, as well as residents, immeasurably.

Dr. Grinker said, "We only turn out five or six psychiatrists a year but if we can do that and if the University of Illinois Neuropsychiatric Institute can turn out five more and Chicago State two or three and the VA and Northwestern five more—well, you've got a sizable number of new people coming into practice in Chicago every year. We hope to continue training people until and after psychiatrists begin to find competition heavy in the big city and they spread out over the country. It's very difficult. They don't like to move, they send down roots here while they're in training. Their training takes so long, especially if they go on to psychoanalytic training. But the good training centers are changing the picture of psychoanalysis. We are training our students in dynamic psychiatry, the psychodynamics of mental illness, which in America means largely the principles of Freudian psychiatry—training them to do a really good job in psychotherapy. They don't need to be analysts, to spend seven years in training and hundreds of hours treating each patient. They can do a good job with a more superficial psychotherapy. And it enables them to deal with a larger number of patients."

5.

Out on the gray West Side of Chicago in the sprawling collection of hospitals and research institutes called the West Side Medical Center—another vast monument to man's attempts to cure his afflictions—stands the Neuropsychiatric Institute of the University of Illinois. A stone and brick building, it rises in two towers, one the "neurology tower," the other the "psychiatry tower." The Illinois NPI is an example of a good university psychiatric hospital. It is a complex institution. It is headquarters for the Department of Psychiatry of the College of Medicine of the University of Illinois; thus, since psychiatry is taught through all four years of the medical course, it is used by the University to teach students in the general medical courses. But it trains psychiatric specialists too—residents in psychiatry; usually there are nine or ten of them, and they rotate among this hospital, Chicago State Hospital and other public and private hospitals. NPI's third function is the treatment of patients: It has forty beds for in-patients and an out-patient clinic. And finally NPI carries on research.

Dr. Francis J. Gerty, director of the Psychiatric Department of NPI and in 1958 president of the American Psychiatric Association, said a while back, "Our responsibilities here are threefold. First, the teaching of undergraduates, so that the principles and practice derived from psychiatry that ought to be of use to the general physician are provided to him. This is the primary purpose of all departments of psychiatry in a medical school. Second, we train residents. But all teaching is behind the frontier of knowledge—it's got to be—and you need some relationship with the front line trenches, and that means research. Research is the community fight against mental disease. Man is a pretty complex being. In our research we're interested in the physical man, in the emotional relationships of man, and in the spiritual side of man which probably underlies the whole business.

"As to physical man, this involves anatomy and physiology, particularly as they focus in the nervous system and in metabolism. We've very much interested in his chemistry, especially in the chemistry that goes on in the individual cells—intracellular biochemistry. Gray matter is made up of certain kinds of cells. We are never going to come near a solution of what mental disease is all about until we understand what goes on inside these cells.

"Now, dealing with the personal man—the mental-emotional man—

we can think of him only in relation to other men. So there is the important area of psychology.

"In tracing these relationships, research leads further. It leads to anthropology, sociology and so on. But here questions arise. How much should an undergraduate medical school devote of its resources to these other frontiers? Right away you're into problems of budget and facilities. How much is going to be the job of other agencies of government? This whole matter has to do with the burden of the state, particularly the burden of the chronically ill. For out of our research something is supposed to arise that will result in treatment, which will, in turn, relieve this burden. Human beings are like gamblers. They want the jackpot, that is, quick results. The whole object of research and training becomes treatment. Our expense for research has to be justified. This is hard. Research depends on discovery. So expenditures are large and results problematical. Once in a while the expenditure pays off—insulin for the treatment of diabetes, penicillin for the treatment of syphilis, and so on. But many times, it doesn't. Before the war the budget of the Department of Psychiatry was the second smallest in the University Medical School—only ophthalmology was lower. Now it's the highest, or nearly so, due mainly to research."

Originally the present Illinois NPI was an Institute of the Department of Public Welfare of the State of Illinois, built in 1941 with state funds. It was conducted jointly by the Department and the University, and Dr. Gerty was first director of the Psychiatric Division. It was intended that all the Chicago medical schools use it for teaching and research. But it was too small. About 1951 it was taken over entirely by the University of Illinois. Today a Psychiatric Institute is being built on the West Side, with state money derived from mental health funds, big enough for all the Chicago medical schools to use.

Illinois University NPI rigidly selects its patients according to what it needs for training and research. Those whom it rejects it sends to state hospitals, mental hygiene clinics, the Institute for Juvenile Research, veterans' hospitals, family service agencies, clinics for alcoholics or other agencies. A staff doctor has said, "There aren't enough facilities but at least they get something." Those who are admitted are assigned to wards on the upper stories of the psychiatry tower. The wards are long tiled halls with bedrooms opening off them; they look much used and rather bleak. On one ward are several children suffering from severe psychosomatic disorders—kids from five to nine with ulcers and other serious physical ailments thought to be of psychic origin. They have been here two or three years under study and treatment. Chicago has been a center of psychosomatic medical studies since the late 1930s when Franz Alexander, then head of the Chicago Psychoanalytic Institute, did his studies of peptic ulcers.

On the fifth floor is a locked ward chiefly for schizophrenics. Somehow it seems darker than the other wards, and perhaps it is. These are disturbed patients, severe acute young schizophrenics, six men and twelve women. For training purposes residents treat them intensively with drugs and psychotherapy. (EST and insulin are rarely used.) In his first year a resident may treat ten patients. "You can't beat it for residency training," says a resident.

6.

It seems a century from the care given a patient in a back ward at Columbus State to the care given a patient in one of the hospitals we have visited in this chapter. Yet these institutions—the psychopathic hospital, the university hospital, the private sanitarium, the psychiatric wing in a general hospital—use no magic. They use no therapies not used in state hospitals. State hospitals could care for patients as well did they but have the manpower.

In this century the proliferation of institutions and agencies to fight mental illness has been enormous. Indeed, it is bewildering. For example, a historian of Illinois psychiatry, Dr. Gerty, writes that Chicago until 1889 had no place other than jail for the detention and observation of the mentally ill but today it has more than fifty such places—is covered by a complex network of institutions and agencies of all sorts. It has five institutions operated by the State of Illinois' Department of Public Welfare—Chicago State Hospital, a big old prolonged-care hospital like Columbus State; the Institute for Juvenile Research, which performs child guidance services on an out-patient basis; the William Healy Residential School, which houses and treats forty-eight children too disturbed to benefit from the out-patient service of the Institute for Juvenile Research; a Mental Health Center, to aid the readjustment of patients on conditional discharge from state hospitals; and the State Psychopathic Institute, which promotes and performs research. A new Psychiatric Institute is abuilding. Chicago has three agencies operated by Cook County—the Cook County Psychopathic Hospital, which diagnoses and briefly cares for patients awaiting commitment to state hospitals; the psychiatric department of the Family Court of Cook County; and the Behavior Clinic of the Criminal Court of Cook County, which diagnoses criminal defendants and advises the court. Chicago has two agencies operated by the City of Chicago—the Psychiatric Institute of the Municipal Court and the Mental Health Division of the Chicago Health Department. In and near Chicago are four U.S. Veterans Administration hospitals—which among them provide psychiatric treatment for veterans, two- and three-year approved residency programs and research facilities. Chicago has, as we have seen, thirteen psychiatric wings in general hospitals. It has fifteen private sanitariums. Its five medical colleges have departments of psychiatry and associated psychiatric hospitals and out-patient facilities. Chicago has the Illinois Society for Mental Health, a citizens' group affiliated with the National Association for Mental Health. It has numerous mental health clinics to which people can take their troubles. And in recent years two new agencies were formed to promote research and training—the Associated Psychiatric Faculties of Chicago, now superseded by other private school and interhospital participative effort, and the Psychiatric Research and Training Authority, established by the state legislature in 1957, which will make grants of money collected from patients in state hospitals to support research and training projects all over the state, much as the National Mental Health Institute of the USPHS at Bethesda does on a national scale.

In addition to all this, Chicago has the Chicago Institute for Psychoanalysis. Founded in 1932, it is one of the nation's seventeen psychoanalytic institutes and training centers approved by the Board on Professional Standards of the American Psychoanalytic Association, the organization of American analysts. The Institute is independent of any hospital or university. It was started with money from the Rockefeller and Rosenwald Foundations; today its annual budget is near $300,000, most of which is provided by its students, some by its patients and some by private foundations and federal grants. The Institute's primary purpose is to train psychoanalysts. Some commence their training while still taking psychiatric residency training, others after they have completed it. Psychoanalytic training starts with a personal analysis. It includes didactic courses and clinical conferences. And each student must treat by analysis at least four patients, under the direction of senior analysts. The Institute operates as a "weekend school" so that out-of-towners can commute for training. It turns out about a dozen analysts a year.

The Institute also performs research. And it treats a number of Chicagoans. From among the neurotics who come to the Institute seeking treatment, the Institute selects those who are amenable to analysis and who are in its judgment "worth while"—in the words of the director, Gerhart Piers, "people whose cure will mean something not only for themselves but for a growing family and people they are bound to influence." Such patients are treated by the students in training and they pay according to their ability; the average fee is about five dollars per hour, the lowest fifty cents an hour. (An average fee in private practice in Chicago is twenty-five dollars per hour.) Recently the Institute has expanded its treatment program—some of its graduates have agreed to treat at least one low-fee patient referred by the Institute. Last year the Institute treated 230 patients, gave consultations to 200 more and gave advice and referral by telephone or letter to about 1,000 more. Dr. Piers said recently, "The number of patients in analytic treatment [at the Institute] is not very high. . . . If you count the treatment hours, however, you arrive at what I believe to be an imposing figure, 19,400 a year. Add to this 3,500 supervisory hours and the hours spent by the diagnostic committee, etc., and you get well over 23,000 hours spent more or less directly on patients. . . . These figures compare only with the largest social agencies. . . . Several institutes now have low-fee clinics as we have, and although we are still far from 'psychoanalysis for the masses,' we have been making headway in that direction."

7.

The first line of defense against mental illness is the community clinic. People with troubles but little money can obtain early diagnosis and treatment at such clinics in their home communities. Many, it is thought, will thus be prevented from going to mental hospitals. Not only do clinics diagnose and treat adult ailments; they consult with the public schools, thus picking off disturbed children early in life.

The original impetus for such clinics came from local groups of doctors and laymen, often supported by the National Mental Health Association. Until recently they were financed largely by local private and public agencies. Then the National Institute of Mental Health began contributing. And today all over the country state governments are giving money to local community clinics.

But here, as everywhere in the field of mental illness, the problem is not so much a shortage of money as a shortage of people. New York

State alone could use all the psychiatrists in America. If New York and California established mental health centers in every town, the country could not begin to staff them. One solution has been to make more use of psychiatric social workers. But these too are in short supply. And there is a certain danger in using social workers indiscriminately. Some clinics located near universities are inclined to use young graduate students not yet fully trained in social work; it is one thing to allow such students to gather family data but quite another to allow them to attempt to use such strong medicine as psychotherapy. Some have memorized the Freudian lingo but have no real understanding of Freudian psychology or appreciation of the power of psychotherapy. One clinic doctor, apparently rationalizing a shortage of help, said, "Anybody can do psychotherapy." It is a frightening dictum. Of what use are millions of dollars in state aid if they employ half-trained youngsters to mess around in people's lives?

8.

Although this book deals with the mentally ill, it cannot totally ignore the mentally defective. There were 151,636 persons in American institutions for the mentally defective in 1956. Probably there is no more tragic and neglected group in American society. In recent years doctors have learned a good deal about how to teach defectives, and research promises further advances, but little use is made of all this in most state institutions, where little is provided but care—food, clothing, shelter and sometimes kindness. A few states, such as New Jersey, have good programs. But not many do. In most states the institutions are ancient and overcrowded and undermanned, and in some they are horror chambers, "boarding houses for idiots," as the head of one in Illinois said recently, "and the staff only the keepers of these boarding houses." In nearly all states waiting lists are long—there are more than three hundred names on the waiting list for the mentally retarded children's unit at Dixon State Hospital in Illinois—and so for months or even years a family must keep a defective child in its midst, perhaps doing daily damage to other children as well as offering daily mute reproach to the parents, certainly denying the child the expert hospital care and training it deserves.

14

The New Drugs

■ Since ancient times men have known that certain drugs influenced the human mind. Alcohol, hashish, opium, mescaline—these and more were in use centuries ago. And indeed one drug prepared from the root of a plant, Rauwolfia, was actually used more than 2,500 years ago for the treatment of mental disorder in India.

But in modern times, drugs played little part in psychiatric practice until 1953. True, penicillin, by controlling syphilis, had dramatically reduced paresis. True, patients suffering from pellagra, who once filled Southern mental hospitals, had practically disappeared as a result of the discovery that pellagra is a dietary ailment preventable by proper diet and curable by niacin. And, true, Dilantin and other drugs had controlled epilepsy to a point where institutions for epileptics were closing all over the country. But these were all organic disorders. Aside from such sedatives as Sodium Amytal and phenobarbital, and aside from insulin in shock treatment, drugs played no part at all in the treatment of the mysterious functional psychotic disorders.

Suddenly in 1953 all that changed. And today many think that the new psychiatric drugs are in the process of transforming psychiatry.

2.

The first psychiatric use in America of Rauwolfia, the ancient Indian drug, came about almost by chance. It happened in 1953. Rauwolfia is the powdered root of a small bush, *Rauwolfia serpentina;* in ancient times it was regarded as a panacea, and it has been used in Colombia and Guatemala and elsewhere as well as in India. In 1947 a biochemist, Sir Robert Robinson, had become interested in an alkaloid of Rauwolfia and had persuaded Dr. Emil Schlittler of the Swiss pharmaceutical firm of Ciba to prepare it. After Schlittler had crystallized the alkaloid, a muddy residue remained; tested on animals, this residue had produced a peculiar tranquilizing effect. Dr. Schlittler and a colleague, Johannes Muller, working with a pharmacologist, Hugo Bein, had set out to isolate the chemical substance responsible for the tranquilizing effect.

At approximately this point, Dr. Nathan S. Kline, director of the research facility at Rockland State Hospital in New York, wandered onto the scene. In 1953 Dr. Kline needed twelve hundred dollars to buy an apparatus to measure blood gases. The state disbursing machinery moves slowly; Kline was in a hurry. He sought a grant from Squibb, a drug manufacturer. But the company gave grants primarily for product development and related activities or for public relations purposes, and there were no products to test in the field of mental disease. "As for public relations," Kline says, "who cared whether a state hospital got a grant—there's no good will in that." But it happened that Squibb had sponsored some work on hypertension by a friend of Kline's, Dr. Robert W. Wilkins, of Boston University, and Kline chanced to have dinner with Dr. A. Dale Console, medical director of Squibb, and the subject of Kline's need for twelve hundred dollars came up. "In his work on hypertension, Wilkins had been using a Squibb drug called Raudixin, the whole root of Rauwolfia," Kline recalls. "He had noted that it lowered blood pressure and that it also had some sedative effect. So I got Squibb to give us some to test for its sedative effect on mental patients with the idea it might replace phenobarbital. Subsequently they gave us a research grant of twelve hundred dollars. Well, having got it, I was trapped by my own insistence on adequate testing—I had to go ahead. At the same time we happened to be trying to talk Ciba into supporting some endocrine research. They were interested to hear that we were getting a grant from Squibb for Raudixin. Ciba had just isolated the active principle in Rauwolfia, which seemed to be the part that brought about the sedative effect. They named it reserpine and later marketed it as Serpasil. They asked could we include this on the testing. This is how we got started using reserpine on mental patients at the hospital. Our first report was published in February, 1954."

Kline took reserpine himself, as is the practice among research men. He gave it to members of the research staff who volunteered. He tried it on two manic-depressive and two schizophrenic patients. Then he started 414 female and 205 male patients on it, nearly all chronic schizophrenics. Then, working with hospital staff, he gave reserpine to 400 consecutive admissions and gave Thorazine to the next 200, and he is now doing a five-year follow-up study on this last 600. He has published numerous professional papers on the results and has become perhaps the country's leading exponent of the new psychiatric drugs.

Working in collaboration with the staff of the hospital, he and Dr. Joseph A. Barsa found that in a series of 150 chronically disturbed psychotics who had failed to respond to EST or insulin shock, 84 per cent showed improvement on reserpine. Reserpine acts slowly. When it is given by mouth, there is little response for several days. Then the patient becomes sedated—less excited, assaultive and agitated—and he eats better and gains weight. After the first week he sometimes enters the "turbulent phase"—delusions and hallucinations increase, the patient does not "feel like himself" and has no control over his impulses; he seems "worse," and an inexperienced physician may discontinue the drug in alarm. But if he does not, the patient finally enters the "integrative phase": He becomes quiet, friendly, co-operative, interested in the world around him, and freer of hallucinations and delusions. Many for the first time in years enjoy eating, talking to others, touching others. Reserpine seems to release the patient, to free him to re-integrate himself. It works on neurotics as well as psychotics.

3.

Chlorpromazine, marketed by the Smith, Kline & French Laboratories as Thorazine, came into use about the same time. Unlike Rauwolfia, it is not a plant; it originated in a laboratory. Its full name is 3-dimethyl-amino-propyl-2-chlorphenothiazine hydrochloride. It was synthesized by French chemists working on antihistamines, and Dr. Douglas Goldman of Longview State Hospital in Cincinnati published one of the first reports on its large-scale use in a mental hospital. He wrote in the *Journal of the American Medical Association:*

The initial observations justify a sense of optimism that has rarely resulted from the trial of new techniques in the treatment of psychotic states. . . . In patients who show a great deal of initial excitement . . . the medicament is practically specific. . . . Patients cease to be loud and profane. . . . In states of excitement associated with the prolonged use of alcohol, the drug is practically specifically effective. . . . In the more chronic psychotic states, the effect of the drug is much less immediately dramatic. . . . After a period of one to six weeks, various psychotic components gradually resolve. Hallucinations are almost specifically relieved in many patients relatively early in the treatment. . . . Severe paranoid ideation subsides more gradually.

4.

Since Thorazine and Serpasil came along, the drug houses have plunged heavily into the field. They have sometimes been criticized for making overenthusiastic claims for their products. At the same time they have done immense amounts of research and have provided huge quantities of free drugs for testing in state hospitals.

Kline has said, "The pharmaceutical houses deserve a lot of recognition. Sure they made money at it. So what? We live in a competitive capitalistic society. So Ciba made money from reserpine. It cost them over a million dollars to develop it. They had 80 per cent of their research facilities devoted to this particular job. It paid off. But at that they didn't get what they had coming because of the patent laws—you can't patent a botanical. SKF did better—they could patent Thorazine."

In recent years the drug houses have marketed a large number of other drugs, and more keep coming. Many are related chemically to Thorazine. Among those which have received the most attention are Frenquel, Miltown, Pacatal, Compazine, Vesprin and Trilafon.

So far we have noted only the tranquilizing drugs. Doctors used them eagerly, and they wrought an almost miraculous change in state hospitals—screaming died out on disturbed wards, patients kept their clothes on, restraint virtually ended, EST declined dramatically. But all the while the doctors recognized that there was one class of patients whom the tranquilizers did not help: depressed patients. They were already tranquil, much too tranquil. Indeed, sometimes the tranquilizing drugs made them worse.

In the past Benzedrine and Dexedrine had been tried on depressions but while they had some limited use they had serious side effects—they reduced appetite and they overstimulated the nervous system so that sleep became difficult or impossible. So during the early years of the new drug era, EST remained the only treatment for depression.

And a search began for a drug that would act on depression.

Several were marketed. Meratran seemed to be useful only in states of pure depression, according to Robert S. deRopp—"Where depression is mixed with anxiety it tends to make the anxiety more severe."* Ritalin has been used successfully in some cases. But "on the whole it must be admitted," deRopp wrote, "that the ideal drug for the treatment of melancholia seems not yet to have been discovered. It is a hard problem for the pharmacologist, for one cannot produce melancholia in experimental animals. What we really need is a naturally melancholic guinea pig, the depth of whose gloom can be measured by some means or other. We could then try, by chemical agents, to restore its *joie de vivre*."

Since deRopp wrote—and his book was published in 1957—another antidepressant drug has come out, Marsilid (and no doubt others will be out before this book is published). Dr. Kline said, "Meratran and Ritalin and the others help mild depressions. But Marsilid seems so far to be the only one that helps severe depressions." Marsilid is a trade name for iproniazid, a drug introduced in 1952 for the treatment of tuberculosis but abandoned because the patients it helped seemed better than they really were and because after prolonged use several patients developed psychoses. Everybody noted that the TB patients showed a remarkable sense of well-being, that iproniazid affected their mental state. When Thorazine and Serpasil came along, iproniazid was tried as a tranquilizer on mental patients. It failed. In the spring of 1956 laboratory investigators attempting to nail down the mode of action of reserpine found that if they gave Marsilid to an animal and then gave it reserpine, instead of becoming tranquilized it became agitated. "On Marsilid," Kline recalls, "the mice looked like supermice." After further experiments, Kline tried Marsilid on depressed patients and found that it worked. Whereas the tranquilizing drugs seemed to reduce psychic energy, Marsilid increased it. Kline calls Marsilid a "psychic energizer," pointing out that "psychic energy" is Freud's term. Marsilid acts slowly, sometimes showing no effect for three months; its action can be speeded up by adding Dexedrine to it. Another doctor has warned, "You should be suspicious of any drug that takes three months" —he feels that in so long a period a depression may lift spontaneously.

---

* Robert S. deRopp, *Drugs and the Mind*. New York: St. Martin's Press, 1957. This is the liveliest and wisest book I have seen on the new drugs.

But Kline maintains that cyclic depressions do not recur when the patient is on Marsilid. In the spring of 1958 several patients who had been given Marsilid died, and New York City health officers forbade the sale of Marsilid in bottles bearing a label recommending a dosage so high as 150 milligrams a day.

5.

In addition to the psychotherapeutic drugs—the tranquilizers and the energizers—there is another class of drugs which has interested psychiatrists greatly of late. These are the psychotogenic drugs—drugs which seem to produce symptoms of insanity.

Many of these are very ancient—hashish or marijuana, derived from the hemp plant; cohoba, a West Indian snuff; peyotl, derived by the Aztecs from a cactus; teonanacatl, the sacred mushroom of the Aztecs; caapi, a drug prepared from a jungle vine in the rain forests of the Amazon; and others. Some are modern synthetics—mescaline, the active substance in peyotl which produced the visions and hallucinations of the peyotl eater, and a new synthetic, d-lysergic acid diethylamide tartrate, called LSD-25, probably the most powerful of all the psychotogenics.

At the end of the nineteenth century an American doctor, Weir Mitchell, drank an extract of peyotl and reported that for two "enchanted" hours he beheld a splendrous display of stars, filmy color, a "rush of points of light," a white spear of gray stone which became a richly furnished Gothic tower, a cliff projecting over a gulf of unseen depth, and other visions. Havelock Ellis, upon drinking peyotl, reported a consciousness of energy and intellectual power, lethargy, visions of kaleidoscopic spiked objects and golden jewels. Baudelaire and others reported the effects of hashish. Humphrey Osmond of Canada, who recently has done much work with modern synthetics, has written in the *Annals* of the New York Academy of Sciences, "Most subjects find the experience valuable, some find it frightening, and many say that it is uniquely lovely. All, from . . . unsophisticated Indians to men of great learning, agree that much of it is beyond verbal description. . . . For myself, my experiences with these substances have been the most strange, most awesome, and among the most beautiful things in a varied and fortunate life. These are not escapes from but enlargements, burgeonings of reality."

Most of the experimental work in recent years has been done with

LSD-25 and mescaline. A few mental patients have been given the drugs—some were affected, some were not, and schizophrenics seemed less affected than normals, a suggestive circumstance. But interest has centered chiefly on the effects that LSD-25 and mescaline produce on normal people. They seem to produce a false schizophrenia.

Dr. Solomon and his colleagues at Boston Psychopathic found that a person who swallowed LSD-25 or mescaline soon began to display physical symptoms—restlessness, weakness, sweating, tremor. Within an hour he became hostile, anxious or irritable. He was withdrawn, apathetic, confused. He began to entertain delusions and hallucinations—a feeling that a part of his body had vanished, visual hallucinations. Sounds seemed extraordinarily loud to him, and he conceived them as persecutory—he thought persons talking in low voices in the next room were shouting threateningly about him. He became inarticulate, unable to describe his strange sensations and ideas—a catatonic-like state. He developed delusions of grandeur and persecution—a paranoid-like state. His feelings swung wildly from elation to despair. Suicidal and homicidal impulses appeared.

Mescaline and LSD-25, then, produce what is called a "model" psychosis. Investigators have sought to learn how they do it. Some have thought that could we but learn how LSD-25 and mescaline produce a "psychosis," we might know what causes schizophrenia. They thought perhaps schizophrenia is caused by a poison within the body which results from an "error in metabolism"*—is the "metabolic error" caused by substances acting as mescaline or LSD-25 does? And they reasoned that if another drug could be found which would block the effect of LSD-25, this drug might also block the unknown, naturally occurring substance which caused schizophrenia. To date, however, this theory has not worked out. Some investigators have come to believe that the resemblances of the "model" psychoses to schizophrenia are only superficial. Dr. Julia Apter, of Illinois, has reported that these drugs will not cause animals to hallucinate when the optic nerve has been severed, and she has concluded therefore that the effect in the brain is dependent on transmission from the retina. Some investigators have abandoned the whole LSD-25 and mescaline lead, concluding that the symptoms they produce are not schizophrenic at all. Nonetheless, the peculiar

* Similarly it has been theorized that cancer is caused by "metabolic error."

properties of mescaline and LSD-25 have opened up new avenues of research in neurochemistry.

A paper by two Canadians, Humphrey Osmond and John Smythies, drew attention to a chemical resemblance between mescaline and two body hormones, adrenalin and nor-adrenalin. Perhaps a failure in body chemistry could produce not adrenalin but some poisonous chemical allied to it. Investigating reports that asthmatic patients sometimes suffered hallucinations when they took large doses of adrenalin that had begun to deteriorate, they found that such adrenalin contained adrenochrome, a substance chemically related to LSD-25 and other psychotogenic drugs; and Osmond reported that when he injected adrenochrome into his own arm, he experienced hallucinations. Max Rinkel and others in Boston disbelieve this claim and suggest that the hallucinations were caused by another breakdown product of adrenalin, adrenoxine. But that adrenochrome, adrenoxine or any other toxin is the "secret poisoner" of schizophrenia has not been shown.

In 1954 J. H. Gaddum of the University of Edinburgh showed that LSD-25 interfered with the action of serotonin. Serotonin is a chemical substance, a hormone, which occurs naturally in the body. Isolated only a few years ago, its role in living processes is still obscure. Serotonin has been shown to cause the smooth muscle tissue in a rat uterus to contract. In the human body it occurs in blood platelets. Serotonin first interested scientists working on the possible causes of high blood pressure. But then it was discovered in the brain. It may act as a neuro-humor, helping to maintain normal mental processes. It causes its effects in specific sites in the body. It will "fit" into them and into nowhere else. As has been said, Dr. Gaddum showed that LSD-25 blocks the action of serotonin on smooth muscle. Drs. D. W. Woolley and E. N. Shaw of the Rockefeller Institute for Medical Research synthesized other antiserotonins and recognized that among them were substances that caused mental aberrations. They theorized that LSD-25 might produce mental disturbance because it interfered with the action of serotonin, or, contrariwise, because it competed with serotonin for its inactivating enzyme, thus permitting the accumulation of abnormally large amounts of serotonin in the brain. They went on to suggest that schizophrenia might result from either too much or too little serotonin in the brain.

But the evidence is confusing. A bromine derivative of LSD-25 blocks the action of serotonin, as LSD-25 itself does—but it produces no hallucinations; and as Dr. Irvine H. Page has written, "Why the substitution of one atom of bromine should so profoundly alter the molecule's effect on the psyche is a problem of major importance." Again, bufotenin, a compound structurally related to serotonin, produces bizarre behavior, indeed it is an active principle of the cohoba snuff used by Haitian and South American Indian necromancers for many centuries. "It is just possible," Dr. Page writes, "that when dealing with psychic processes the specificity of action is of a very high order. . . . If thought is indeed associated in some way with cerebral metabolism . . . then it is possible to understand how disturbing [are] substances that interfere with normal metabolism of brain cells."

In the mammalian brain, the largest concentrations of serotonin appear in the more primitive brain areas—in the brain stem, especially the hypothalamus. A lower concentration appears in the cortex, virtually none in the cerebellum. And it is precisely in the regions of the brain where serotonin levels are highest that the tranquilizer reserpine is thought to act. Reserpine appears to liberate extra amounts of serotonin in the brain and may produce its beneficial effect in this way. Reserpine enters the brain rapidly and disappears entirely in eight hours but its sedative effects last forty-eight hours. Similarly although LSD-25 is metabolized in about an hour, its effects last twelve hours or more. All this suggests that neither reserpine nor LSD-25 acts directly but rather causes a chemical change which produces delayed psychic effects.

Much research on how the tranquilizing and psychotogenic drugs act is focused on the autonomic nervous system—the nervous system not subject to control by the will—and on three chemical substances in the body. These substances, all hormones, are acetylcholine, adrenalin and nor-adrenalin, and upon them depend the outward signs of inner emotional life. We could not move a muscle unless the cholinergic nerves produced acetylcholine and unless an enzyme, cholinesterase, promptly destroyed acetylcholine. It is known that acetylcholine acts as a chemical mediator, or aid to conduction, in transmitting nerve impulses across the gap, called a synapse, between two nerve fibers and across the gap at the neuromuscular junction. A nerve impulse coming along a nerve fiber results in the liberation at the synaptic gap of free acetylcholine; it diffuses across the gap, depolarizes the membrane of the nerve cell body on the other side of the gap and thus helps transfer the impulse to the other side of the gap. If a cholinesterase inhibitor is present, the acetylcholine released is protected from destruction and produces a volley of impulses to depolarize the nerve cell body on the far side of the gap. But if an excess of cholinesterase inhibitor or acetylcholine itself is present, the cell is flooded with acetylcholine, which results in persistent depolarization and thus prevents activation of the nerve cell body on the other side of the gap. Thus the impulse is blocked. Bernard B. Brodie and Parkhurst A. Shore of the National Institute of Mental Health have suggested that serotonin and noradrenalin may function similarly as synaptic transmitting agents in the hypothalamus and other subcortical areas of the brain itself.

They suggest that some of the tranquilizing and psychotogenic drugs may work by interfering with the action of serotonin and noradrenalin. Numerous other investigators think so too. But Brodie and Shore caution,

If the role of serotonin [or nor-adrenalin] in brain function is that of a chemical mediator, especially of subcortical centers, it seems unlikely that the many kinds of mental illnesses could possibly be explained by the single premise of faulty nerve transmission. This seems too easy a solution of the problem. The chemistry of the brain that could account for the specialized functions capable of memory, evaluation, and selection is undoubtedly extraordinarily complicated, far more so than that which is responsible for the specialized functions of other organs, about which we still know relatively little. The abundance of research with the tranquilizing and hallucinogenic agents and with serotonin may not lead to a profound understanding of schizophrenia, but it may well result in a better comprehension of the integration of the subcortical centers in the brain that regulate the autonomic [stabilizing] mechanisms. Perhaps it is even more important that research with serotonin and LSD-25 has channeled our thinking concerning brain function and the action of the drugs thereon along [new] lines. . . . It is probable that subtle biochemical events, peculiar to the brain, will ultimately explain normal brain function and the changes responsible for mental illness.

Neurochemistry began in 1884 with the appearance of a paper in London by J. L. W. Thudichum, "A Treatise on the Chemical Constitution of the Brain." It lay dormant until about 1928 when, along with psychopharmacology, it was resurrected in Germany and England. Dr. Page, commenting on this, has said:

But the growth and delineation of a field of endeavors requires . . . more than merely a desire to cultivate it. What is needed is a specific discovery that points to the usefulness of something. The [psychotogenic drugs],

the tranquilizers, and their metabolic partners have, I think, provided this.
. . . We are witnessing, and participating in, the rebirth of a new branch
of knowledge dealing with the chemical substrates of thought, from a
theme established long ago. Unless I exaggerate, a new era is indeed upon
us."

6.

Nobody knows with certainty how or why the new tranquilizing and
energizing drugs work. Theories are legion—we have outlined a few.
Research is proceeding—we have noted a little of it and shall note more.
If we knew how and why the drugs work, we might know what causes
schizophrenia. Even this is by no means certain. In the study of the
brain the unknown comprises a realm many times the size of the
known, and only to consider a few of the speculations, as we have done,
is to indicate the enormity of the unknown.

State hospital doctors are inclined to be a trifle indifferent to all this.
They are inclined to be pragmatists—and no wonder, confronted as
they are with vast assemblages of psychotic patients. Nobody knows
why aspirin works but it does; nobody knows how anesthesia works,
but it does. The new drugs work; enough.

New York State jumped into the lead in the use of the psychiatric
drugs. In 1953 and 1954 Kline had done his original work with
reserpine at Rockland State Hospital and others had reported on Thorazine. The pharmaceutical houses gave New York a million and a quarter
dollars' worth of drugs free for trial. Dr. Henry Brill, Assistant Commissioner of the New York State Department of Mental Hygiene,
recalls, "By November of 1954 we had collected two thousand cases,
patients to whom we'd given the new drugs. We held a meeting. With
unprecedented unanimity all the psychiatrists agreed that they were
good. So we plunged in and asked for large appropriations." In 1958
New York State spent two million dollars for the drugs. It provides
drugs for all patients who need them.

Other states were slower to act. Some hospitals, including Columbus,
struggled along for several years with small supplies, and patients
had to buy their own. This is still true in some hospitals, although state
appropriations for drugs have increased astronomically. It has been
estimated that one-third of all medical prescriptions written are for the
psychiatric drugs.

Somewhat surprisingly, no definitive evaluation of the drugs has yet been made. Kline and others have criticized the National Institute of Mental Health for not making one. The Institute set up a Psychopharmacology Service Center in 1956, which was at first advised that "not enough was known about the best methods for studying drug effectiveness to warrant the development of an expensive multi-hospital co-operative study of drug effectiveness," but later it took a more "sanguine view" and in 1958 allotted $752,616 for clinical evaluation.

Kline's and Barsa's original study at Rockland State showed that 22 per cent of the patients who received reserpine were able to leave the hospital. But how many relapse and return? Nobody is sure. A two-year follow-up study at the Langley Porter Clinic in San Francisco of sixty-two schizophrenic patients treated with Thorazine showed that 60 per cent made a social recovery, ten relapsed, seven were retreated and made a social recovery, and the majority did not require maintenance drugs; 22 per cent showed marked improvement and usually needed maintenance therapy; 13 per cent showed slight improvement; and 5 per cent made no improvement. This and other studies at Langley Porter have led Lester H. Margolis of that clinic to a "conservatively enthusiastic" acceptance of the "values and limitations" of Thorazine. Margolis has written, "An overwhelming mass of evidence points to the fact that chlorpromazine and reserpine yield results superior to insulin-coma or electroconvulsive therapy in the treatment of schizophrenia." He adds that EST is still superior in treating depressions and that certain cases, including classical obsessive-compulsive states and such borderline states as pseudo-neurotic schizophrenia, respond only to lobotomy.

To date, no newer drug has replaced chlorpromazine (Thorazine). It is the clinical impression of most authorities that chlorpromazine is superior to reserpine (Serpasil), though both have their uses. Some believe that the two work well in combination, though this is disputed. No new side effects of either have come to light. Doctors are still not sure which of the many drugs works best on which psychiatric conditions. Kline feels that both chlorpromazine and reserpine have lived up to expectations. He has said, "They get patients out of the hospital. Many of them don't have to return. They prevent others from ever coming in. Cures? We don't even talk about cures. We can't. If you'll tell me what schizophrenia is, then I'll tell you when we've cured it. I've seen patients on drugs who were symptom-free. Is that a cure? I don't know. In many fields of medicine we're satisfied if we patch up a patient so he has only a limited disability. In surgery, for instance—an amputee isn't cured, but he can function to a limited extent. Only in psychiatry do people insist on total cures. Only in psychiatry do people say, 'You've only reduced his symptoms.' The drugs do get people out of the hospital. Even though sometimes they're partially disabled, they can function. In any other branch of medicine this would be enough.

"But," Kline went on, "the major importance of the new drugs is the idea that chemical factors can influence the course of mental disease. From now on it's a question of improving and exploring. Prior to this, nobody had much faith in chemical treatment. From a practical point of view, the drugs represent the biggest breakthrough in the history of psychiatry."

Dr. Brill of New York State has termed the use of drugs, especially Thorazine, "a major identifiable influence" in the present trend toward stabilization of the New York state hospital population. On March 31, 1954, the census of New York mental hospitals was 90,893, four times the 1900 figure. The increase had been steady and no amount of work had stopped it. In 1955 the large-scale use of reserpine and chlor-promazine began. Almost at once the use of restraint and seclusion dropped dramatically, and by midsummer it was clear that a shift in population equilibrium was taking place. On March 31, 1956, the hospital population showed a reduction of 452 for the year instead of the anticipated increase of from two to five thousand. The same trend continued in the second year—the population fell another 453 patients. And as we have seen, other states reported the same thing. Dr. Brill reports in the *American Journal of Psychiatry* that only once before in modern times, during World War II in 1942-43, had the hospital population dropped. But during that period admissions also dropped, while they remained high in 1955-56; the 1942-43 drop was gradual and reached a maximum, then receded, while the 1955-56 drop was sudden and seems to be sustained; and, perhaps most significant, the 1942-43 shift affected both functional and organic cases, while the 1955-56 shift was felt most strongly in those functional disorders which are known to respond best to drugs. (It is true, however, that in 1955-56 the increase in geriatric and alcoholic cases was less than had been expected, a curious and unexplained fact.)

On the other hand, some hospital administrators feel that the decline in the number of patients in their hospitals is due to other factors. Jack R. Ewalt, Commissioner of Mental Health in Massachusetts, has said,

"I attribute it to the increase in hospital personnel—to group activity by nurses and attendants supervised by psychiatrists. Our decline started a year and a half before the drugs came along. The drugs accelerated the decline. Most of us feel that the drugs don't do anything to the underlying psychotic process but that they make it easier to get at."

The new drugs are not accepted universally. Some doctors deny they are any good. (Dr. Kline believes that some oppose the drugs because their use originated "in the backwoods state hospitals.") One doctor said, "All we really know is that they keep the patient quiet without putting him to sleep. They may have some more specific effect but we don't know." A canvas of leading investigators for the New York *Annals* showed that, while most considered the drugs efficacious, a minority did not and said so vehemently. One thought Thorazine "useless . . . with the exception of one or two dramatic cases," another felt the drugs should be used only after EST has failed, another that the drugs had no lasting effect and another that the drugs were no help in office practice and often were a hindrance. Some state hospital doctors believe that the drugs, though virtually useless themselves except as sedatives, brought about improved attitudes in the hospital personnel which resulted in the discharge of more patients.

The drugs revived the ancient quarrel between those who attribute mental disorder to organic factors and those who attribute it to psychic factors. Some psychiatrists are skeptical of the drugs because they believe the case for them not proved. The first enthusiasm for the drugs has faded a bit. For a time nearly everybody agreed, for example, that if the drugs did nothing else they at least facilitated psychotherapy; but recently even that has been questioned. At the APA meeting in 1957, Drs. Charles Savage and Juliana Day of the National Institute reported on the results of giving reserpine to four chronic regressed schizophrenics who had received continuous intensive psychotherapy for two years without result. On reserpine the patients improved dramatically— their hostility decreased, they were no longer assaultive, they participated in group activities, they talked more freely and rationally, they made visible efforts at self-control and were concerned about the doctor's reaction. "Psychotherapy was more comfortable for both patient and doctor," the investigators reported. "In the sense of therapy as a collaborative investigation into the patient's difficulties in living, psychotherapy was not facilitated. The patients avoided sensitive areas as effectively as they had before reserpine. . . . Eventually the patients reached a plateau which they were unable to transcend and none became well enough to leave the hospital. Environmental stress was able to reverse the favorable effects of reserpine. After six months reserpine was temporarily discontinued. The patients all relapsed to their former state."

At the 1957 APA meeting Dr. Werner Simon and six other Minneapolis investigators reported on what they called the first research project to compare chlorpromazine and reserpine with other treatments, with each other, and with spontaneous remission in schizophrenia. Eighty consecutive first-admission schizophrenics were randomly assigned into four treatment groups—those treated by whatever method seemed indicated, including EST, insulin shock, psychotherapy, drugs or these in combination; those treated by chlorpromazine alone; those treated by reserpine alone; and those given no therapy except hospital routine. After thirty days it was found that the four groups had improved in this order: miscellaneous treatment, chlorpromazine, reserpine and hospital routine. Chlorpromazine was "significantly" more effective than reserpine, which was little better than hospitalization alone. In the total group, twice as many patients were unimproved as showed definite improvement. Dr. Simon concluded:

We consider it, therefore, premature to discard such treatments as insulin coma, electroshock, and psychotherapy in favor of the tranquilizing drugs, as has been recommended by others and has become actual practice in many hospitals. In addition, our study re-emphasizes (at least for short-term treatment) that schizophrenia is exceedingly resistant to any form of treatment, and also that in some cases [any] treatment [or none] results in some slight improvement.

7.

Dr. L. G. Abood, a biochemist who directs the laboratory research work at the Illinois University NPI, takes a somewhat skeptical view of the uproar over the drugs. He has said, "Marsilid is the bandwagon of the moment. Now that all the patients have been properly depressed by Thorazine and reserpine, suddenly everybody wants to stimulate 'em. Some drug house in the country comes out with a new drug every day. It isn't rational or useful, it spends a lot of talent in the wrong direction. We ought to pause and try to understand what happens—the chemical nature of the compounds and the mechanism of their action. The therapeutic effectiveness of the tranquilizers is now being questioned. It's not as good as was thought at first. Patients are relapsing, how many nobody knows. Of course the drugs have done a lot of good. You don't see the disturbed patients now that you used to. Instead of being in a locked seclusion room they're staring at the TV set in a stupor. It's easier on the attendants and the psychiatrists. Whether it's really easier on the patients is doubtful.

"Some people don't think the drugs are any better than EST," Dr. Abood went on. "Almost every new therapy produces a sudden improvement in the hospital. EST, Metrazol, insulin, are only a few examples. But then the effect eventually levels off. We feel this is happening with the existing tranquilizers. You can't get around the fact that the real answer lies in understanding the chemistry of the brain. We need fundamental research that has nothing directly to do with mental health. Research on the chemistry of the brain, on enzyme systems, on how the brain functions at the neurophysiological level, on the relationship of the autonomic system and the higher nervous system—the ultimate answers lie in those directions.

"In the last twenty years there has been a great impetus given neurochemistry. It would be unfortunate if clinical research would get in the way of this now. If you make an application for a grant today and mention that drugs are to be tested on patients, the application meets with favor. But all the time, what you should be doing is trying to understand the chemistry of the brain and the chemistry of these drugs. If you want to find out what goes wrong with an organ system, you have to find out first how it functions normally. We know less about the chemistry of the brain than about the chemistry of any other organ. Today in the rush to find new drugs we've lost sight of the fact that the real value of substances such as Thorazine and reserpine concerns their use as research tools. How are they acting upon the nervous system? Where do they act? What is it about their chemical properties that gives them this peculiar activity? In what way have they improved our understanding of brain function as well as mental illness?"

8.

When the new drugs first appeared, the public was greatly interested. Many people started taking them without doctor's prescription. Doctors became concerned. Repeatedly they have warned, as Dr. Margolis did in the *Annals,* that "the clinical application of [Thorazine] is attended by important and sometimes dangerous reactions, and it should not be administered indiscriminately."

Dr. Kline has written:

> The tranquilizing drugs, as I have repeatedly and strongly urged, should be used only for the treatment of those whose mental and emotional state *disables* them. They should not be resorted to for the treatment of anything less than an incapacitating illness. The picture of the snarling vicious dangerous monkey transformed by a few milligrams of a chemical into a friendly "tranquil" and "happy" animal fascinates me in a horrendous way. Such a creature is a pleasure to have around the laboratory, but he would not last ten minutes in his native jungle. Similarly, mankind is perfectly capable of tranquilizing itself into oblivion.

Dr. Kline was concerned because people were taking drugs for the wrong reasons.

> If somebody feels low on Monday morning, that's no reason to medicate himself up. Or because he's inefficient and may get fired. What's needed is to bestir himself and not get fired. He can tranquilize himself out of a job. Anxiety, guilt, tension—all these uncomfortable things are the things that keep us moving.

Psychiatric drugs are developing so fast that it is almost impossible to keep up with them. No doubt by the time this book is published, this chapter will be sadly out of date.

9.

Just as the drugs have radically changed the mental hospitals, so have they started to alter the office practice of psychiatry.

Of the approximately 6,500 psychiatrists in the United States who are in private office practice, about seven hundred are psychoanalysts. The reception room of the psychoanalyst is likely to be small, soft-lit, furnished in the modern style, decorated with a picture of Freud. To a stranger the most striking thing about it is that there is no nurse or receptionist in sight; rather, there is likely to be a sign, "PLEASE BE SEATED," and nothing more. Nor is the waiting room cluttered with other patients waiting to see the doctor. The patient is all alone. Here he awaits his appointed hour. Promptly on that hour, the door of the analyst's inner office opens, the previous patient leaves, and the new one goes in. In the inner office, another soundproofed soft-lit chamber, the patient lies on a couch, the analyst seated at his side or even behind his head, and for forty-five or fifty minutes the patient verbalizes whatever comes into his mind—ideas, associations, dreams, memories, fantasies, images, bodily sensations. Occasionally the analyst interprets this material for him, or guides him slightly, or jogs him when he falls silent—"Yes?" Most of the time the analyst says nothing. His role is to direct the patient in his effort to discover the truth about himself and the inner meaning of his own experience. The patient spends forty-five or fifty minutes a day, three or four or five days a week, like this for two or three or even six or seven years. Analysis proceeds according to certain laws of its own; it is underlain by certain theoretical analytical concepts. But the patient in the hands of a good analyst knows and hears little of these matters. To him, it is simply his own inner life that is being revealed, as though he were the first man learning about himself at earth's dawning. Such phrases as "Oedipus complex" and "anal fixation" are heard far more often at cocktail parties than in an analyst's office. Analysis is an extremely—even an excruciatingly —personal thing. Not everybody benefits from analysis. Some persons go through seven or eight years of analysis without notable improvement. Others are helped greatly in a couple of years. People who have been through analysis successfully have termed it the most fascinating, painful and helpful experience of their lives.

Analysis is a far cry from a universal pill which heals all men's troubles. One man's troubles lie buried in his memories of his mother; another's are deeply intertwined with his feelings about a younger brother born thirty years ago; but to all this the universal pill is indifferent, it treats all alike, chemically precipitating in the unseen cells of the brain relief from pain, operating in a dark world where all cats are gray. Is it possible that an indifferent pill can do the work of hundreds of hours of skilled and intensely personal analysis? To date, no. Someday, who knows? Freud himself believed that in the long run the value of analysis might well lie more in the insight it provided into mental processes than in its value as a therapy.

Clearly, there being about fifty forty-five- or fifty-minute hours in a working week, an analyst can treat only ten to fifteen patients at a time in full-scale analytic office practice, and many probably treat but eight, in order to leave more time free for one-time consultations, hospital work and research. Since there are only seven hundred certified analysts in America, if each treats ten it is clear that all the analysts in America can treat by analysis only seven thousand patients in any given year. But (to overstate the matter a bit) a single doctor with a jar of pills can fling them to thousands of patients in a year; and the ten thousand psychiatrists in the country who are not analysts, not to mention all the general practitioners, can dose tens or hundreds of thousands of patients with pills. And hundreds of thousands, millions even, need help, help of some kind. Individual analysis never could catch up. There are eighty million people in Indonesia and only twelve psychiatrists, one of whom came to America and trained in analysis. What can he hope to do for the masses? Nothing, obviously; he is almost certain to become something akin to a court functionary.

For years psychiatrists have sought means of short-cutting the lengthy expensive process of psychoanalysis. They have tried hypnoanalysis, narcoanalysis and group therapy. They have found merit in all but none was precisely what they sought. Some feel the drugs may be the answer. Resist the idea as one will, it seems inescapable that psycho-analysis was a nineteenth-century technique appropriate to a time when the individual was supreme and when individuals were less numerous than today; but the psychiatric drugs are a twentieth-century technique suitable for large masses of men—for mass man—whose individuality is becoming obliterated in other ways, whose individual idiosyncrasies need be attended less than their mass metabolic errors; and because the mass has gotten so huge we have no alternative but to turn from individual analysis to mass drug dosage.

Will, then, the drugs make the old-fashioned analyst obsolete? Kline does not think so, nor does deRopp. They envision the use of drugs as an aid to analysis. Kline says: "With drugs, the analyst will lose the patients he shouldn't have had in the first place, those ill-suited to analysis, and he'll be able to reach some of the suitable ones he wasn't able to help before, those who sought analysis too late."

DeRopp says that analysis is "frequently rendered impossible by the inner fears of the patients which persistently 'block' those very memories and damaging experiences from rising to the surface from the depths of the unconscious." He says that such drugs as Pentothal and LSD-25 can "unlock the closed rooms of the mind," bring back forgotten child-hood experiences, reach those deeper levels of consciousness which sometimes prove unreachable by psychotherapy alone.

Analysts might be expected to have a built-in resistance to drugs: Drugs run counter to their theory of the mind, that mental disorder is of psychic, not organic, origin. Nonetheless, a few of them have begun to use the drugs as adjuncts to analysis. One has reported on eight patients to whom he has given Marsilid. In one of these the analyst had seen the patient for 144 analytic sessions. The patient went into a deep depression. The analyst felt he would probably come out of it but meanwhile the analysis was threatened by three hazards—the patient might kill himself, might fail in business or might stop coming to analysis. The analyst hesitated to give him Marsilid but did so. It brought the patient out of his depression, overcame the hazards and permitted the analyst to conclude the analysis successfully. He administered lighter doses of Marsilid than are usually recommended, feeling they would interfere less with the analytic process though they might prolong it. The analyst wrote:

A question will occur at this point to the non-analyst. Why should one think of retarding a recovery? In fact, if Marsilid can relieve depression, why should it not replace analysis rather than merely supplement it? The answer, of course, lies in the goal of therapy. If one is interested, as the non-analytic psychiatrist generally is, in relieving an acute episode of illness, Marsilid can be used as electroshock is now being used. This, however, is not the goal of the analyst. He sees an episode of depression . . . as merely a phasically recurrent symptom in a sick personality. In other words, for the analyst, the depression is not the illness. The personality in which the depression appears is a sick one, and it requires treatment as much in symptom-free intervals as during the depressive episode. Although it is usually the depression which brings the patient for treatment . . . the analyst will attempt to see the total problem. If the patient satisfies the usual criteria for analysis he will recommend analysis. In other cases, the patient will be referred for one of the symptomatic therapies, hitherto shock and now, probably, Marsilid.

10.

The impact of the drugs has been considerably greater on the general private office practice of psychiatry than on analysis.

The office of the psychiatrist is likely to be a busier place than the analyst's, to resemble that of a general practitioner of medicine—receptionist, ringing telephone and a waiting room filled with patients in all stages of neurological and psychological debilitation (for often the psychiatrist is also a neurologist). In his inner office, before the drugs came along, the psychiatrist gave a patient electroshock or psychotherapy or both. After shock the patient rested awhile in a darkened little room, then arose and went about his day's business. Psychotherapy might be conducted with the patient supine upon a couch or upright in a chair facing the psychiatrist. It usually lasted the conventional analytic forty-five or fifty minutes. But it was a much more superficial therapy than analysis, similar to what we have observed at Columbus State. It took the form of a dialogue between patient and doctor, not of free association by the patient and occasional interpretation by the doctor. It was intended to give the patient insight into his problems or perhaps intended only to support and encourage him. It was not aimed, as the analyst quoted above pointed out, at treating the underlying sickness of the personality but at relieving the acute symptoms. Its goal was approximately the goal suggested by Dr. Kovitz at Columbus State—not to "cure" the patient but to help him feel better.

Since the drugs have appeared, the goal in the office practice of psychiatry has remained the same but the treatment has differed. In many psychiatrists' offices, drugs have replaced EST. And in many they have shortened the psychotherapeutic hour radically. Dr. Kline's practice is a case in point. In addition to his duties at Rockland State's research facility, Dr. Kline treats a number of patients in private practice in an office off Fifth Avenue in New York. A while back, seated in a deep upholstered chair in his office, a slender youngish graying friendly man with lean face and a keen wide-ranging mind, Kline said, "Three or four years ago my practice was quite different. I saw patients for the traditional fifty-minute hour. Nowadays I give many of them drugs and talk to them for twenty minutes or a half-hour, and that's enough. This way I can see three or four times as many patients as formerly, and it costs each one less—fifteen dollars or so for a twenty-minute session instead of twenty-five dollars or fifty dollars for a fifty-minute hour. Formerly the therapy I did was close to classical Freudian therapy, using free association and dream interpretation, though I'm not an analyst because I'm not formally trained. I still use it a little. But I intervene more, interpret more, talk more myself. I keep my time flexible—some patients can only talk usefully for twenty minutes, some I see for as much as forty minutes. So my office is likely to be full of patients who have to wait to see me. It's more like going to an ordinary doctor."

A man of enormous energy, Dr. Kline sees private patients in his New York office two nights a week, often working till midnight or later, interviewing new patients, treating old ones, and dispensing pills from bottles in a closet. One evening a while back patients streamed in an out, and one of them was a heavy middle-aged woman with a kindly face and graying hair and a Middle European accent; she moved slowly and spoke slowly, her head bowed down with pain and trouble. She had had psychotherapy with various doctors off and on for seven and a half years. She had had a variety of physical complaints, including almost unbearable headaches and gastric ulcer. She had found it impossible to work or indeed to leave her room. Finally her doctor had sent her to Kline because he was afraid she might kill herself. She had first arrived at Kline's office in a deep depression. Kline had put her on Marsilid, one of the first patients to get it in private practice. She had begun to improve almost at once.

Now, sitting in a chair in Kline's office, she said, "I'm much better. Thanks to Marsilid I'm able to control this terrible depression. In addition, too, I am able to work at my different things." She was a baby nurse but always had quit after a short while, fearing to become too attached to the child. Now she had been with one family eight months. Her headaches had disappeared. Her ulcer no longer gave her pain. Her depression had lifted. She said, "Thanks to Marsilid somehow I feel I can untie the knot." She was far from completely well. Her voice was flat and slow, her face expressionless, she seemed almost to be walking and talking in her sleep. Or to be walking carefully lest she jar and break something in her mind. She said, "I am very conscious of controlling myself. I go at a very slow pace. Now it does not take so much effort." Kline broke in, "Marsilid really is a psychic energizer. She used to do things but the price was bloody murder."

She nodded. "There's not the helplessness that there was before. There is blue sky above. I couldn't even plan for the next day. I couldn't buy anything for myself. I couldn't invest in myself. I couldn't go to concerts or the opera. Now I do all these things. I feel I can go. I no longer feel I am an outcast."

15

The Hope and the Need: Research

■ Research is the thing—is what we need, is the hope of the future. Research into mental illness is difficult. Often it takes peculiar turns. Let us see what sort of thing occupies the attention of some of the best researchers in the United States, how they go about their work, and what difficulties they face. Let us call on the research people at the Illinois NPI, at Boston Psychopathic, at Michael Reese, at Rockland State and elsewhere.

All of them have one thing in common: The mind of man is working on the mind of man. But research in this field is of infinite variety. It can mean almost anything, from studies of job placement for ex-patients to investigations of the fundamental nature of life itself. Our purpose will be to indicate the variety of research, not to elucidate what is important. No one can say what research is important, what is not—the realm of the unknown is too enormous; and a man working with homemade tools in a woodshed in the Dakotas may be closer to the heart of the mystery than anybody in a gleaming New York laboratory. In a little laboratory in the basement of Columbus State Hospital, surrounded by microscopes and slides and charts, Dr. James W. Papez, an elderly neuroanatomist, says that, by dissecting the brains of dead psychotics and studying the nerve cells under a microscope, he has found a fungus-like organism that invaded the cells and caused the psychosis. Who knows? Though the other doctors at the hospital do not accept his findings, they do not laugh at them—or at other work in a field where so little is known and so much hoped for.

2.

The research facility at Rockland State Hospital employs seventy-five or eighty people. Its state budget is about $165,000 a year plus about $150,000 in grants from federal and private sources. Soon it will spend $600,000 on a new addition. "It's big," says the director, Dr. Kline. "But it isn't big enough. New York State does better than most states since it puts 2 or 3 per cent of its budget into research. Any private industry that tried to get by with only 2 per cent of its budget for research would be out of business in very short order."

Rockland State's buildings are scattered about wooded acreage in the countryside up the Hudson River from New York City, a setting not unlike a college campus. Kline's laboratories are housed in a converted ward, a low stucco building, rather old and very crowded and cluttered. In his office, seated before a window overlooking the hospital grounds, Kline said a while back, "We're attempting to elucidate the ways schizophrenic behavior differs from normal. This is an interdisciplinary attack—psychological, neurophysiological, biochemical and so on. Soon it develops into a problem in methodology. So we're working on new instruments and procedures. Now we're off on the use of analogue computers. The man who's doing it was formerly working on guided missiles but he felt he was not very socially useful so he came to us."

As he walked down a corridor, a rumpled young man stopped him and said, "I've got something exciting to show you," and took him into a back room. He was the refugee from the guided missile program; he wanted to show Kline some graphs he had produced with his analogue computer, an apparatus into which he fed various equations and produced effects analogous to bodily processes, thus simulating on a machine such natural processes as heartbeat and respiration.

In the radiation laboratory, filled with large heavy complicated equipment, were researchers who inject a radioactive isotope of iodine into schizophrenic patients and normal subjects; within a minute it reaches the thyroid gland in the neck; by counting the radiation with a scintillometer—an advanced Geiger counter—the scientists can determine the level of thyroid activity. After several years' study they have concluded that the thyroid gland functions differently in schizophrenics than in normals but they cannot be sure to what extent nor whether the difference is the cause or the effect of the disease or indeed whether it is the effect of hospitalization.

For several years researchers have known that the adrenal and pituitary glands function differently in schizophrenics than in normals. A biochemist at Rockland State is working on steroid metabolism, an index of adrenal activity. He has found correlations between the various catatonic phases and steroid production, "but I don't know if it means anything or not—this is the sort of basic research that may pay off thirty years from now."

In the biochemical laboratory three chemists are studying the metabolism of amino acids in the body. One says, "We're tackling one phase of it—tryptophan metabolism. We're attempting to determine what the pattern of metabolism is in schizophrenics. We think it differs from the pattern in normals. We've been at this for three years. The Japanese have been studying it twelve years or more. So far the chief thing we've done is devise some new study methods."

In the perception laboratory a young psychologist and his wife are trying to determine whether the visual perception of schizophrenics differs from that of normals. Schizophrenics have always said the world looks strange to them, that things look bigger or smaller than life size; they have always described reality inaccurately. The psychologists are attempting to determine whether they actually see the physical world differently than we do. The problem has to do with the constancy of vision—how we maintain our stability of consciousness. For example, if a person walks toward you, his image on your retina becomes larger, but you know he is not really growing larger. The experimenters at Rockland State have shown that the schizophrenic has lost this ability to adjust his consciousness to external reality; he is, so to speak, at the mercy of his retina. Apparently the integrative parts of his brain don't work.

Kline said, "All this is designed to see how schizophrenics differ from normals. The answer to schizophrenia is not going to be a simple one. It's not an X substance, or a deficiency of riboflavin in tomato juice, or any other one thing."

3.

Much of the research being done today revolves around the action of the new drugs. Dr. Harold E. Himwich and his colleagues at Galesburg State Hospital in Illinois are trying to find out where and how the drugs work, especially whether serotonin is involved. Out in Nebraska, Dr. Jackson A. Smith and his colleagues at the Nebraska Psychiatric Institute have studied the effects of thirteen different drugs on metabolism in brain tissue and enzyme systems. Doctors at the Menninger Foundation are doing research on the clinical problems of thyroid gland dysfunction. Dr. Fred Elmadjian of Worcester and Dr. Justin M. Hope of Tufts Medical School have studied the excretion of adrenalin and nor-adrenalin in hockey players, boxers, normal subjects in anticipatory states, psychiatric patients receiving LSD and psychiatric patients in various degrees of emotional disturbance. Boxers and hockey forwards and defensemen showed active aggressive behavior and an increase in nor-adrenalin excretion but not necessarily with an increase of adrenalin; normals in anticipatory states and a hockey coach and goal keeper showed tense, anxious but passive behavior and increased adrenalin but normal nor-adrenalin excretion.

Dr. Stig Akerfeldt of the Nobel Medical Institute in Sweden has reported that the blood serum of schizophrenics contains abnormally high amounts of an enzyme called ceruloplasmin, a copper-containing protein, and has devised a dyestuff to detect it, which may one day lead to a blood test for schizophrenia. Dr. Abood of Illinois' NPI and Dr. Robert G. Heath of Tulane have also reported abnormally high levels of ceruloplasmin in schizophrenics. Ceruloplasmin functions in the oxidation of amines. The amines are substances found in body proteins and in such hormones as adrenalin and nor-adrenalin. Dr. Heath believes that in schizophrenics there is a deficiency in amine metabolism. With amine deficiency, adrenalin and nor-adrenalin cannot be broken down properly. A "metabolic error" results. Dr. Heath believes that ceruloplasmin is present in higher quantities in schizophrenics in order to act as a defense against the amine deficiency. He has gone on to inject schizophrenics with an extract taken from the brains of cattle and has found it restored their metabolic balance. He warns that this does not mean he has found a cure for schizophrenia, although in monkeys, induced schizoid symptoms did disappear after injection of the extract.

Another group of researchers at Tulane headed by Dr. Byron E. Leach gave taraxein, a substance obtained from the blood of schizophrenic patients, to normal human volunteers, most of them convicts from the Louisiana State Penitentiary. He reported: "The subjects who received taraxein have developed consistent basic alterations in behavior which fit the description of primary schizophrenic symptomatology as described by Bleuler. In the different subjects there have been varying secondary elaborations which are felt to be influenced by the pre-existing psychodynamic adaptation of the individuals." He also reported that a very small dose had little effect upon the normal volunteers but when given to schizophrenic patients in remission it produced a clear-cut psychotic reaction.

Not only psychiatrists but neurologists have of late turned to biochemistry in their investigations. Some of the new drugs appear to have an effect upon such neurological disorders as Parkinson's disease and several of the little-known choreas. Dr. Benjamin Boshes, chairman of the Department of Neurology and Psychiatry at Northwestern University in Chicago, and a leading neurologist, has fitted up a new laboratory to carry on biochemical and carefully quantitated physiological measurements, using recently developed electronic devices, in a number of neurological diseases, including the choreas. Biochemistry and electron microscopy are already shedding new light on multiple sclerosis.

4.

The principal research at the Institute for Psychosomatic and Psychiatric Research and Training at Michael Reese Hospital in Chicago is a large program of research on anxiety and other primary emotions, such as anger and depression. It is a multidisciplinary program—psychiatric, psychological, physiological and biochemical. "Anxiety," says Dr. Grinker, "is the basis of all psychiatric and psychosomatic disease. We are trying to see what are the really fundamental problems in anxiety as related to functions and disturbances of mind and body." In one experiment, the patient lies down on a table and the wires of a polygraph are connected to his body. A psychiatrist who knows where he is vulnerable then interviews him in a way that makes him anxious, or a psychologist shows him objects with distorted dimensions which convince him his perception is distorted, making him anxious. As the experiment progresses, the polygraph records his physiological changes, a technician takes blood specimens, and, from behind a one-way mirror window, psychiatrists observe his reactions. One result of these and other experiments, which have been carried on for several years, suggests that anxious people produce hydrocortisone, a secretion of the adrenal gland, at a rate several times greater than the normal individual.

They also react with responses in heart rate, blood pressure, respiration, etc., indicating their bodily sensitivity to psychological stimuli.

In addition to the anxiety program, there are many other studies under way at Michael Reese. Scientists are removing parts of monkeys' brains and cats' brains to test the effects on their behavior; studying the chemical constituents of blood and urine; studying the effects of endocrine secretions on the nervous system; testing the effect of thyroid on the mental and emotional activity of rats; and studying the effect of handling on infant rats, finding that rats handled in infancy become in adulthood more emotionally stable and better learners than rats who were not handled as infants.

5.

There are about 130 research projects afoot in Massachusetts state hospitals. Worcester State Hospital, for example, working with the private Worcester Foundation, is using radioactive carbon in a search for the site of the metabolism of adrenalin. Jack Ewalt, Commissioner of Mental Health, has said, "We have a lot of work going on in our hospitals. But we have a lot of help—Harvard, Boston University, Tufts, the National Institute. It's an old tradition in Massachusetts. It's like pushing a truck—no trick if you've got a lot of people to push."

Boston Psychopathic alone spends upward of a quarter of a million dollars a year on research. It has sixty or seventy researchers. Research here is directed less at basic questions concerning the biochemistry and electrophysiology of cells than toward clinical research and sociological and psychological projects.

One group at Boston Psycho is studying the rehabilitation of the mentally ill through the use of halfway houses, day hospitals, ex-patient clubs, job placement. Another is working on the prevention of hospitalization. Another is studying nursing techniques—"A new schizophrenic patient is drowning and floundering," says Dr. Milton Greenblatt, research director, "and the doctor can't get out there to him, but the nurse can, she can bring him back to shore so the doctor can sit with him for an hour. It's a nonverbal technique, a laying on of hands, dressing, feeding, bathing the patient." Another group is studying the effect of climate on psychotherapeutic interviews. Another is studying hospital sociology—what goes on in a hospital and how it affects the patients. Another is studying "sensory deprivation"—putting people in an isolated insulated room and leaving them there, deprived of all stimuli, a condition which may lead to a psychotic-like state. Another group, studying the relationship between the new drugs and social milieu, has put forty-eight chronic schizophrenics in a mainline state hospital on drugs, left half of them there, and brought the other half here to Boston Psycho; after six months, nine of those brought to Boston Psychopathic had gone home but of the twenty-four left at the mainline state hospital, only one had gone home.

Boston Psycho owns a polygraph, a complicated apparatus which measures and records on graph paper numerous physiological reactions such as respiration, blood pressure, skin temperature, perspiration and heart rate. It has hitched it up to both patient and doctor during a psychotherapeutic session, discovering that the doctor's reactions follow the patient's: When the patient becomes anxious, his heart rate rises, and so does the doctor's, though not so high as the patient's. It has used the polygraph, along with psychological tests and psychiatric interviews, to compare the effects of various new drugs. "We are going to run this test systematically year after year," Dr. Greenblatt says, "so we'll know where the hell we are. We don't even know now whether Thorazine is better than phenobarbital."

Boston Psychopathic has studied at length the effects of LSD-25, and among its findings is this: that social relationships affect hallucinations and delusions, and if a man is given LSD-25 by someone he likes, he will see him as bigger than life size, but if he is given it by someone he dislikes, he will see him as smaller. It has studied the effect of EST and insulin on adrenalin and nor-adrenalin, the effect of Thorazine on autonomic nervous system reactions of healthy subjects, and the effectiveness of Frenquel. It did a five-year follow-up on 116 lobotomized patients. It has studied the spinal fluid of schizophrenics and found that it differs in some ways from that of normals. It has carried through a large family project, including these studies: one comparing families in which schizophrenia occurs with "nonschizophrenic" families, a cross-cultural study of differences in value systems of paranoid and depressed patients in Boston and Burma, and a study of parental roles in schizophrenic patients, peptic ulcer patients and healthy subjects.

6.

In the psychiatry tower of the Illinois NPI, a man in a white coat, Dr. Nahman H. Greenberg, now in his third year of resident training but with a wide background, and ten other doctors are studying the psychic and physical organization of infants before the age of two. They are working with fifteen sets of mothers and babies. They start their studies of the mother before the child is born. They study her during labor. After birth, they study her and her baby continuously, finding out how she treats him, how he reacts, how his psychic and somatic organization proceeds under her influence. They have found that mothers who themselves are distant, apathetic and disorganized tend to have babies who mirror these traits. But how do they study a child so young he cannot talk? They observe him; more, they study his skin temperature, cardiac rate, respiratory rate, gastric action and other indices of autonomic nervous system activity. Such indices measure psychic reaction and organization. A mother, for example, who is anxious, distant, apathetic, or who can't feed her baby satisfactorily, tends to have a baby who shows a progressively disorganized cardiac activity. "Some of the mechanisms seen in infants are mechanisms seen later in schizophrenia," Greenberg said. "For example, we see a baby who is in rage constantly and who is somatically disorganized: such a baby is predisposed to later trauma which will send it back and reactivate the same mechanism—the regression of schizophrenia. It can be seen in infants as somatic regression."

Another psychosomatic study at the Institute, already mentioned briefly, is that by Dr. George J. Mohr, Dr. Irene Josselyn and others of small children with ulcerative colitis. All the mothers were emotionally disturbed during pregnancy or shortly after birth. They became anxious and fearful mothers themselves and developed domineering and controlling patterns superficially similar to those of their own mothers. Three of the children's fathers were mentally ill; the other three were aloof and withdrawn. The children's biological security was threatened by the mothers' early inability to provide care. The children attempted to provide for themselves the protection and security their parents could not provide; their failure was associated with the onset of the illness or exacerbation of the symptoms.

But the NPI has always been better known for its work in biochemistry than in psychosomatic medicine, and this probably is still its major field. In a basement laboratory Dr. Abood, a big tall dark-complexioned biochemist with the big hands and rangy physique of a football end, said, "Right now our principal work is with a class of psychotogens but a different class from LSD. The compounds we're working with are cholinergic nerve-blocking agents. They act peripherally by blocking the activity of acetylcholine."

Acetylcholine, adrenalin and nor-adrenalin, as we have seen, are three body chemicals which act as nerve hormones, and serotonin probably is another. Still another is histamine. The tranquilizing drugs are antihistamine and antiadrenalin, Abood said, and LSD-25 is antiserotonin and also antiadrenalin. The drugs Abood is studying are antiacetylcholine. Abood said, "Acetylcholine is the only neurohumeral agent in the body for which we have definitely established a role in nerve conduction. It is speculated that the psychotogenic and tranquilizing drugs act by interfering with the action or production of the neurohormones. Our group of compounds are esters of piperidine and benzilic acid, that is, piperidyl benzilates. A compound similar to them is atropine. They were synthesized by Dr. John Biel, an organic chemist at the Lakeside Laboratories in Milwaukee. They are extremely powerful. The psychotic symptoms they produce seem to be closer to a true psychotic episode than those caused by LSD or mescaline. They produce a feeling of detachment, loss of control and decrease in ability to concentrate or verbalize. Subjects are often totally confused and disoriented. They talk to imaginary people. The hallucinations may be tactile and olfactory as well as visual. They are so vivid that subjects begin to interact with them. The hallucinations involve people, animals and other objects with definite shapes in situations often dating back to childhood. The effect is quite prolonged and may last for days. Working with Biel, we've synthesized about a hundred different compounds of this sort and we're working out the relationships of their chemical composition to the effects they produce."

Abood got started on these drugs almost by accident. "I'd always been interested in the fact that the psychotogens seem to block essential neurohumeral agents. I felt that not only serotonin and adrenalin are important, but so are other neurohumeral agents as well. I knew that atropine blocks acetylcholine and is known to produce psychic disturbances. When I heard that Lakeside was developing atropine-like agents to treat ulcers, I became curious. They had produced a couple of drugs that had psychotogenic effects. They'd shelved them of course, since such properties were presumably undesirable. Dr. Adrian Ostfeld of the University of Illinois College of Medicine and I tested them first on Siamese fighting fish, rats and other animals. They seemed to produce behavioral effects similar to LSD. Then we tried them on human volunteers—myself, medical and divinity students, nurses."

All this, however, is clinical research, and Dr. Abood's principal interest is not in clinical research but in basic research. "I'm especially interested in mitochondria," he said, smiling a little and spelling it. "These are tiny granules in the cytoplasm of all cells. They're only one micron in diameter. They are the powerhouses of the cells. They produce all the energy the cell needs. I'm interested in their role in brain function, that is, in nerve conduction and excitation. Although mitochondria are concerned with the fundamental character of the nervous system, they do have practical clinical application—Thorazine's effects are apparently due to its ability to block energy production in the mitochondria. Many of these neurohumeral agents—adrenalin and serotonin and so on—seem to be bound to mitochondria. Perhaps it's at this level that these agents are acting. LSD and the tranquilizing drugs may act there too. But I'm primarily interested in basic research on the mitochondria themselves. They are complex structures of enzymes and chemical substances, organized in a very precise geometrical arrangement, more intricate than the cell itself. This high degree of organization is essential for carrying on the process of energy production. The rearrangement of enzymes and chemical substances could disturb their function. Many drugs act by causing such a rearrangement."

How does he study such a thing? "You can get at them by breaking up the cells in a solution of sugar. By gradually increasing the speed of centrifugation the granules can be separated from other cell particles. Mitochondria prepared in this manner are in such a state that they are still metabolically active—the enzymes are active and their structure is not altered appreciably.

"There are a great many problems at the basic level. For example, when you stimulate a nerve, what happens to the energy mechanism? We're studying the link between function and chemistry. I think this is where the ultimate secret of life itself lies. How to get from the mitochondria to an idea"—smiling—"is one of our questions."

He talked about other research at the NPI. Ruth Geiger was growing human brain cells in test tubes and studying their response to drugs and other stimulation. She obtained the cells by biopsy incidental to a brain operation and put them into human serum or rooster serum. Abood said, "Mrs. Geiger has tried schizophrenic serum on them and seen bizarre changes in their growth. She's tried LSD and our group of hallucinogenic drugs and seen characteristic changes in the mitochondria. She's found a similarity between the effects produced by

LSD, our drugs and schizophrenic serum—but there are differences too. It's a unique and effective tool. She can grow muscle cells too, and the cells from patients with muscular dystrophy are completely different in their growth characteristics and their response to drugs than normal cells. If there are differences in the brain cells of psychotics and normals, this is one way of pointing out the difference. She hopes to get hold of some schizophrenic brain cells. But few lobotomies are being done these days."

Her husband, Alexander Geiger, was studying brain metabolism. He anesthetizes a cat, cuts off the blood vessels leading to the brain, and attaches them to an artificial heart, thus isolating brain circulation from the rest of the body and enabling him to control what goes into the brain and to collect what comes out. Other scientists here were studying the electrical activity of single nerve cells. Abood said, "There are complicated components to the electrical activity of a neuron. Some drugs act on one phase of the pattern, some on another. Ultimately, we may have to go down to single-cell chemistry and physiology before we can understand how the new drugs act. So you see in general what this laboratory is primarily directed toward—basic research, approaching the cell from all angles, chemical, electrophysiological, pharmacological, psychological."

Biochemistry's modern development, he said, had begun about 1920. Only in the last ten years had it been applied to the nervous system. At the same time, new tools had come along—radioactive isotopes, chromatography, advanced electronic instruments. All had given impetus to biochemical research. The coming of the new drugs had been only coincidental to the broader stream of development of biochemical research on the nervous system.

"This field is still a new frontier," Abood said. "Biochemistry and electrophysiology—the electrical characteristics of the nervous system —are the important fields now. There's a lot going on. Public interest has been aroused but I'm not sure the public understands the need for patience. All the spectacular happenings are not really so important. The ultimate answers lie in a slow intellectual progress—in basic research and ideas which are very remote from the immediate problem of mental illness. These are the things that Sputniks are made of. And it's hard for the public to grasp the importance of such basic work." One recalled former Defense Secretary Charles Wilson's scornful dismissal of basic research as the investigation of "what makes grass

green and fried potatoes brown." Abood went on, "Abnormality in behavior must be referred back to a single nerve cell and how it functions. The stages involved are infinite, endless. When you submit a
grant application to the National Institute, you have to attach a state-
ment on how this applies to the public health, for the Senator to see if
he happens to pick it up. Because who in heck cares about basic
research on a neuron?" Smiling, "What the heck is a neuron anyway?"

7.

Out in the rolling hills of Maryland at Bethesda, ten miles from
Washington, rises an imposing tower of brick, the clinical center of
the National Institute of Mental Health. It is a symbol of America's
search for new knowledge to combat mental illness.

National Institute scientists have learned how to measure and analyze
blood flowing through the living, thinking brain. They are doing
laboratory research on the chemistry of the nervous system, studies of
the prepsychotic personalities and social environments of patients,
studies of the role of heredity in mental illness, studies of emotionally
disturbed children, work on the development of a proper therapeutic
milieu and much more.

But the research that is actually conducted here at the Institute is
only a part of the research in which the Institute is involved. One of
its prime functions is to support financially research being carried on
all over the United States. In 1958 it made research grants totaling
$12,402,000. (But the National Cancer Institute, another federal
agency, made grants totaling $22,675,000 and the National Heart
Institute made grants totaling $19,364,000. Of the seven national
Institutes, only the Dental Research Institute spent less money on
research grants than the Mental Health Institute.)

Merely to glance at a few of the projects the Institute supported last
year gives some idea of the scope and variety of American research:
research in electron microscopy of the central nervous system, at the
University of Minnesota; in the sense of reality in schizophrenic children, at Topeka State Hospital; in the relation of personality to social
structure, at the Department of Health, Santurce, Puerto Rico; in
psychologic change in the hospitalized mentally ill, at the Pinel
Foundation, Seattle; in human behavior in disaster, at the National
Academy of Science, Washington; in an exploratory study of visiting
at a mental hospital, at the University of Vermont College of Medicine.

8.

Traditionally research has been carried on primarily at university hospitals. In recent years, however, state hospitals have gone heavily into research, a tendency Dr. Nathan Kline applauds. Himself director of research at Rockland State, Kline has said, "There are dangers in the university hospital setup. It's usually under the aegis of a professor from the medical school. He's a three-job man—teaching medical students, directing the psychiatrists in their care of patients, and research. In about that order. You can always push research off to tomorrow, but the medical students are there and have to be taught, and the patients are yelling and have to be attended." Moreover, Kline says, only state hospitals have the enormous collection of research material which is needed—patients, patients of all kinds. "If you're working on a problem of nerve conduction, you can work anywhere, you don't need the state hospital. But as soon as you move to a problem such as how schizophrenics differ from the normal, then you can't do without it. Most neuropsychiatric institutes are small. In one in New York City there are 144 beds, at the National Institute there are 79. But here at Rockland we have 8,000 patients. We have 150 kids under twelve, 500 from twelve to seventeen, we have everything but epileptics and defectives, and even a few of these who happen also to be psychotic, and about 60 per cent of our patients are schizophrenics. Whatever we need in research, we can put our head out the window and see it."

New York State has eleven major research installations and more planned. Ohio's 1955 law set up research institutes at the receiving hospitals. Pennsylvania, Massachusetts, Michigan, Illinois, New Jersey, Connecticut, California, Nebraska, Kansas and other states have gone into research. Any list of the best research centers in the U.S. would have to include Boston Psychopathic, the Lafayette Clinic in Detroit, the University of Michigan at Ann Arbor in conjunction with Ypsilanti State Hospital, the Langley Porter Clinic in San Francisco, the Illinois NPI, New York Psychopathic, the Worcester Institute, Galesburg State Hospital in Illinois and Walter Reed Hospital in Washington, D. C.

9.

Working outside the main stream of research, the leading exponent of the genetic theory of mental disease, Dr. Franz Kallmann of New

York, is continuing his studies of schizophrenic twins, which have tended to show that schizophrenia is hereditary. Kallmann has reported that the mathematical probability of coming down with schizophrenia is only 0.85 per cent in the general population but is 16.4 per cent among the children of one schizophrenic parent; it is 14.0 per cent for a *nonidentical* twin of a person who has schizophrenia, but it is 85.8 per cent for the *identical* twin of a schizophrenic. Most psychiatrists do not consider the case for heredity proved, Dr. Noyes pointing out that Kallmann ignored "all those life situations and intrafamily influences generally recognized to be psychopathologically conducive to the development of schizophrenia." But the case for heredity has never been disproved either.

Parallel to Kallmann's work is that of Dr. William Sheldon of Columbia University. Sheldon believes there is a necessary relationship between human physique and human temperament. In order to understand the human personality, Freud started with the most deeply buried aspect of the human, the unconscious. Sheldon starts with the most external aspect, the physique. He is attempting to ground psychology in biology. He calls his specialty constitutional psychiatry. He holds that "behavior is a function of structure." Some of his early studies showed a direct relationship between certain types of mental illness and certain body types. (And anybody who has visited a mental hospital is immediately struck by the large number of schizophrenics who are tall and thin.) Sheldon has photographed thousands of human bodies, measuring them and classifying them on a mathematical scale. His three main body types—somatotypes—are endomorphs, mesomorphs and ectomorphs, named according to the type of embryonic tissue suggested by the mature individual. The inner embryonic layer, which develops into the functional part of the digestive system, is prominent in the fat endomorph; the middle embryonic layer, which becomes the bone, muscle and sinew, is prominent in the muscular mesomorph; and the outer layer, from which develop the skin and nervous system is prominent in ectomorphs. Everyone's body contains the three primary components in some varying degree. Sheldon set up a 7-point scale to cover the wide range of variation within each component. Thus a man who is graded 4 in endomorphy, 4 in mesomorphy, and 3 in ectomorphy—he is middling fat, middling muscular and a little below the halfway mark in fragility—is identified as somatotype 443, the commonest male somatotype. Of a man graded 117—1 in endomorphy, 1 in mesomorphy, and 7 in ectomorphy—Sheldon has written, "Encountered more frequently on college campuses than in the general population, and there the diagnosis is sometimes Phi Beta Kappa." Sheldon, a man of nimble mind, once proposed a study of "human development planned to continue for at least one century." His idea was to follow a group of people throughout their entire lifetime and then to follow their descendants for at least a hundred years. He wrote:

> The useful study of human beings cannot be merely a matter of recording the individual development of persons taken at random from a genetic vacuum, i.e., samples of children whose antecedents are not even described and whose descendants are to be disregarded. There is also a genetic or or pedigree factor in human personality, and when we study animals other than ourselves we do not ignore it. The object of the project now under consideration is to follow a sample population of human beings for at least 3 or 4 generations, from both a genetic and an environmental or developmental point of view. This has never been done.

Most psychiatrists, especially those psychoanalytically oriented, discount Sheldon's work on the human constitution—the old quarrel between psychic and somatic theories. (Sheldon is rather violently and sometimes amusingly anti-Freudian, referring to analysis as "Freudianity.") Dr. Kline is one of the few psychiatrists who have attempted to work with Sheldon's discoveries. Some years ago, studying the results of lobotomy and other types of psychosurgery, Kline found a significant correlation between body type and surgery's success. Four out of five mesomorphs in his study who had undergone lobotomy or topectomy had been discharged from the hospital and, perhaps more significant, of the thirteen patients who were not mesomorphs—were endomorphs or ectomorphs—only one was discharged. Kline wrote, "The use of psychosurgical procedures on nonmesomorphs should be undertaken with caution." In transorbital lobotomy Kline found that the best results were obtained in mesomorphic males and endomorphic females. In a study of schizophrenics, Kline found a significant correlation between mesomorphy and good prognosis and between endomorphy and poor prognosis. Indeed, he found a more basic relationship between prognosis and somatotype than between prognosis and the subdiagnostic categories of paranoid, catatonic or hebephrenic schizophrenia. He found significant correlations between somatotype and diagnosis—

mesomorphs tended to be paranoid and not hebephrenic, whereas ectomorphs tended to be hebephrenic and not paranoid. Kline thought that the somatotype would prove a "much-needed factor" in the study of schizophrenia. That was in 1950. Since then little use has been made of Sheldon's work. It is not impossible, however, that the ascendancy of the new drugs and the organic view they imply may reawaken interest in it.

10.

Some investigators are studying the epidemiology of mental disease. A paper published by the Milbank Memorial Fund reports evidence that both the prevalence and types of psychiatric disorder are significantly related to the class structure. The wealthiest class in the community it studied included 3.1 per cent of the total population but only 1 per cent of the psychiatric cases; the lowest class, ill-educated laborers and factory hands who inhabit the tenements and cold-water flats of town, included only 17.8 per cent of the total population but contributed 36.8 per cent of its psychiatric patients. Moreover, the neuroses were concentrated at the higher levels, the psychoses at the lower levels. Schizophrenia was eleven times as prevalent in the lowest class as in the highest.

New experiments are under way with EST. Dr. D. Ewen Cameron of Montreal attempted the "complete depatterning" of a patient's mind by deep sleep and massive EST in order to break the chain of schizophrenic thinking and give the patient's mind a chance to reorganize itself. He gave a series of patients Thorazine and barbiturates for a week, making them sleep deeply for twenty or twenty-two hours a day. On the tenth day intensive EST began—four or five shocks in two or three minutes each day. "Complete depatterning" was achieved between the thirteenth and sixteenth days, after about thirty shock treatments, and was maintained five to seven days. During this time of "depatterning" the patient recognized no one, had lost his sense of space and time and didn't care. Then barbiturates were withdrawn gradually and shock was cut to three a week. The patient was attended by a nurse for a month of reorientation. He was then discharged from the hospital. He returned every week for EST during the first month and once a month for the next two years. Dr. Cameron reported that of ten patients who had been ill less than two years, none relapsed. Of sixteen ill longer, three were unable to leave the hospital and thirteen went home, though two had to be readmitted.

Drs. Irving Wright and William T. Foley of the Cornell Medical Center in New York have been working with arteriosclerotic patients and anticoagulants. They are co-operating with Dr. John Whittier on an extensive controlling program at the New York State Hospital at Creedmore. Several anticoagulants are known and others are being sought. One, Dicumarol, was discovered because pregnant cows in Wisconsin were bleeding and having miscarriages: Researchers in the University of Wisconsin's Agriculture Department found that certain types of spoiled clover seemed to be causing the hemorrhaging, chemists isolated the active substance, and drug firms synthesized it. Other researchers are attacking the same problem from another angle —by working on arteriosclerosis itself, or, more properly, atherosclerosis, the process of narrowing of the arterial wall. Arteriosclerosis—and accompanying "heart attacks" and "strokes"—has been called America's medical public enemy No. 1. Of all the Americans who died in 1956, over 46 per cent died of arteriosclerosis and hypertension. Yet only $1,787,970, one-fourteenth of what Americans spend on face powder, is being spent by the federal government on research on arteriosclerosis, despite the fact that promising research leads pointing toward its control have been uncovered. Until fairly recently it was considered that nothing could be done about arteriosclerosis. This idea has been discarded.

11.

"The main problems of research today," said Dr. Kline a while back, sitting in his office, "are a shortage of money and a shortage of people. And above all a lack of imagination. Somebody comes out with a promising lead and everybody else follows it up instead of dreaming up their own leads."

And there are other problems. One is bureaucratic red tape which requires researchers to spend too much time writing reports and requisitions. It sometimes takes months to get an order for glassware through the complex purchasing system of state government. One biochemist spent twelve hours of his time convincing the business manager he needed seventy-five dollars' worth of chemicals. "And there's eight million dollars going up in the Jupiter-C missile," Kline remarked wryly. Another is the problem of communication among scientists so that all can know what each is doing and will not waste time by duplicating each other's efforts, a problem apparently solved in Russia.

The shortage of trained research personnel is probably the biggest single problem today and is likely to become bigger. Graduate school enrollment has dropped in biochemistry and physiology, the fields that produce researchers, yet we are building more and more research institutes. Nobody knows how to staff them. Already competition has developed among the states and universities for researchers. Industry attracts them too—it pays double or treble the university salary.

The question of whether we need more money for research is not an easy one. Some experts believe that so much money is now available that it is embarrassing—it can't be spent because of the shortage of trained personnel and laboratories. In Illinois, for example, all money paid by patients in state hospitals is earmarked for research and training, and it is piling up at the rate of six million dollars a year. The state, unable to spend it, is putting more than nine million of it into a new institute and has set up the Illinois Psychiatric Training and Research Authority to make research grants. It is an American tendency when faced with a problem to appropriate a sum, pass a law or build a building. But in this field none of these may suffice.

Expenditures for research into mental illness have risen enormously in recent years. Until a few years ago the sum was usually figured at about six million dollars a year, nearly all provided by the federal government (which spent vastly more for research on hoof-and-mouth disease). Today the states alone are probably spending in the neighborhood of fifteen million, though firm figures are hard to get, and important private money has become available: In 1955 the Ford Foundation set aside fifteen million dollars for research. The total national expenditure on research today—state, federal and private—is probably close to thirty million dollars a year, five times what was available a few years ago.

Nevertheless, it is not a large sum compared to what is spent for research into other diseases. It is far less than the amount spent on cancer research, more than $53,000,000. It is only one-tenth of what Americans spend for chewing gum.

Dr. Kline has said, "There probably are some research projects languishing for lack of money, though I imagine the federal government would deny it." If he had more money for equipment in his own establishment, he said, he could get twice as much work done with the same number of people. Highly trained scientists are spending part of their time at carpentry—making their own equipment because the state can't or won't buy it. A biochemist, walking through a corner of his laboratory, patted a power saw lovingly and said, "Here's one thing I couldn't be without. I made my own tables with it. You learn you have to make stuff if you want to do anything."

Dr. Foley of New York has said, "There's a lot of research being done on arteriosclerosis but it's far from being solved. There's a lot of money available but no over-all project. My department has a fifty-thousand-dollar budget. We think it's a hell of a lot. But when I think of putting a billion into the missile program," and he laughed. "I've felt if I could spend a million, in two or three years I'm damned sure I could get the answers on arteriosclerosis."

Scientists everywhere say it is especially hard to get money for basic research. People who make grants want results, and often basic research shows no practical results for many years. It was forty years between Einstein's discovery that $E = MC^2$ and the first atomic explosion at Alamogordo, and the discovery was not aimed to that end anyway. And it is precisely basic research that is needed in the field of mental illness today. For many years there was a great shortage of doctors, nurses and attendants to care for tuberculars and epileptics. But suddenly major discoveries were made in how to treat both. And immediately the tuberculosis sanitoriums and epileptic hospitals began to close, and there was a surplus of personnel. Today we have a great shortage of doctors and nurses in mental hospitals. It can only be relieved, in the long run, by major scientific breakthrough.

Dr. Abood said, "All around the country we have good laboratories, but there isn't enough basic work being done. In the last few years we've been putting up more and more research institutes. The new drugs provided the impetus—they gave new hope, and the legislatures were encouraged to spend some money. The Russians too are putting up brain research institutes at a great rate and encouraging people to go into brain physiology. Our research is superior to theirs so far, we think, but how long it will be is another question."

The dictates of the cold war may seem a poor reason to push the fight against mental illness, but it is a fact that a major breakthrough in schizophrenia (or in cancer or other world-wide dread disease), shared with the peoples of the world, would win for America more friends than any other technical aid, and that purely as an investment in national policy, money spent on biological research is well spent.

Even aside from such considerations, research pays. Dr. Kline has said, "It costs us $1,680 to keep a patient in the hospital a year. Our state research budget here is about $165,000. So if we can, by research, get one hundred patients out of the hospital, we've paid for ourselves." (The drugs are getting nearly five hundred a year out.) According to figures compiled by the National Health Education Committee, between 1937 and 1954 the American life expectancy increased ten years solely because medical research discovered antibiotics and other new drugs to control pneumonia, syphilis, tuberculosis and other diseases. Moreover, since 1944 the Salk vaccine, anticoagulants and other discoveries have cut the death rate further, according to the Committee's figures, so that 1,654,069 more Americans were alive in 1956 than would have been had the discoveries not been made—which meant that the federal treasury gained in taxes in 1956 alone $356,000,000, two times as much as Congress appropriated that year for all the National Institutes of Health.

Of course, however much money is available, research into mental disease is not easy. This is, inherently, a field difficult to research. A false lead can cost a great deal of time. Dr. Seymour S. Kety of the National Institute has pointed out an inherent difficulty in testing theories on the origin of schizophrenia: often, material is obtained from the back wards of hospitals and so what is being tested may not be schizophrenia at all but the effects of long-term hospitalization. Again, are the abnormal body functions of schizophrenics the cause of the disease or its effect? And all this goes back to a fundamental difficulty: Nobody is really sure what schizophrenia is. It is not easy to research the causes of something so ill-defined. But it is not impossible. It took four hundred years to trace paresis to syphilitic infection. Perhaps we should not be impatient that the far greater mystery of schizophrenia, which was only named fifty-odd years ago, has not yet been solved.

16

The Future

■ A while back a visitor, after touring a big state hospital in the Midwest, returned to the superintendent's office and said, somewhat shaken, "This is a fearful problem."

The superintendent replied, "The problem is the hospital. Not the illness, but the hospital."

What is the future of the state mental hospital?

Dr. Solomon of Boston Psychopathic has said, "The big state hospitals are bankrupt without exception. So far as usefulness goes, if it ever existed. The big state hospital is on the wane. What will come to take its place I don't know. There are certain currents you can see now. For one, the accretion of large numbers of private psychiatric practitioners in the United States who are equipped to treat patients in their offices and keep them out of hospitals. Then, the increasing number of psychiatric pavilions in general hospitals. And the increasing number of university hospitals. Then, another current—the trend toward day hospitals—patients sleep at home at night but spend their days in the hospital. This is an extension of the hospital into the community, and it prevents patients from entering the hospital permanently. More broadly, we've got to build a new group of mental health workers in the community, and a good place to start would be with our teachers. Then we could give better service in the community."

Traditionally, state hospitals have been walled off from the community. So isolated, prison-like, the hospital itself and the community's

351

fear of it created the need for severely restrictive custodial care. Most current thought sees hospitals moving toward greater freedom and closer ties with the community. This is seen as taking place in a number of ways—through out-patient and after-care clinics, home-care plans even for acute patients, vocational guidance, halfway houses, day hospitals, night hospitals, unlocked wards and so on. New York State has two day hospitals, patterned after one in Montreal. A day hospital can serve two shifts of patients and thus save money. But its big advantage is that its patient remains in the community and with his family, he can go home at night, he isn't locked in, isn't hospitalized. Hospital confinement is not the only resource for people with physical ailments; just so should the mentally ill be able to look to other resources. The community ought to be the place for prevention, for prehospital treatment, for short-term care. The state hospital is the place for patients needing longer treatment. And the community again ought to help the patient while he is in the state hospital and after he leaves it. The open hospital, with unlocked wards, is currently the hottest thing in American mental hospital administration—at least in the talk of American hospital administrators. For years some English hospitals have been open; and today two or three American hospitals are completely or nearly open, and many are unlocking some wards. St. Lawrence State Hospital in upstate New York was easy to open up—it was small (two thousand beds), had a stable personnel and a long tradition, and it drew from a small homogeneous rural area. Dr. Francis J. O'Neill, Director of Central Islip State Hospital on Long Island, has warned, "To unlock the doors alone would bring little progress. It must be incorporated into other progressive steps aimed at integrating the mental hospital with the community."

Dr. Brill, of the New York State Department of Mental Hygiene, has said, "Because of the drugs and other things, these hospitals will change their nature. Their tremendous rate of growth will cease. We'll come to a stabilized population or a gradual decrease. The tremendous accretion of chronic schizophrenics will gradually dissolve. But because of the growing total population, they will be replaced by other elements of the population, other unsolved psychiatric problems." He did not say so but may have had in mind alcoholics, the aged and narcotics addicts, among others. "None of this is going to happen tomorrow," he went on. "In New York we're still 25 per cent overcrowded. Till three years ago we were in an impossible situation. We were piling up two thousand cases a year. And there was no end in sight. When we had to talk about finances, everyone said, 'What's the use—they fill up faster than we can build them.' But then the piling up stopped. Our hospital population actually declined. This doesn't mean that we've solved at once all the problems that had accumulated over the years. We can't move into new fields yet. Our admission rates are still going up, and so are England's. There's no evidence yet that people are being kept out of hospitals by the new drugs or by community clinics. But those who do come in stay a shorter period of time.

"The drugs had an effect on our building program. We passed a bond issue of $350,000,000 for new buildings. We've opened about five thousand new beds in the past four or five years. In some buildings we built wards for disturbed patients, then the drugs came along, and now we have to take out the inside security screens—we don't need 'em any more. We built a building for disturbed patients with TB, and by the time it was done TB was cut in half and disturbed behavior had disappeared—so we're using it for geriatric patients. There's been a tremendous and a rapid change."

2.

It is fortunate that today, at the very time when the new drugs, the open hospital and other innovations have generated a great ferment, American medicine has undertaken a nation-wide survey of every aspect of mental illness—a survey which may become a landmark in medical history. Such a study was recommended in 1953 by Dr. Kenneth E. Appel, then president of the American Psychiatric Association, who urged a "Flexner-type report" on how we treat the mentally ill. (The Flexner Report of 1910 improved medical education enormously.) Surveys in the field of mental illness have been numerous but narrow. Dr. Appel wanted a wide-ranging survey that would cover the field as a whole and challenge its basic assumptions. In January of 1955 under the leadership of Dr. Appel and Dr. Leo Bartemeier, chairman of the Council on Mental Health of the American Medical Association, the AMA and the American Psychiatric Association established a Joint Commission on Mental Illness and Health. Other national organizations joined. It asked Congress to help finance the survey.

In testifying before a House committee Dr. Bartemeier said, "Underlying the proposal is the thought that out of such a project might evolve some fundamental departures from our traditional concepts and methods of dealing with mental illness. . . . Within comparatively recent times the 'pesthouse' concept of treatment for the physically ill has fallen to the assault of intensified medical research and the wide application of new and healing techniques to diseases long thought to be incurable has been substituted. Smallpox, typhoid fever, yellow fever, malaria, all dreaded killers in their time, have fallen. Tuberculosis, pneumonia, diabetes and infectious diseases of childhood are no longer great threats. New hope exists for success in the fight against polio-myelitis, cancer and heart disease.

"Mental illness can succumb to the same attack."

Dr. Braceland thought such a survey was needed now to prevent us from "running off madly in all directions" at a time when the promise of psychiatry seemed so great. He said, "Psychiatry at present is in a ferment. There are several new drugs about. . . ."

Dr. Daniel Blain, medical director of the American Psychiatric Association, said the survey was needed because "there is no central, integrated, organized body of knowledge in this field." The APA had made surveys of mental health needs in several states but the information was not collated. Excellent World Health Organization reports were virtually unknown in the U.S. Thousands of worth-while reports of mental hospitals were merely gathering dust. Each state was left to report individually. Statistics in the field were bewildering. Dr. Blain said, "There is crying need to re-examine our basic assumptions in the field, to see what actually takes place in hospitals with high discharge rates as compared with others with low discharge rates; to assess the factors which account for the tragic lag between the development of psychiatric knowledge and its application in the public mental hos-pitals; to determine the extent to which community services pay off in keeping people out of mental hospitals; to discover the most effective ways of utilizing present personnel; to find out more about the epidemiology of mental illness; to discover why it is that young pro-fessional students resist entering the field of mental illness; to find out exactly what our personnel needs are; to review our whole statistical system for gathering data on mental illness; to assess the contribution that psychiatry can make to the various social ills in which mental illness is a component."

Congress appropriated $1,250,000 for a three-year study; states and private sources supplied more. Dr. Bartemeier called it "the chance of a lifetime to develop guideposts for the American people that will point to a fundamentally new attack on this staggering problem." The Joint Commission opened an office in Cambridge, Massachusetts, and set to work under the direction of Jack Ewalt, Massachusetts Commissioner of Mental Health.

The Commission began major studies of various aspects of the care of mental patients and of mental health manpower. It undertook a nation-wide sampling to find out what kind of troubles people have and how they handle them. It began smaller studies of nonpsychiatric mental health resources, the roles of the schools and churches, the epidemiology and etiology of mental disease, the economics of mental illness, others. Ewalt has said, "We're not trying to paint a picture of the average hospital. We're trying to pick out the best things and see what makes them the best, so that we can tell a superintendent how to improve his hospital. The same with the drugs—what makes them work better some places than others? The same with open hospitals—why do they work well one place and not another? We're looking for all the new ideas we can find. We're interviewing the leaders in psychiatry. We're trying to figure out what should be the future of these mausoleums, the big state hospitals. We're trying to figure out how we can get the psychiatrists and other personnel we need without wrecking the tax structure of the states. We're helping local communities make self-surveys. In general, we're trying to figure out where we are now and what we ought to do next." The Commission will make recommendations to Congress and to the states in the summer or fall of 1959. Its report may at last provide a rational basis for a national mental health policy.

3.

Already experts have envisioned an ideal hospital, and it is instructive to compare Columbus State—and other state hospitals—with the ideal. This yardstick was embodied in a report made by experts for the World Health Organization, an agency of the United Nations.

They commenced by asking what provision a society ought to make for psychiatric care. They said it needed a minimum number of hospital beds for the custodial care of the mentally ill who must be removed from society and treated because their behavior was dangerous to themselves or others or because they otherwise created a "grave social problem." It was hard to fix this number; most Western countries probably needed at least one bed per thousand population but in rural tropical Africa a tenth as many was enough. (Most Western countries have about three beds per thousand.) Once the minimum has been reached, however, the next step is not to build more beds, though in the past this is what has usually been done. Rather, as soon as the hospital can provide essential custodial care, its staff members should reach out into the community and devote a third of their time to a community mental health program. They should inform the public about the hospital and the nature of mental illness. They should encourage private physicians and general hospitals to deal with simple psychiatric conditions and promptly recognize those beyond their scope. They should set up an out-patient service for patients who need treatment but not hospitalization and a day hospital for patients who need more than out-patient treatment but yet can go home to their families at night and perhaps never slide into chronicity. They should set up special clinics for special problems, such as alcoholics, epileptics and children. And they should form and direct clubs of patients who have been discharged from the hospital.

Now, the experts recognized that when the hospital undertook all these activities its own burdens would increase, and so the hospital would have to enlarge its staff. This would mean spending more money. But, the experts argued, the amount of money spent does not alone test a hospital's quality. They said quality is better measured by the average length of stay, the ratio between the number discharged and admitted, the capacity the hospital has to absorb patients from society and take care of them, the percentage of discharged patients who relapse and return, and, above all, "the atmosphere" of the hospital. On this last intangible point of "atmosphere" the experts wrote, "Too many psychiatric hospitals give the impression of being an uneasy compromise between a general hospital and a prison. Whereas, in fact, the role they have to play is different from either: It is that of a therapeutic community."

The "atmosphere" of a hospital can be evaluated in numerous ways, they thought. How good are the relations between the medical director and the doctors under him, between the doctors and the attendants, between the attendants and the patients, among the patients themselves? Does the hospital preserve the patient's individuality? ("In too many psychiatric hospitals still the patient is robbed of her personal possessions, her clothes, her name and, should her head be lousy, even her hair. Every step, therefore, that can encourage the patient's self-respect and sense of identity should be taken.") Does the hospital assume that the patients are trustworthy? ("The locking of wards creates the urge to escape; the removal of knives and other elaborate and insulting precautions have provoked many suicidal attempts. High walls, bars, armor-plated windows, bunches of keys, uniform clothing and all the other paraphernalia of prison make modern psychiatric treatment impossible.") Does the hospital reward patients' good behavior rather than punish bad? Is it, for that matter, punitive at all? Does the hospital encourage patients' initiative and responsibility? Does it encourage visitors? Does life inside the hospital resemble as closely as possible life in the outside community? ("In a Western country where men and women mix freely at work and in recreation, it is obviously desirable that they should do so when in the mental hospital.") Are the patients active—not merely busy, but busy at planned and purposeful activity? ("The planning of the patient's day is probably the most important therapeutic task of the hospital psychiatrist.")

Once the proper atmosphere of the therapeutic community has been established, the experts wrote, the staff can build upon it specific types of treatment. They merely mentioned electroshock; they emphasized much more occupational and recreational therapy. They stressed group activities of all kinds, ranging from habit-training for grossly deteriorated patients to art and music for others. "In their gradual return to social effectiveness, patients often seem to need to recapitulate, not only the development of the interests and activities of the human being from childhood to adult life, but also the development of the human race itself." For some patients sand and water play are better than technical or craft activity. At first a nurse must supervise the activity; but as soon as possible the patients must be given responsibility. They should be encouraged to form clubs.

"It is evident from this conception of treatment that more space should be devoted to such common activities than most mental hospitals provide. It is also evident that during the greater part of the day the patients will be away from their own sleeping quarters." So would the nurses; scrubwomen and janitors must clean the living quarters "if the patients and the nurses are to be free to devote their day to therapeutic activity." Patients should not be locked into their wards; neither should they be locked out, for if they need solitude and rest they should have it. There should be one doctor for every 150 patients;

one nurse for each five or six patients. More use should be made of group psychotherapy. As for full-scale classical psychoanalysis, it is probably never justified except for research purposes. Each patient, however, should "feel that there is one doctor who is his—one doctor who knows him well and whom he knows." Moreover, each patient's case should be reviewed regularly by another psychiatrist, however chronic the patient's condition.

When a new patient is admitted "everything" should be done to make him feel at home—he should be given a guidebook and a map and should, as a right, meet the medical director personally. Leaving the hospital, he should be prepared by gradual trial visits and numerous interviews and be helped by social workers to find a job and home. Some patients should be allowed to remain at the hospital, or at a hospital-operated hostel, for a time after being discharged.

As to architecture, the experts said, "If [the hospital] is to support and recreate the sense of individuality in patients, it must not dwarf them by its size and by herding them together in thousands in giant monoblock buildings." No hospital should contain more than a thousand patients. (The experts doubted that large hospitals are cheap to operate.) Moreover, hospitals were built to last too long. "Many countries will be burdened for a long time to come with large obsolete mental hospitals built years ago to fit a conception of the role of the mental hospital which is now completely rejected." New hospitals should be designed to become obsolete in twenty or thirty years, and their interior walls should be movable. The hospital should be composed of several small buildings, not of a single large building. "The therapeutic community should take the village as its model." Day space and night space should be separated, not be part of a single locked enclosure. Enormous existing hospitals could be improved by breaking them up administratively into units of four hundred to seven hundred patients, each complete in itself with its own medical director and staff, its own admitting, acute and chronic wards. (Interestingly, in another field, penologists have advised breaking up the huge maximum-security prisons which were built in the 1920s and which, because they are unmanageable and because prisoners of all sorts are dumped into them, damage inmates and retard their rehabilitation.)

Finally, the experts warned that the psychiatric wards of general hospitals are not necessarily the best places for psychiatric care. Too often they keep patients in bed, emphasize neurological diagnosis, and ignore patients without neurological symptoms. Moreover, they sometimes are "very detrimental" to the community mental hospital, because they treat and return to society all patients capable of early recovery and send to the community hospital only grossly disturbed or chronic patients. "There is no more certain way of turning the community mental hospital into a 'madhouse' and depriving it of its role of a therapeutic community," they wrote, words of interest to Ohio, with its receiving hospitals.

Now, it is obvious that Columbus State does not come very close to this picture of an ideal community mental hospital—big old Columbus State, with its locked wards, barred windows, untrained attendants, overburdened doctors, isolation from the community, idle patients and almost total lack of planned activities.

And yet Columbus State is not very different from most American state mental hospitals. The only hospitals in America that even approach the WHO ideal are the best psychopathic hospitals and private sanitariums. These care for few people at present. Yet they may point the way to the future. And so does research, and so do the new drugs, and so do the open hospitals, halfway houses, day and night hospitals, community clinics, the whole tendency to reintegrate the state hospital with the community and to erase public ignorance and fear of mental illness. Indeed, under the impact of all these things, it is not impossible that the state hospital as we have known it may wither away. Tuberculosis hospitals are closing, and epileptic institutions. What a day it will be when the state hospitals close too!

4.

Dr. Felix of the National Mental Health Institute said recently, "The best guess is that there are nine million people in the United States today suffering from psychiatric disturbances which require assistance. Of these one million are cared for in mental hospitals during each year and probably another million get private treatment. So about seven million get nothing. Many of these live in rural areas far from any help. You take a town in the center of Nebraska, maybe two hundred miles from Omaha and three hundred miles from Denver, what do people do out there? Well, the state hospital at Hastings is one hundred miles down the road, so their relatives take them there. And after a while forget about them. Write them off. They are technically dead. You can't go one hundred miles every weekend to see Uncle Joe. But these patients are not dumb brutes. They still feel. When visits drop off, they know. And what if he does get better after ten years? Who wants to hire him? What about his family? His ten-year-old boy is twenty, his wife was thirty-five but now she's forty-five and she's arranged her life differently. We've got to find better answers.

"Remember," Dr. Felix went on, "a patient is a double liability—he not only costs money to keep but he's not contributing anything himself to the economy. This problem is so enormous it's staggering. Until a few years ago a few of us were voices crying in the wilderness. But not now. There are answers. These patients can be gotten out—though not next year, we've got a long way to go, a lot to learn. But we haven't whipped cancer yet either. People put up millions to fight cancer. Or heart disease—a big shot can give to the Heart Association and announce proudly he has a heart condition. But let Senator Big-shot have a moderate nervous breakdown—is he going to get out and beat the drums? Of course not—they won't re-elect him. Mental illness is terrifying in a way cancer or heart disease is not. People think these are wild men, they'll kill people in their beds. If a tubercular leaves the sanitarium without permission there's nothing in the paper. But let a maniac escape and it's in every paper."

And in the long run it is indeed only a change in public attitude that can bring about important changes in the care of the mentally ill.

5.

Partly because so many discoveries have been made in the last twenty years—and particularly because of the latest, the new drugs—a feeling is widespread today that psychiatry itself is on the threshold of a great future. Even cautious medical men find it difficult to restrain themselves. Dr. Blain of the APA told a House committee, "The despair that consigned the mentally ill to simple custody for life in mental institutions is rapidly being displaced by the realization that mental illness is not hopeless and that the great majority of the mentally ill can be treated and returned to the community in a relatively short period of time. . . . Dramatic advances are being made in psychiatric therapies on all fronts, and most dramatically so with the new drug therapies. . . . Increasingly the mental hospital is thought of as merely part of a network of community services. . . . So I say a new spirit is rampant in the field."

Of all the therapies used on insanity from the beginning of time, including bloodletting and purging, these, listed with their dates of introduction, have been in use recently: moral treatment (c. 1800); hydrotherapy (c. 1870); rational psychotherapy (1893); fever treatment of paresis (1917, succeeded by penicillin, 1944); insulin shock (1933); lobotomy (1935); EST (1937); psychiatric drugs (1953). Though the history of human mental disorder is ages long, virtually everything known today about physical treatment has become known in the last twenty-five years. Not a single physical treatment—not insulin shock, EST, psychosurgery or the new drugs—was discovered in America. Nor for that matter was the foundation of psychotherapy. Today moral treatment is little used—too little. Fever treatment has all but vanished. Hydrotherapy and insulin shock have declined greatly. So, under the impact of the drugs, have lobotomy and EST. At various times one or the other of these was hailed enthusiastically. All disappointed. Hydrotherapy had been recognized as little more than restraining sedation when EST came along; it was known that EST "didn't hold" when lobotomy came into widespread use; the terrible results of many lobotomies were recognized when the drugs came along. There had been many lean years of little hope, during which psychiatrists gazed helplessly at thousands of patients for whom they knew they could do little or nothing. Today, the new drugs have reawakened hope as nothing had for many years, not only because of their therapeutic effect but because of the avenues of exploration they have opened up.

Dr. Kline wrote a while back:

An older brother, a research pathologist, once chided me for going into research in such an uncertain field as mental disease. "Doing research in psychiatry," he wrote me, "is like playing poker with the deuces wild." But it is this very factor of chance—chance that the cards we are now being dealt may fall into some unexpectedly happy combination—that held many of us fascinated through the lean years which *deo volente* are now ending.

Dr. Brill of New York State believes that in not many years the state hospital as we have observed it at Columbus will be remembered as a curiosity in medicine's history. He has said, "A hundred years ago or more the movement to get the mentally ill into hospitals began. We overorganized mental illness—developed enormous collections of mental patients before we had any effective methods of treatment. That's how the problem developed that we call the state hospital problem—not entirely for a lack of finances and personnel, but because we collected all these people—for the best motives—before we knew what to do for them. Now at last we do know. The concentration of schizophrenic patients started in 1840 and reached a crescendo in 1950. Even before 1950 a rounding-off tendency had begun in the United States. Now a decline has set in here and all over the world. British mental hospitals dropped twelve hundred in 1956. There are empty beds in mental hospitals in Denmark. This cannot be coincidence.

"I feel that we're at a new threshold in psychiatry. I base it on simple logic. We have pretty nearly incontrovertible evidence that mental illness can respond to drug therapy. If the principle is established that a drug can do a job, then medical history shows that a better drug can be found to do a better job. And that can lead to the cause of the illness. This has happened with other diseases and other drugs. Take the history of quinine—Cromwell died of malaria because he wouldn't use Jesuits' bark. Jesuits' bark was the old cinchona bark, containing quinine. For hundreds of years quinine was used on malaria, though nobody knew what malaria was. Finally in the course of treating and studying malaria, the cause was discovered—in 1880 a Frenchman saw the plasmodium. In fact, it's the usual course in medicine that the drugs for treating a disease are discovered long before the cause of the disease is found. They were treating syphilis with mercury over three hundred years before anyone ever saw a spirochete. You can pile this evidence up—treatment precedes knowledge of causes."

Over the years, the trends of thought in psychiatry have swung more widely, perhaps, than in any other science. During the materialistic eighteenth and nineteenth centuries, mental illness of all kinds, and criminality as well was ascribed to gross organic alteration of the brain determined in large measure genetically. Toward the end of this period it was said that insanity was caused by the invasion of the brain by the newly discovered microorganisms and it was freely predicted that once these were properly identified and counterattacked, hospitals for the mentally ill would empty. This did not happen. Freud came along, and his great discoveries for half a century pushed the organicists into the background. Though Freud himself never forgot the biological factors underlying the psychological, some of his followers did, and the pendulum swung too far in the other direction, the psychic direction. Today, largely because of the new drugs, once more the danger is that the pendulum will swing too far, this time toward the organic.

Is it possible that it may be found, as William Sheldon has suggested, that "delinquency may reside in the cellular morphogenotype"; that not only schizophrenic hallucinations but also *The Divine Comedy* and all the other sublime works of man's mind may be ascribed to brain chemistry? Perhaps. But many doctors resist the idea. Among them, of course, are the analysts—and America, perhaps because of its veneration of the individual, has become peculiarly the home of psychoanalysis. But there is another American psychiatric tradition, broader than the analytic tradition, which also resists the purely organic explanation of the mind. Since early in this century American psychiatrists from Adolf Meyer on have striven to view man not as a purely "physical" nor a purely "mental" being but as a psychobiological whole. Psychosomatic medicine has grown out of this effort. Today in response to this tradition many doctors seem aware of the danger in the wide swings of the past—the danger to knowledge that always accompanies ironclad dogma. They seem to be attempting, amid the rising tide of biochemistry, to keep afloat Adolf Meyer's idea of the psychobiological whole man. Encouragingly Dr. Boshes of Northwestern University has observed, "In the neurological societies now we almost always hear psychiatric papers, and in the psychiatric societies it is common to hear neurological papers, including chemistry." Even such a leading exponent of the new drugs as Dr. Kline has said, "For years you couldn't get anyone to look at biochemistry. Now nobody will look at anything else. This is dangerous. You have both aspects of man to take into account. Despite all we know about syphilis of the brain, no one yet really understands how the damage to the cells of the frontal brain caused by syphilis can produce delusions of grandeur. We still need the link between the two. The great appeal of psychodynamic theory is that it gives an answer though it has no evidence, and the great appeal of biochemistry is its promise of a simple cure. What we need is a system that relates these two."

Dr. Kovitz at Columbus State, asked a while back at lunch in the noisy hospital cafeteria whether he felt psychiatry was on the threshold of a new age, said, "This is possible. Let's put it this way. For years there's been a great gap between the understanding of the function of the brain and nervous system and the understanding of people and

personality. I suppose a lot of us have a feeling that the gap is beginning to narrow now. I don't feel I know enough about the forefront
of investigation to talk about it," smiling a little. "I don't know how
close we are to the time when the clinical psychiatrist, the physiologist
and the neurologist will talk the same language but that's what we're
working toward."

6.

In this period of new hope and accelerated interest in psychiatry,
people are inclined to expect more of psychiatry than it can produce.
It has become the fashion to call almost every social and individual
malady "primarily a psychiatric problem." The sex offender, the drug
addict, the alcoholic, the criminal, the juvenile delinquent, the divorcee,
the child who can't read—all these and many more we tend to hand
over to the psychiatrist.

Legislature after legislature passes new laws committing sex offenders
to the care of psychiatrists, or establishing conciliation services in
divorce courts to be staffed by psychiatrists—all without asking where
the psychiatrists are to come from. Psychiatrists cannot begin to carry
the burdens already imposed. We have seen how scarce psychiatrists
are in mental hospitals; the situation is worse in prisons. There are only
forty-three full-time psychiatrists in all American prisons and reforma-
tories, and the care of psychotics in prison today is no better than the
care given the insane one hundred years ago. Moreover, as we have
seen, even were there enough psychiatrists they don't know enough
to deal with all the problems brought to them. The parents of one
teen-age schizophrenic murderer were indignant—and rightly—because
they had sought treatment for him repeatedly before his crime but had
got none; and yet what treatment is there? None, really. Their faith
in psychiatry is touching and, sadly, misplaced. It is not an uncommon
faith. People everywhere who have seen one attempt after another fail
to solve the ills of society have not unnaturally turned to psychiatry
in the hope it can save them. Perhaps someday it can. But not yet.
Nonetheless, it must try. Today mental hospitals are full, and so are
prisons and juvenile institutions, and unless research makes a major
breakthrough on schizophrenia, and until the states find means of
identifying and treating disturbed children, we can only expect that
our institutions will overflow.

Even in the care of patients in mental hospitals psychiatry can work no miracles. Serious men in the field fear that the hopeful public may vote them all the money they ask but then, if they fail to empty the hospitals quickly, turn on them indignantly, with the result that psychiatry will be set back many years. Dr. Blain of the APA has said, "All this public interest is wonderful, of course—but what if we don't deliver? By gosh, there's going to be a slump in interest for twenty-five years." And Dr. Solomon of Boston Psychopathic says, "Oh, sure—we're on the threshold. But I would also bring to your attention that these things go in cycles. We work in the social climate of the times. The new drugs have given rise to great expectations. I feel sure we can accomplish a very great deal. I'd guess we can cut the patient population 15 to 20 per cent in five years. But that's a long way from emptying the hospitals."

Hope should not blind us. Despite all advances, so recently as at the end of 1957 Dr. William Menninger of Topeka called government-run hospitals a disgrace, "human warehouses," and said, "Sixty per cent of their population never comes out alive." Money, personnel, research and public understanding—these, he said, are what we need today to make them what they ought to be.

The end of the pesthouse is not in sight. But its existence has been challenged. A while back Dr. Blain, after speaking of the difficulties and disappointments in his field, quoted Dr. Alan Gregg of the Rockefeller Foundation, who recalled that at the dedication of the Mount Palomar telescope a few years ago the guests were allowed to look at a star never before seen by man—a star whose light has been on its way to earth at 186,000 miles a second for 195,000,000 years. In so awesome a context of time and space, the guests felt insignificant indeed. But one of the speakers reminded them that although the philosopher may say, "Astronomically speaking, man is completely negligible," the psychologist may reply, "Philosophically speaking, man is the astronomer."

"And in that heartening answer," said Dr. Gregg, "lie the consolation and the glory of those who study the mind and spirit of man."

17

Columbus State Revisited

■ Meanwhile, pending the millennium, the state hospitals struggle along. Out on the hilltop in Columbus, many things have changed since our first visit in 1955—yet all is really much the same.

2.

In the state of Ohio as in the nation the number of patients in state hospitals has declined since 1955—from 28,663 on July 1, 1955, an all-time high, to 26,616 on July 1, 1958. Ohio authorities attribute the decline to an increase in the numbers of doctors and nurses and attendants, to the drugs, and to increased efforts by social service to get patients, especially the aged, out into family-care homes and other halfway houses. Ohio hospitals are still overcrowded but no patients are sleeping in the Cleveland jail because they can't get into the state hospital, as they were in 1955.

Following the passage of the $75,000,000 bond issue for the new building program authorized by the 1955 legislature, the first ground-breaking ceremony was held February 15, 1957, and by 1958 the building program was progressing well. Three intensive-treatment facilities at state hospitals were being built to supplement the eight intensive-treatment hospitals. As for the program to train psychiatrists, two of the three institutes for training and research authorized in 1955

366

were operating in 1958 at two receiving hospitals, one in Columbus in conjunction with Ohio State University and the other in Cleveland with Western Reserve. Some of the residents in training were on a three-year program, paid $375 a month as a starting salary; others were on a five-year plan, paid $600 a month and interspersing two years of service in Ohio state hospitals among their three years of training. Early in 1958 the institute at Columbus had twenty-two or twenty-three residents in training, nine of whom were on the five-year plan. In 1957 six residents had finished their training at the institute and, according to Dr. Ralph Patterson, all have stayed in state service. The results of this new training program are only beginning to be felt in the mainline state hospitals.

Since our first visit, Dr. Porterfield, then Director of the State Department of Mental Hygiene and Correction, has resigned and Dr. Haines has replaced him. Others in the downtown office have departed or changed jobs. Governor Lausche has been elected to the U. S. Senate. Dr. Haines, a bright youngish psychiatrist, feels that the reform impetus has been maintained. Ohio citizens are becoming increasingly interested in the state hospitals, he says. Volunteer groups, organized by service clubs, are visiting them. "People are starting to come into the hospital," Haines says. "We want to open up the hospitals but first the community has to get interested in the hospitals. You can't have just an open-door policy. It has to be a swinging door."

3.

There were 2,712 patients at Columbus State as of July 1, 1958, compared with 2,781 on July 1, 1955. Superintendent Wedemeyer died July 30, 1957. His place was taken by Dr. Lowell O. Dillon, a gray-haired crew-cut psychiatrist of forty-seven who has been in the Ohio state hospital system most of the time since he finished medical school in 1941. Whereas Dr. Wedemeyer had seemed an easygoing warmhearted somewhat old-fashioned psychiatrist, the sort who might be expected to believe in "moral treatment," Dr. Dillon seems a modern administrator, sharp-minded, cool and canny.

Dillon considers more space for patients his "No. 1" need—Columbus State is still seriously overcrowded. He has other problems—the ancient building is in constant need of rehabilitation and remodeling, recreational and occupational therapy need more space, the power-house needs overhauling, the TB building should be rebuilt or scrapped.

But on the whole, asked how he's doing, he is likely to say, "Real well. I'm real happy with the place."

Dr. Haines' annual budget is $3,336,341, including $2,407,944 for salaries. In 1955 Dr. Wedemeyer's total budget was only $2,431,104. The state's building program has so far not benefitted Columbus State at all. It will give it one new building, a badly needed million-dollar structure for the admission of all new patients and the treatment of acute ones. But it won't get the medical and surgical building which Dr. Wedemeyer wanted.

The biggest change is in the number of doctors. Where Dr. Wedemeyer had seven residents, Dr. Dillon, in January of 1958, had twenty-nine. This is a direct result of the legislature's appropriating more money to train psychiatrists. The money for training at all state hospitals was put into a common pool and became available in July, 1957. Dr. Wedemeyer promptly hired a dozen residents in order to tie up funds before other hospitals could. Dr. Dillon, replacing Dr. Wedemeyer, hired still more residents in order to tie up still more funds. If some of those hired at first turned out to be of little worth, he could replace them with more carefully selected and better qualified men, sending in a new application with each resignation so as to keep the funds tied up, and thus gradually amassing a large staff of able people.

When the floodgate thus first opened, the residents came not from U. S. medical schools but from foreign countries. Only six of the twenty-nine residents in Dr. Dillon's first group were born in the United States. The rest came from all over the world—the Philippines, Italy, Germany, Turkey, Japan, Greece, India, Czechoslovakia, Rumania, Austria, France. Twelve of the twenty-nine were here temporarily on a student exchange program and when they had finished their training must return to their native countries. The remaining eleven were immigrants who would stay in the United States and, presumably, become citizens. Dr. Richard Johnson, whom Superintendent Dillon brought with him and put in charge of the residency program, said, "The exchange students bridged the gap. They held their finger in the dike."

The influx of residents has meant great changes in the hospital. Now there is one doctor to a ward. The four acute female wards that Dr. Smith used to try to take care of alone are now served by four doctors. The doctors' offices have expanded. Walking through the hospital in 1955 one saw few doctors; now they are everywhere, often traveling through the wards in clusters of two or three. Indeed, sometimes they seem to be falling over one another. New patients no longer are staffed as they were in 1955; rather, Dr. Kovitz or Dr. Kirch goes to the admission ward and, with the residents there, conducts staff. Their remarks are noticeably more elementary than in 1955, assuming little knowledge on the part of the residents.

To supervise all these residents there were in January, 1958, only four certified psychiatrists at Columbus State—Dr. Johnson and three left from the old regime: Kovitz, Kirch and Agosten, the analyst. The hospital had in addition six experienced doctors who were Board-eligible—Dr. Dillon; his new administrative assistant, Dr. W. P. Addison; three left from the old regime, Dr. Madi, Dr. Lande and Dr. Bookspan; and one new man, Kurt Witton. One doctor said, "It's a rat race—two or three people trying to supervise thirty residents." Superintendent Dillon felt he needed twelve more senior staff members to supervise residents and treat patients. He hoped to get two before long, a full-time neurologist and a second analyst, one experienced at group therapy; but money was lacking for more. He had a full-time pathologist. He had 290 attendants and 37 registered nurses in January 1958. In 1955 Dr. Wedemeyer had had 248 attendants and 28 nurses.

Did additional personnel mean better treatment for the patients? It was hard to say. One doctor said, "They don't do any harm. More patients get more attention given to their problems. More patients are getting individual psychotherapy—but its quality is doubtful, especially in view of the foreign residents' language handicap plus their lack of experience. All in all, I don't think we're getting more people out of the hospital in spite of all this help." The number of patients is going down instead of up but this is probably due more to the new drugs than to the new residents. In sum, it is probably fair to say that the new expanded residency program has improved treatment, though not yet sufficiently to justify its expense, and that it has added to the potential supply of psychiatrists in Ohio, though not yet to the fullest extent possible. The legislature's main objective was to train psychiatrists and hold them in the Ohio state hospital system. It probably did not contemplate training psychiatrists who had every intention of practicing in, say, Pakistan. Just the same, while foreign residents are here, they serve. And if the time comes when the superintendent can select residents who are U.S. citizens or intend to become citizens,

Ohio is likely to benefit greatly from the expanded program.

For years leading psychiatrists around the country have urged that more doctors, nurses, attendants, money and drugs will inevitably mean better treatment and more discharges. This principle, as applied at Columbus State, seems to work out imperfectly—but perhaps it is too early to tell.

4.

Some of the wards have been changed around—Ward 8, for example, our acute male disturbed ward, is used now for chronic deteriorated untidy infirm patients, and an upstairs ward, 16, has become the acute male disturbed ward. No wards are unlocked, though some could be if privileged patients were collected; the hospital thinks it better to scatter them, since they provide encouragement to sicker patients.

Dr. Kovitz thinks that more patients are getting therapy of some kind today than in 1955. At that time only about one-third of the patients were getting anything. The percentage has gone up because of increasing use of the drugs, especially among chronics. The hospital has performed no lobotomy since 1955. A little more use is being made of OT and recreational therapy. EST has declined greatly—whereas in 1955 117 patients were on EST, by 1958 only about thirty were, nearly all depressed patients. The hospital spent $54,000 for psychiatric drugs in 1957. Patients no longer have to buy their own. Drug prices are coming down. The hospital still could use more money for drugs for chronic and aged patients and for patients who leave on trial visit; many who cannot buy their own drugs soon relapse and return. The hospital is using Thorazine, Compazine, Vesprin, Pacatal, Trilafon, Miltown, Serpasil (reserpine), Ritalin, Frenquel and Sparine. Like most hospitals, it is still using them on a trial-and-error basis. In January of 1958, months after Kline started using Marsilid extensively in New York, Columbus State had "heard of" it but had not yet tried it. Little more research is going on at Columbus State than in 1955, nor is more in prospect. The hospital has begun to develop a volunteer program. It has hired a director of volunteer services, and he has spoken to service clubs in Columbus, and about fifty citizens have formed a volunteer organization. They visit the hospital regularly, go on the wards to help with OT and recreational therapy, talk to patients, write to them, take them out for rides and home for meals, send them gifts at Christmastime and give parties for them on the wards. Dr. Kovitz says, "The hospital is rejoining the community."

Kovitz's own duties have changed somewhat. Now that someone else directs the residency program, he is freer to supervise the treatment of patients. He supervises the doctors on admissions in order to get a good diagnosis and lay the foundation for treatment. He supervises the residents on the female side. Dr. Kirch, now assistant clinical director, handles the male side. Residents come to Kovitz and Kirch to consult on patients. Kovitz teaches a weekly seminar for beginning residents. He sees three patients for individual psychotherapy. He supervises residents' psychotherapy. He watches each new drug that comes along.

5.

What has happened to the doctors and patients we met here in 1955?

Of the doctors, only the senior staff members remain. Only one resident of 1955 stayed at the hospital after his training, Dr. Bookspan. In 1955 he had been taking care of chronic patients, including the dangerous men on Ward 24; in 1958 he was working in the out-patient department.

The other doctors had scattered widely. Dr. Dane, the bushy-haired young resident who had been interested in the child Peter Bell was now at a new children's out-patient clinic in Columbus. Dr. Mary Lou Hippert, the young resident who had taken care of the disturbed ward, 8, and other acute male wards, had been divorced from her husband, had married a psychologist at the hospital and had moved to Illinois, where her new husband worked at a clinic; she herself had abandoned psychiatry and was keeping house. Dr. Roper, the young resident who had handled chronic women, had gone into military service and decided to remain in service; he was completing his training at Walter Reed Hospital. Dr. Handcock, the elderly woman whom we observed giving EST on Ward 8, had retired. Dr. Smith, the resident who had taken care of four acute women's wards single-handed, had gone to Indiana to take his third-year residency. The doctor whose wife had strangled her baby had gone to a state hospital in another state and had remarried. His former wife was still in Lima State Hospital for the Criminally Insane. Dr. Beitzel, who had handled physical afflictions, had gone into private practice in Paris, Illinois. Dr. Shortridge, the young man who handled female admissions, had gone to Columbus Receiving Hospital (now renamed Columbus Psychiatric Institute) to complete his residency. Columbus State was approved for third-year residency in 1958 and so might expect to hold more of its residents.

6.

And what of the patients we met in 1955? Where were they by January, 1958?

Sally Bennett, the lovely blonde schizophrenic, was out of the hospital. After Dr. Kovitz had interviewed her, she had been put on Thorazine, and in seven months had been deemed well enough to go home on trial visit. She had returned in a month for an interview with Dr. Smith, who had reported she was doing well, though having trouble finding a job. She had found a boy friend. Once returning to the hospital for a checkup she had wept while talking about the broken romance of long ago. She had had a rash on her face, and the doctor had stopped Thorazine. He had resumed it later: She seemed to need it. She finally had found a job, and the last time she visited the hospital she said she was happier than ever before in her life. But she still needed Thorazine.

Nancy Wilton, the smiling girl who had hallucinated the girls in red dresses and whom we saw with Dr. Smith just before she left the hospital, had indeed gone home but a few months later had returned to the hospital. She said she had heart trouble because she could feel her heart beat, she was so afraid of people she had been staying indoors, she was "afraid to live and afraid to die." The hospital had taken her in and put her back on heavy doses of Thorazine, and she had improved quickly. After about six months she had gone home again on trial visit. But when she returned for a checkup she had been much worse—tense, grimacing, quiet, her eyes closed. She had run out of Thorazine. Not much later, in for another checkup, she had said she wanted to stay in the hospital—there were too many conflicts at home. Her sister, who had come here earlier with the same diagnosis, hebephrenic schizophrenia, and who had been lobotomized, is on Ward 17, a chronic ward. There she receives Thorazine, as she used to receive EST, when she becomes disturbed. No doctor has written a progress note on her since 1955.

Chris Haverford, the brilliant young law student whose psychotic break became known when he wired to his parents, "Her name is Judy and she loves me" though there was no Judy, had been in and out of the hospital several times since 1955. "I saw Chris the other day,"

Dr. Kirch said. "He was pretty badly disturbed. Once I saw him and he was ready to clobber me." In mid-1957 a new doctor had taken over Ward 16, to which Chris Haverford and the other disturbed patients had been moved from Ward 8, and as many other doctors had done, he had taken an interest in Haverford and had commenced psychotherapy with him. As other doctors had, he had felt he was making good progress with him. Haverford had gone home on trial visit, which the doctor regarded as a triumph. But then he had relapsed and returned, violent and combative, and now, quieted, he is once more running errands for the ward attendants, back where he was in 1955; and Dr. Kirch says, "His doctor still has high hopes for him—he's a young doctor and a good therapist. But Chris is the kind of a boy that I think will always be here."

Sam Adams who used to reach for his nerves on Ward 8 had contracted tuberculosis and been moved to the TB cottage, disturbed as ever. "Poor Sam Adams," the doctors still say but there seems nothing they can do for him.

Donald Stone, the dancing drum major who wanted to be a magician before he came here in 1933 and whom we met on one of the back wards, had suddenly come to life. For years he had sat motionless or had gone through his dance, then subsided. Suddenly in 1956 he had become excited, tense, restless; he had begun to talk rapidly, had felt rushed all the time. Instead of listening passively to grand opera on the radio, he had wanted to work in the hospital's carpentry shop. His ward doctor, spotting the change, had put him on Thorazine and let him work. He had become a skillful carpenter, adept at repairing smashed furniture. Thorazine had had little effect but the doctor had given him full privileges anyway. He must have gone downtown, for one day he said he wanted to leave the hospital—he had been offered a job downtown in a carpentry shop. It was true. The hospital, mystified, let him go. Dr. Kirch says, "Nothing we'd done changed the underlying schizophrenic process. The next thing I knew he had a job and was gone. Something had happened inside him, we don't know what. In so many of our patients there's so much normal mixed with the abnormal. I'm sure the people Donald works with don't think he's half as crazy as we do. They think he's a little odd. Nowadays he keeps Thursday afternoons open so if we need any of our furniture fixed he can come out and do it. He fooled everybody."

Barbara Little fooled no one. She is the tall girl who twice had undergone psychosurgery; and she is still wandering around Ward 15, a disturbed ward, with a turban wound around her head. Just so, Roland Smith, the huge Negro roustabout, still sits in restraint on Ward 24, the security ward. Nor has Millicent Parker surprised. She was the sad young girl to whom Dr. Dane and Dr. Smith long ago gave psychotherapy, and though she had gone out on trial visit in 1956, she soon had come back into the hospital, and though occasionally now she seemed to improve on a new drug she soon relapsed, sat staring at space, spoke slowly, said she would be better off dead. The doctors tried one drug after another on her—Thorazine, reserpine, Equanil, Frenquel, Ritalin. Nothing availed. Today she is on Ward 11, a good ward. But that is where she was in 1955.

Theobald Tuttle, the excitable little schoolteacher on Ward 8, had gone home several times on trial visit. But he hadn't been able to keep a job, and his wife would bring him back for checkups and confide that she considered a breakdown imminent, and usually it had turned out she was right. Early in 1958 he was home; indeed, he was staying in the house, doing the housework, while his wife, a courageous woman, worked to earn their living. The hospital expected him back.

Lillian Hill, who was one of the first in Columbus State to get the new drugs and who made an almost miraculous recovery on them, is still out of the hospital, still on Serpasil, and, so far as the hospital knows, doing fine. As for Peter Bell, the boy, the hospital has heard nothing of him. On its records he is diagnosed, "Adjustment reaction of adolescence with epilepsy," and, "Discharged July 30, 1956."

7.

Today, although doctors are more numerous and money more plentiful than in 1955, old Columbus State seems essentially unchanged. The same patients sit in the rocking chairs on the chronic wards, the attendants on the disturbed wards perform their onerous tasks, the doctors pursue their rounds, occasionally heartened by a good hour's talk with a new patient or another patient's surprising recovery on Thorazine. Day and night the struggle against mental disease goes on without end. And the clinical director hurries from staff meeting to individual patient to admission ward. And the superintendent goes on hoping for larger appropriations, more experienced psychiatrists and fewer indignant relatives. They all are doing their best with what they have. And occasionally they are rewarded. Not long before he died Superintendent Wedemeyer, a big man in a white coat in an old varnished office, said, "Once in a while something nice happens," and passed a letter across his desk. It was from a woman whose aunt had died in Columbus State, and it said:

I want you to know that I shall always appreciate the kindly interest that you, the physicians, nurses, and other members of the staff took in her during the time she was in the Columbus State Hospital. I feel that in your position you are rendering a great service to society. Best wishes for continued success in all that you do.

Acknowledgments

■ Many people have contributed to the making of this book, a project which consumed more than three years; and I am deeply indebted to them.

I am indebted first to the *Saturday Evening Post* and its editors, Ben Hibbs, Robert Fuoss, Robert Sherrod and Stuart Rose; it was they who made possible my first researches in this field and who in 1956 published the series of articles on Columbus State Hospital, "Inside the Asylum," out of which this book grew.

I am indebted to Mrs. A. D. Lasker and the National Committee Against Mental Illness; she gave me a grant which made it possible for me to spend many months traveling, researching and writing—expanding the scope of the magazine articles.

I am indebted to my agents, Harold Ober and Ivan Von Auw, who encouraged the preparation of the magazine articles and the book.

I am indebted to my wife, Frances R. Martin, who encouraged the preparation of the articles and the book; to my friend, Francis S. Nipp, who performed editorial labors upon the manuscript; and to Alton B. Smith, who typed it.

The information for the book came from many sources—from books and papers but, perhaps more importantly, from people whom I interviewed. Among the latter were many patients and their relatives, and these I am unable to thank here by name; but I am grateful to them. Among them, too, were many doctors and laymen who work in this field. These I can and wish to thank here by name. All of them furnished information. Many of them read parts of the manuscript. I alone, of course, am responsible for the use to which I put the material they so generously gave me; and any errors which remain in the book are mine.

I wish, then, to acknowledge the help of Dr. L. G. Abood, Dr. W. P. Addison, Dr. Tibor Agosten, Dr. Julia T. Apter, Dr. Paul L. Barone, Dr. Alfred Paul Bay, Dr. Raymond T. Beitzel, Dr. Daniel Blain, Alvin Block, Dr. Saul C. Bookspan, Dr. Benjamin Boshes, Dr. Francis J. Braceland, Dr. Henry Brill, Dr. Bernard B. Brodie, Dr. D. Ewen Cameron, Dr. Joe T. Carter, Dr. Louis Cholden, Rev. Maurice Clark, Roger Cloud, Dr. John Cowen, Dr. Robert Dane, Dr. Lowell O. Dillon, Dr. Jack R. Ewalt, Mrs. Margaret M. Farrar, Dr. Robert Felix, Dr. William T. Foley, William O. French, Dr. Francis J. Gerty, Mike Gorman, Rev. John Francis Grady, Dr. Naham H. Greenberg, Dr. Milton Greenblatt, Dr. Roy R. Grinker, Dr. Kalman Gyarfas, Dr. Dan Haffron, Dr. R. A. Haines, Harold P. Halpert, Dr. Charles E. Hamner, Dr. Esther Handcock, Dr. Robert G. Heath, Lister Hill, Dr. Mary Lou Hippert, Dr. Paul H. Hoch, Fred K. Hoehler, Dr. Edward J. Humphreys, Dr. George W. Jackson, Dr. Richard Johnson, Dr. Paul Kirch, Dr. Nathan S. Kline, Dr. Julius Kolacskovszky, Dr. Benjamin Kovitz, Bernard M. Kramer, Morton Kramer, Dr. Elizabeth Lande, Frank J. Lausche, Donald Lawder, Jr., Dr. Zigmond M. Lebensohn, Dr. Maria L. Madi, Dr. William C. Menninger, Dr. Robert T. Morse, Dr. Hans B. Mulholm, Dr. Arthur P. Noyes, Dr. James W. Papez, Dr. Ralph Patterson, Dr. Darwin K. Phelps, Dr. Gerhart Piers, Dr. John D. Porterfield, William G. Reidy, Robert L. Robinson, Dr. John Roper, Dr. William H. Sheldon, Dr. Wilson P. Shortridge, Donald E. Smeltzer, Dr. Gordon L. Smith, Dr. Harry Solomon, Sidney Spector, Dr. George S. Stevenson, Dr. H. Sinclair Tait, Dr. J. S. Tarewater, Dr. M. R. Wedemeyer, Greer Williams, Dr. Harry J. Worthing, Sidney Yates.

Bibliography

■ Much of the material in the book came from interviews—the spoken word. Some came from printed sources. This bibliography is not intended to be exhaustive but represents some of the printed sources I used that may give the reader a chance to go further and deeper into the subject. Many of the works in the first section have useful bibliographies. In the second section many are continuing publications. I have not listed a great many technical papers I used, such as those by Dr. Kline on the new drugs. Such literature is enormous. Except for a few not yet published, these papers can be located in the *Index Medicus* under the names of the people mentioned in the text and the Acknowledgments of this book.

I. General Works

A. Mental Hospitals

American Psychiatric Association, Mental Hospital Service, *Standards for Psychiatric Hospitals and Clinics, Revised 1954.*

Deutsch, Albert, *The Shame of the States* (New York: Harcourt Brace and Company, 1948).

————, *The Mentally Ill in America: A History of Their Care and Treatment from Colonial Times,* 2nd ed. (New York: Columbia University Press, 1949).

Greenblatt, Milton, Richard H. York, Esther Lucile Brown in collaboration with Robert W. Hyde, *From Custodial to Therapeutic Patient Care in Mental Hospitals: Explorations in Social Treatment* (New York: Russell Sage Foundation, 1955).

Hyde, Robert W., in collaboration with the attendants of Boston Psychopathic Hospital, *Experiencing the Patient's Day* (New York: G. P. Putnam's Sons, 1955).

Mental Hospitals, published monthly 10 times a year from 1950 by the American Psychiatric Association Mental Hospital Service.

Stanton, Alfred H. and Morris S. Schwartz, *The Mental Hospital: A Study of Institutional Participation in Psychiatric Illness and Treatment* (New York: Basic Books, Inc., 1954).

B. Psychiatry

Aichorn, August, *Wayward Youth: A Psychoanalytic Study of Delinquent Children, Illustrated by Actual Case Histories,* foreword by Sigmund Freud (New York: Meridian Books, 1955; 1st pub. 1925 by Internationaler Psychoanalytischer Verlag, Vienna; 2nd ed. 1931).

The American Journal of Psychiatry, official journal of the American Psychiatric Association, from 1844; January issue currently carries "Review of Psychiatric Progress" for the preceding year.

Alexander, Franz, *The Fundamentals of Psychoanalysis* (New York: W. W. Norton & Company, Inc., 1948).

Bell, John Elderkin, *Projective Techniques: A Dynamic Approach to the Study of the Personality* (New York, London, Toronto: Longmans Green and Company, 1948).

Bleuler, Eugen, *Dementia Praecox or The Group of Schizophrenias,* trans. by Joseph Zinkin, Monograph Series on Schizophrenia No. 1, (New York: International Universities Press, 1950).

Cleckley, Hervey, *The Mask of Sanity: An Attempt to Clarify Some Issues about the So-called Psychopathic Personality,* 2nd ed. (St. Louis: The C. V. Mosby Company, 1950).

Hall, Bernard H., "Early Development of the Psychiatrist," *Quarterly of Phi Beta Phi,* Vol. LI, No. 1, March, 1955, pp. 16-25.

Henderson, Sir David and the late R. D. Gillespie, *A Text-book of Psychiatry for Students and Practitioners,* 7th ed. (London, New York, Toronto: Oxford University Press, 1952).

Hinsie, Leland E. and Jacob Shotsky, *Psychiatric Dictionary with Encyclopedic Treatment of Modern Terms,* 2nd ed. with supplement (New York: Oxford University Press, 1954).

Jones, Ernest, *The Life and Work of Sigmund Freud,* 3 vol. (New York: Basic Books, Inc., 1953, 1955, 1957).

Interrelations between the Social Environment and Psychiatric Dis-

orders, Papers presented at the 1952 Annual Conference of the Milbank Memorial Fund (New York: Milbank Memorial Fund, 1953).

Kallmann, Franz J., *Heredity in Health and Mental Disorder: Principles of Psychiatric Genetics in the Light of Comparative Twin Studies* (New York: W. W. Norton & Company, 1953).

Kretschmer, Ernst, *Physique and Character: An Investigation of the Nature of Constitution and of the Theory of Temperament*, 2nd ed. rev. with an appendix by E. Miller (New York and London: The Humanities Press Inc. and Routledge & Kegan Paul, Ltd., 1951).

List of Fellows and Members of the American Psychiatric Association, published biennially.

Menninger, Karl A., *The Human Mind*, 3rd ed. (New York: Alfred A. Knopf, 1949).

Myerson, Abraham, *Speaking of Man* (New York: Alfred A. Knopf, 1950).

Noyes, Arthur P., *Modern Clinical Psychiatry*, 4th ed. (Philadelphia and London: W. B. Saunders Company, 1948).

The Scientific Papers of the Annual Meeting of the American Psychiatric Association in Summary Form, annually from 1949 meeting.

Sheldon, William H., with the collaboration of Emil H. Hartl and Eugene McDermott, *Varieties of Delinquent Youth: An Introduction to Constitutional Psychiatry* (New York: Harper & Brothers, 1949).

Sheldon, William H., with the collaboration of C. Wesley Dupertuis and Eugene McDermott, *Atlas of Men: A Guide for Somatotyping the Adult Male at All Ages* (New York: Harper & Brothers, 1954).

Sheldon, W. H., with the collaboration of S. S. Stevens, *The Varieties of Temperament: A Psychology of Constitutional Differences* (New York and London: Harper & Brothers, 1942).

Sullivan, Harry Stack, *Conceptions of Modern Psychiatry*, the first William Alanson White Memorial Lectures (Washington, D.C.: The William Alanson White Psychiatric Foundation, 1947).

Zilboorg, Gregory, in collaboration with George W. Henry, *A History of Medical Psychology* (New York: W. W. Norton & Company, Inc., 1941).

II. Specialized Studies

American Psychiatric Association, *A Descriptive Directory of Psychiatric Training in the United States and Canada*, 2nd ed.,

September, 1955 (Washington, D.C.: American Psychiatric Association, 1955).

The Central Inspection Board of the American Psychiatric Association, *Report on the State Mental Hospitals of Ohio,* 3 vol., 1953.

The C. S. H. Echo, published monthly from Oct., 1954 for patients and personnel of Columbus State Hospital.

Commission on Organization of the Executive Branch of the Government, *Federal Medical Services: A Report to the Congress, February, 1955.*

Conference of Mental Hospital Administrators and Statisticians, *Proceedings,* from 1951.

deRopp, Robert S., *Drugs and the Mind* (New York: St. Martin's Press, 1957).

Expert Committee on Mental Health of the World Health Organization, Technical Report Series.

Facts on the Major Killing and Crippling Diseases in the United States Today (New York: The National Health Education Committee, Inc., 1957).

Gerty, Francis J., *Report of a Consultation for the Texas Medical Association on the Mental Health Services, Nov. 1, 1956 to Feb. 15, 1957.*

Institute for Psychosomatic and Psychiatric Research and Training of the Michael Reese Hospital, Chicago, Illinois, *Annual Report,* from 1946.

Jaffary, Stuart K., *The Mentally Ill and Public Provision for Their Care in Illinois,* Social Service Monographs (Chicago: The University of Chicago Press, 1942).

Joint Commission on Mental Illness and Health, *Annual Report,* from 1956.

Joint Information Service of the American Psychiatric Association and the National Association for Mental Health, *Thirteen Indices: An Aid in Reviewing State Mental Health and Hospital Programs* (1957).

Kansas Legislative Council, *Part II. Special Report and Recommendations: Charitable and Benevolent Institutions and Mental Hospitals of the State, Submitted to the 1955 Legislature, Dec. 15, 1954.*

Kramer, Morton, Hyman Goldstein, Robert Israel and Nelson A. Johnson, *A Historical Study of the Disposition of First Admissions to a State Mental Hospital: Experience of the Warren (Pa.) State Hospital During the Period 1916-50,* Public Health Monograph No. 32, Public Health Service of the U.S. Department of Health, Education and Welfare, 1955.

Menninger, William C., *Address before the Joint Session of the Texas Legislature, Feb. 12, 1957* (Distributed by the Texas Society for Mental Health).

Menninger Foundation, Progress Report, annually from 1941.

Menninger Quarterly, from 1946.

Menninger School of Psychiatry Catalogue, annually.

Mental Health Hearings before the Sub-committee on Health of the Committee on Labor and Public Welfare, U.S. Senate, 84th Congress, 1st Session, on S.J. Res. 46 . . . S.724 . . . S.848 . . . and S.886 (Title VI) . . . March 30 and April 13, 1955, (Washington, D.C.: Government Printing Office, 1955).

The Mental Health Programs of the Forty-Eight States: A Report to the Governors' Conference (Chicago: The Council of State Governments, 1950).

Mental Health Study Act of 1955. Hearings before a Sub-committee of the Committee on Interstate and Foreign Commerce, House of Representatives, 84th Congress, 1st Session on H.R. 3458 . . . and H.J. Res. 230 . . . March 8, 9, 10 and 11, 1955. (Washington, D.C.: Government Printing Office, 1955).

Mental Health Training and Research in the Midwest: A Report and Recommendations to the Midwest Governors' Conference on Mental Health . . . 1954 (Chicago: Interstate Clearing House on Mental Health, The Council of State Governments, 1954).

Mental Hospital Institute of the American Psychiatric Association's *Proceedings,* from 1949.

Midwestern Regional Survey on Mental Health Training and Research, Statistical Summary (Chicago: Interstate Clearing House on Mental Health, Council of State Governments, November 30, 1954).

Motive, published by the Ohio Department of Mental Hygiene and Correction, from 1954.

National Institute of Mental Health, *Patients in Mental Institutions 1950 and 1951,* prepared in Biometrics Branch (Washington, D.C.: U.S. Department of Health, Education and Welfare, 1954).

New York State Department of Health, *Health News,* Vol. 34, No. 5, May, 1957 (issue on tranquilizing drugs), published from 1923.

New York State Department of Mental Hygiene, *Mental Hygiene News,* from 1920.

Norristown (Pa.) State Hospital, *Annual Report,* from 1879.

National Health Education Committee, Inc., *Does Medical Research Repay the American People?,* 1957.

National Mental Health Committee, *What Are the Facts about Mental Illness in the United States?* (New York, 1954).

Ohio Department of Mental Hygiene and Correction, *Annual Report Fiscal Year Ending June 30, 1955,* (Columbus, O., August 1, 1955). (Earlier reports under varying titles containing valuable historical material may be consulted at the Department.)

Ohio Mental Health Survey Committee with the American Psychiatric Association, *A Mental Health Program for Ohio* (January, 1957).

The Pharmacology of Psychotomimetic and Psychotherapeutic Drugs, papers read at a conference held by The New York Academy of Sciences and printed in its *Annals,* Vol. 66, art. 3, pp. 417-840 (March 14, 1957).

A Program to Meet Indiana's Mental Health Needs, Final Report of the Survey and Planning Committee on Mental Health Needs (February, 1955).

The Psychiatrist, His Training and Development, Report of the 1952 Conference on Psychiatric Education . . . 1952. Organized and conducted by The American Psychiatric Association and The Association of American Medical Colleges (Washington, D.C.: American Psychiatric Association, 1953).

Psychiatry and Medical Education, Report of the 1951 Conference on Psychiatric Education . . . 1951. Organized and conducted by The American Psychiatric Association and The Association of American Medical Colleges (Washington, D.C.: American Psychiatric Association, 1952).

Public Welfare Statistics, Ohio, from 1944.

Research Conference Group on Psychosurgery, *Proceedings of Conferences, 1949, 1951, 1953* (Washington, D.C.: U.S. Department of Health, Education and Welfare, Public Health Service).

Selected Employment Regulations for Personnel at State Institutions for Mentally Ill and Mentally Deficient: A Compilation of Work Week, Vacation and Sick Leave Provisions and Coverage under State Merit Systems and Retirement Plans (Chicago: The Council of State Governments, July, 1956).

Selected Tables on Resident Population, Finances and Personnel in State Mental Health Programs (Chicago: Interstate Clearing House on Mental Health, The Council of State Governments, December, 1956).

State Action in Mental Health, 1955: A Summary of Financial, Legal and Administrative Developments in State Mental Health Programs (Chicago: Interstate Clearing House on Mental Health, The Council of State Governments, December, 1955).

State of Ohio Department of Mental Hygiene and Correction, *1956 Building Program (request),* prepared for General Assembly . . . Capital Planning and Improvement Board Division of Capital Planning and Improvement (January 5, 1956).

The States and Their Older Citizens: Report to the Governors' Conference (Chicago: The Council of State Governments, 1955).

Summary of Organization and Top Salary Schedules in State Mental Health Agencies (Preliminary Compilation), (Chicago: Interstate Clearing House on Mental Health, The Council of State Governments, Feb., 1955).

Summary of Proceedings Northeast State Governments Conference on Mental Health . . . Asbury Park, N.J., March 22-23, 1956 (Chicago: Interstate Clearing House on Mental Health, The Council of State Governments, 1956).

Salaries of Selected Personnel in State Mental Hospitals and Institutions for the Mentally Deficient; supplement (Chicago: Interstate Clearing House on Mental Health, The Council of State Governments, December, 1956; March, 1957).

State Programs for the Aging: A Review of the Problem and of Recent Action in the States (Chicago: The Council of State Governments, Dec., 1956).

Topeka (Kans.) State Hospital, *Biennial Report,* from 1879.

Training and Research in State Mental Health Programs: A Report to the Governors' Conference (Chicago: The Council of State Governments, 1953).

Turner, Violet B., *Chronic Illness: Selected References (1950-52),* Public Health Bibliography Series, No. 1, supplement (Washington, D.C.: U.S. Government Printing Office, 1953).

U.S. Department of Health, Education and Welfare, Public Health Service, National Institute, *Mental Health Statistics, Current Reports.*

What Are the Facts about Mental Illness in the United States? Facts compiled in January, 1957 by the National Mental Health Committee.

Index

Set in Linotype Fairfield
Format by Nancy Etheredge
Manufactured by The Haddon Craftsmen, Inc.
Published by Harper & Brothers, *New York*